THE LEFSCHETZ
FIXED POINT THEOREM

Robert F. Brown
University of California, Los Angeles

Scott, Foresman and Company *Glenview, Illinois   London*

Library of Congress Catalog Number 70-132567
AMS 1970 Subject Classification 55C20
Copyright © 1971 by Scott, Foresman and Company, Glenview, Illinois 60025.
Philippines Copyright 1971 by Scott, Foresman and Company. All Rights Reserved.
Printed in the United States of America.
Regional offices of Scott, Foresman are located in Dallas, Oakland, N.J.,
Palo Alto, and Tucker, Ga.

Preface

The subject called "Fixed Point Theory" is generally understood to be a certain collection of related topics, some of which come from analysis and some from topology. All of these topics are concerned in one way or another with a question which, in its simplest form, can be stated as follows: "If X is a topological space and $f: X \to X$ is a map (i.e., a continuous function), what can be said about the set of points x in X such that $f(x) = x$?"

Many of the topics in fixed point theory which lie primarily in the area of analysis can be found in the book by Jane Cronin [16].* The present book is concerned instead with some parts of the topological theory and, in particular, with the most famous of the topological results, the Lefschetz Fixed Point Theorem.†

The Lefschetz Fixed Point Theorem states that if X is a sufficiently "nice" space and $f: X \to X$ is a map, then one may associate to f an integer $L(f)$ such that if $L(f) \neq 0$ then every map $g: X \to X$ homotopic to f has a fixed point, that is, a point $x \in X$ for which $g(x) = x$. In this book, the Lefschetz Theorem will be proved for a wide class of spaces which is of general interest, namely, the class of compact absolute neighborhood retracts (ANRs).

We will also be interested in the converse of the Lefschetz Theorem: If $L(f) = 0$, does it necessarily follow that some g homotopic to f is without fixed points? We shall see that the converse is false in general, even for maps on finite polyhedra. However, if one puts sufficient restrictions on the type of polyhedron to be considered, it turns out that the converse is indeed true.

The route from the Lefschetz Fixed Point Theorem to its converse is rather circuitous. It is accomplished by means of an improvement on the Lefschetz number $L(f)$ called the Nielsen number $N(f)$. The Nielsen number is a non-negative integer with the property that, if $f: X \to X$ is a map on an ANR, then

---

* Numbers in brackets refer to the bibliography at the end of the book.

† A good survey of a large part of the topological theory of fixed points can be found in van der Walt's book [50].

every map g homotopic to f has at least $N(f)$ fixed points. Furthermore, if X happens to be a finite polyhedron of the right kind, then there is a map g homotopic to f which has exactly $N(f)$ fixed points. We will also see that, under suitable hypotheses, $L(f) = 0$ implies $N(f) = 0$ and thus the map g with exactly $N(f) = 0$ fixed points is the one we need in order to prove the converse of the Lefschetz Theorem.

The plan of the book follows the outline above. After some preliminary material in Chapter I, the Lefschetz Fixed Point Theorem is proved in Chapters II and III. Chapters IV and V are devoted to the fixed point index which serves as a bridge between the Lefschetz and Nielsen fixed point theories. The theory of the Nielsen number occupies Chapters VI and VII and, in Chapter VIII, we prove the converse of the Lefschetz Theorem. There are a number of digressions along the way, primarily for the purpose of giving topological applications of the theory as we develop it.

Readers who wish to get to the Lefschetz Fixed Point Theorem as quickly as possible can postpone Sections M and N of Chapter I. My experience in teaching fixed point theory has been that students find it easier to follow the lengthy and technical proof of the existence of a fixed point index if they already know why a fixed point index is useful. Therefore, after discussing Section A of Chapter IV, I go directly to Chapter VI and complete the last three chapters before covering Chapters IV and V.

It is assumed that the reader has a good grasp of elementary point-set topology and algebra. The material from homology theory which is used in this part of fixed point theory is explained in some detail, but most proofs are omitted. There is no homotopy theory in the book other than that usually covered in elementary topology courses.

We use the following system in the text for referring to previous results: A theorem in the same section is given only by number, for example, Theorem 2. A result in another section of the same chapter is referred to by section letter as well, e.g., E.2. For a theorem in another chapter, for example Theorem 2 in Section E of Chapter VII, we would use the label VII.E.2. The end of a proof is indicated by the symbol ∎.

Notes of courses which I taught at the University of California, Los Angeles, in 1965 and 1967 have been the main source for the book. The comments of the students in these courses were of considerable assistance in its preparation. My approach to fixed point theory has been influenced by conversations with a number of mathematicians, especially Felix Browder, Edward Fadell, and Barrett O'Neill. Part of the book was written during the summer of 1967 at the University of Georgia. I wish to thank the members of that faculty for their hospitality and I particularly thank Michael McCord for several useful discussions. Burtis Casler read an early version of this material, Eldon Dyer and Edward Fadell read later ones — all contributed many helpful comments. The patient and skillful typists were Donna Bergen, Lorraine Poole, and Alice Hume. Special thanks go to my wife for her encouragement and for her help in proofreading. It is a pleasure to acknowledge the support which I received from the National Science Foundation during the time that this book was in preparation.

Los Angeles, California   Robert F. Brown

Contents

Chapter I

Preliminaries

The background one needs for fixed point theory consists primarily of bits and pieces of standard material from homology theory. We will omit most of the usual technical verifications, so the reader who wishes to see the detailed arguments of homology theory should refer to a basic algebraic topology text, such as Spanier [49].

The main result of this chapter is the Hopf Trace Theorem. Since we consider it a basic part of fixed point theory, we will cover this subject in greater detail.

A. GRADED MODULES

Let J denote the integers. We take Λ to represent a principal ideal domain. A *graded Λ-module* M is a collection $M = \{M_p\}_{p \in J}$, where each M_p is a Λ-module. If $N = \{N_p\}_{p \in J}$ is a graded Λ-module such that N_p is a submodule of M_p for all $p \in J$, then N is a *graded Λ-submodule* of M and we can form the *quotient graded Λ-module* $M/N = \{M_p/N_p\}_{p \in J}$. In the case that Λ is a field, each M_p is a vector space over Λ, and so M is called a *graded vector space over Λ*.

For $M = \{M_p\}_{p \in J}$ and $N = \{N_p\}_{p \in J}$ graded Λ-modules and i an integer, by a *morphism $h: M \to N$ of graded Λ-modules of degree i* we mean a collection $h = \{h_p\}_{p \in J}$ where each $h_p: M_p \to N_{p+i}$ is a Λ-module homomorphism. The *kernel* of h is the graded Λ-submodule $\text{Ker}(h) = \{\text{Ker}(h_p)\}_{p \in J}$ of M where

$\mathrm{Ker}(h_p)$ denotes the kernel of h_p. Similarly, we have $\mathrm{Im}(h) = \{\mathrm{Im}(h_{p-i})\}_{p \in J}$, the *image* of h, a graded Λ-submodule of N.

Given a morphism $h\colon M \to N$ of graded Λ-modules of degree i, we will be making use of the *alternating sign morphism* $\boldsymbol{h}\colon M \to N$ defined as follows: $\boldsymbol{h}$ is the morphism $\boldsymbol{h} = \{\boldsymbol{h}_p\}_{p \in J}$ of graded Λ-modules of degree i where $\boldsymbol{h}_p\colon M_p \to N_{p+i}$ is characterized by $\boldsymbol{h}_p(x) = (-1)^p h(x)$ for all $x \in M_p$.

From Λ-modules M_p and G, we can form the G-module $\mathrm{Hom}(M_p, G)$ of Λ-module homomorphisms from M_p to G. Thus a graded Λ-module $M = \{M_p\}_{p \in J}$ gives rise to a graded G-module $\mathrm{Hom}(M, G) = \{\mathrm{Hom}(M_p, G)\}_{p \in J}$. If $M = \{M_p\}_{p \in J}$ and $N = \{N_p\}_{p \in J}$ are graded Λ-modules and $h\colon M \to N$ is a morphism of degree i, then we can produce a morphism

$$\mathrm{Hom}(h, G)\colon \mathrm{Hom}(N, G) \to \mathrm{Hom}(M, G)$$

of graded G-modules of degree $-i$ in the following manner: We let $\mathrm{Hom}(h, G) = \{\mathrm{Hom}(h_p, G)\}_{p \in J}$ where

$$\mathrm{Hom}(h_p, G)\colon \mathrm{Hom}(N_{p+i}, G) \to \mathrm{Hom}(M_p, G)$$

is given by

$$\mathrm{Hom}(h_p, G)(\varphi)(x) = \varphi(h_p(x))$$

for all $\varphi \in \mathrm{Hom}(N_{p+i}, G)$ and all $x \in M_p$.

B. TRACES

Now let M be a free Λ-module where Λ is, once again, a principal ideal domain. If M has a finite basis, it is said to be *finitely generated*.

Given a free finitely generated Λ-module M, a homomorphism $h\colon M \to M$ and a basis $x_1, \ldots, x_n$ for M, we can write

$$h(x_i) = \sum_{j=1}^{n} a_{ij} x_j$$

for all $i = 1, \ldots, n$. The matrix $[a_{ij}]$ is called the *matrix* of h (with respect to the basis $x_1, \ldots, x_n$).

From a basis $x_1, \ldots, x_n$ for a free J-module M, we can produce a basis $X_1, \ldots, X_n$ for the Λ-module $\mathrm{Hom}(M, \Lambda)$ by defining each X_i to be the homomorphism such that

$$X_i(x_j) = \begin{cases} 1 & \text{if } i = j \\ 0 & \text{if } i \neq j. \end{cases}$$

The basis $X_1, \ldots, X_n$ is the *dual basis* to $x_1, \ldots, x_n$.

A well known fact is

Lemma 1. *Let M be a free finitely generated J-module with basis $x_1, \ldots, x_n$, let $h\colon M \to M$ be a homomorphism, and let Λ be a principal ideal domain.*

The matrix of h with respect to $x_1, \ldots, x_n$ is the transpose of the matrix of Hom(h, Λ) *with respect to the dual basis.*

We observe that, since the matrix of h is an integer matrix, the matrix of Hom(h, Λ) is an integer matrix (rather than a matrix with entries from Λ) when the matrix is defined in terms of a dual basis.

Let $A = [a_{ij}]$ be an n-by-n matrix, then the *trace* of A is defined to be $\sum_{i=1}^{n} a_{ii}$. If M is a free finitely generated Λ-module and $h: M \to M$ is a homomorphism, then the *trace* of h, written Tr(h), is the trace of the matrix of h with respect to some basis for M. If M is the trivial module then, by definition, Tr(h) = 0. It is a standard result that the definition of the trace of a homomorphism is independent of the choice of the basis for M. The same proof, actually, establishes the following stronger result which we shall use in Chapter III.

Lemma 2. *Let M and N be free finitely generated Λ-modules where Λ is a principal ideal domain and let $h: M \to M$, $\varphi: M \to N$, and $\psi: N \to M$ be homomorphisms such that $\psi\varphi: M \to M$ is the identity function; then*

$$\mathrm{Tr}(h) = \mathrm{Tr}(\varphi h \psi).$$

By a *free graded Λ-module* we mean a graded Λ-module $M = \{M_p\}_{p \in J}$ such that each M_p is free. A *finitary graded Λ-module M* is defined by the following conditions:

(1) $M = \{M_p\}_{p \in J}$ is a free graded Λ-module
(2) each M_p is finitely generated
(3) M_p is trivial except for a finite number of integers p.

If $M = \{M_p\}_{p \in J}$ is a finitary graded Λ-module and $h: M \to M$ is a morphism of degree zero, then it makes sense to define the *trace* of h by

$$\mathrm{Tr}(h) = \sum_{p \in J} \mathrm{Tr}(h_p).$$

Recalling the alternating sign morphism $\boldsymbol{h}$ of the last section, we define the *Lefschetz number* $L(h)$ of such a morphism by $L(h) = \mathrm{Tr}(\boldsymbol{h})$.

C. CHAIN COMPLEXES AND COHOMOLOGY

A *chain complex* is a pair $(C = \{C_p\}_{p \in J}, \partial)$ where C is a graded Λ-module and $\partial: C \to C$ is a morphism of degree -1 such that $\partial\partial = 0$ (the morphism which is trivial on each C_p). Given chain complexes (C, ∂) and $(\bar{C}, \bar{\partial})$, a morphism $h: C \to \bar{C}$ of degree zero is called a *chain map* if the diagram

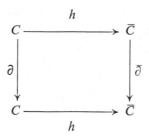

commutes.

Starting with a chain complex (C, ∂) where C is a graded Λ-module (Λ a principal ideal domain) and a Λ-module G, we can form the graded G-module $\mathrm{Hom}(C, G) = C^{\#}(G)$ and a morphism

$$\delta = \mathrm{Hom}(\partial, G): C^{\#}(G) \to C^{\#}(G)$$

of degree $+1$ such that $\delta\delta = 0$. Also, a chain map $h: C \to \bar{C}$ gives rise to a morphism

$$h^{\#} = \mathrm{Hom}(h, G): \bar{C}^{\#}(G) \to C^{\#}(G)$$

of degree zero such that the diagram

$$
\begin{array}{ccc}
\bar{C}^{\#}(G) & \xrightarrow{\ \ h^{\#}\ \ } & C^{\#}(G) \\
\Big\downarrow{\bar{\delta}} & & \Big\downarrow{\delta} \\
\bar{C}^{\#}(G) & \xrightarrow[\ \ h^{\#}\ \ ]{} & C^{\#}(G)
\end{array}
$$

commutes.

Let (C, ∂) be a chain complex and define $Z(C) = \mathrm{Ker}(\partial)$, $B(C) = \mathrm{Im}(\partial)$. Since $\partial\partial = 0$, it follows that $B(C)$ is a graded Λ-submodule of $Z(C)$ and we have the quotient Λ-module

$$H_*(C) = \frac{Z(C)}{B(C)},$$

the *homology* of the chain complex (C, ∂). Observe that a chain map $h: C \to \bar{C}$ induces a morphism of graded Λ-modules of degree zero which we denote by $h_*: H_*(C) \to H_*(\bar{C})$.

Define $Z(C; G) = \mathrm{Ker}(\delta)$ and $B(C; G) = \mathrm{Im}(\delta)$. Then the property $\delta\delta = 0$ makes $B(C; G)$ a graded G-submodule of $Z(C; G)$, so we can form the quotient graded G-module

$$H^*(C; G) = \frac{Z(C; G)}{B(C; G)}$$

called the *G-cohomology* of the chain complex (C, ∂).

A chain map $h: C \to \bar{C}$ induces a morphism $h^*: H^*(\bar{C}; G) \to H^*(C; G)$ as follows: if $[\bar{z}] \in H^*(\bar{C}; G)$ then

$$h^*[\bar{z}] = [h^{\#}(\bar{z})].$$

The fact that $\delta h^{\#} = h^{\#} \bar{\delta}$ guarantees that h^* is well defined.

If the Λ-module G is a field, then homology and cohomology are related in a simple way: The graded G-module $H^*(C; G)$ is isomorphic (by a sequence of isomorphisms which preserve the grading) to $\mathrm{Hom}(H_*(C), G)$. Furthermore, if $h: C \to \bar{C}$ is a chain map, then $h^* = \mathrm{Hom}(h_*, G)$.

When $h: C \to \bar{C}$ is a chain map, the alternating sign morphism $\boldsymbol{h}$ is not a chain map, but it does have the property $\bar{\partial}\boldsymbol{h} = -\boldsymbol{h}\partial$. Therefore, for $\boldsymbol{h}^{\#} = \mathrm{Hom}(\boldsymbol{h}, G)$ we have $\delta \boldsymbol{h}^{\#} = -\boldsymbol{h}^{\#}\bar{\delta}$ and we obtain a well-defined morphism $\boldsymbol{h}^*: H^*(\bar{C}; G) \to H^*(C; G)$ by setting

$$\boldsymbol{h}^*[\bar{z}] = [\boldsymbol{h}^{\#}(\bar{z})]$$

for $[\bar{z}] \in H^*(\bar{C}; G)$. If $[\bar{z}] \in H^p(\bar{C}; G) = \mathrm{Ker}(\bar{\delta}_p)/\mathrm{Im}(\bar{\delta}_{p-1})$ then $\boldsymbol{h}^*[\bar{z}] = (-1)^p h^*[\bar{z}]$. In other words, $\boldsymbol{h}^*$ is the alternating sign morphism corresponding to h^*.

D. THE HOPF TRACE THEOREM

In this section we consider a *finitary chain complex*, that is, a chain complex (C, ∂) where C is a finitary graded J-module. Let F be a field and use the symbol $C^{\#}(F) = \{C^p(F)\}_{p \in J}$ for the finitary graded vector space $\mathrm{Hom}(C, F)$.

Choose a basis $B^p = \{z_1^p, \ldots, z_{r(p)}^p\}$ for the finite-dimensional vector space $B^p(C; F) = \mathrm{Im}(\delta_{p-1})$ and extend it to a basis

$$Z^p = \{z_1^p, \ldots, z_{r(p)}^p, z_{r(p)+1}^p, \ldots, z_{s(p)}^p\} \quad \text{for} \quad Z^p(C; F) = \mathrm{Ker}(\delta_p).$$

Since $H^p(C; F) = Z^p(C; F)/B^p(C; F)$, then $H^p = Z^p - B^p$ is a basis for $H^p(C; F)$.

By definition, δ maps $C^p(F)$ onto $B^{p+1}(C; F)$ so we can choose $c_1^p, \ldots, c_{r(p+1)}^p \in C^p(F)$ so that $\delta(c_i^p) = z_i^{p+1}$ for $i = 1, \ldots, r(p+1)$ where $B^{p+1} = \{z_1^{p+1}, \ldots, z_{r(p+1)}^{p+1}\}$ is the previously chosen basis for $B^{p+1}(C; F)$.

Lemma 1. *The set* $C^p = \{z_1^p, \ldots, z_{s(p)}^p, c_1^p, \ldots, c_{r(p+1)}^p\}$ *is a basis for* $C^p(F)$.

Proof Let $x \in C^p(F)$, then $\delta(x) \in B^{p+1}(C; F)$ so

$$\delta(x) = \sum_{j=1}^{r(p+1)} a_j z_j^{p+1} = \sum_{j=1}^{r(p+1)} a_j \delta(c_j^p) = \delta\left(\sum_{j=1}^{r(p+1)} a_j c_j^p\right)$$

where $a_j \in F$, $j = 1, \ldots, r(p+1)$. This implies $\delta\left(x - \sum_{j=1}^{r(p+1)} a_j c_j^p\right) = 0$ or

$$\left(x - \sum_{j=1}^{r(p+1)} a_j c_j^p \right) \in Z^p(C; F). \text{ Thus we may write}$$

$$x - \sum_{j=1}^{r(p+1)} a_j c_j^p = \sum_{k=1}^{s(p)} b_k z_k^p \qquad (b_k \in F),$$

so C^p spans $C^p(F)$. If $\sum_{k=1}^{s(p)} b_k z_k^p + \sum_{j=1}^{r(p+1)} a_j c_j^p = 0$ then

$$0 = \delta \left(\sum_{k=1}^{s(p)} b_k z_k^p + \sum_{j=1}^{r(p+1)} a_j c_j^p \right)$$

$$= \delta \left(\sum_{k=1}^{s(p)} b_k z_k^p \right) + \sum_{j=1}^{r(p+1)} a_j \delta(c_j^p)$$

$$= \sum_{j=1}^{r(p+1)} a_j z_j^{p+1},$$

which implies $a_1 = a_2 = \cdots = a_{r(p+1)} = 0$ because the set $z_1^{p+1}, \ldots, z_{r(p+1)}^{p+1}$ is linearly independent. Armed with this knowledge, we return to the equation $\sum_{k=1}^{s(p)} b_k z_k^p + \sum_{j=1}^{r(p+1)} a_j c_j^p = 0$ and find that it reduces to $\sum_{k=1}^{s(p)} b_k z_k^p = 0$, so $b_1 = \cdots = b_{s(p)} = 0$, and the elements of C^p are linearly independent. ∎

Theorem 2 (The Hopf Trace Theorem). *Let (C, ∂) be a finitary chain complex and let $h: C \to C$ be a chain map; then, for any field F,*

$$\mathrm{Tr}(h^\# = \mathrm{Hom}(h, F)) = \mathrm{Tr}(h^*).$$

Proof Choose C^p as the basis for $C^p(F)$ and H^p as the basis for $H^p(C; F)$. Now, for $j = 1, \ldots, r(p + 1)$, we write

$$h^\#(c_j^p) = \sum_{t=1}^{r(p+1)} b_{jt}^p c_t^p + \sum_{u=1}^{s(p)} a_{ju}^p z_u^p$$

where $b_{jt}^p, a_{ju}^p \in F$. For $j = r(p) + 1, \ldots, s(p)$, set

$$h^\#(z_j^p) = \sum_{t=1}^{s(p)} d_{jt}^p z_t^p \quad (d_{jt}^p \in F),$$

recalling that $h^\#(Z^p(C; F)) \subseteq Z^p(C; F)$. We know that $\delta h^\# = -h^\# \delta$ so, for $j = 1, \ldots, r(p)$,

$$h^\#(z_j^p) = h^\#(\delta c_j^{p-1}) = -\delta h^\#(c_j^{p-1})$$

$$= -\delta \left(\sum_{t=1}^{r(p)} b_{jt}^{p-1} c_t^{p-1} + \sum_{u=1}^{s(p-1)} a_{ju}^{p-1} z_u^{p-1} \right)$$

$$= -\delta \left(\sum_{t=1}^{r(p)} b_{jt}^{p-1} c_t^{p-1} \right) = \sum_{t=1}^{r(p)} (-b_{jt}^{p-1}) z_t^p.$$

The matrix of $h_p^\#$ with respect to the basis C^p therefore looks like Figure 1,

$$
\left[
\begin{array}{cccccc}
-b_{11}^{p-1} \cdots \cdots -b_{1,r(p)}^{p-1} & 0 \cdots\cdots\cdots 0 & 0 \cdots\cdots\cdots 0 \\
\vdots \qquad\qquad \vdots & \vdots \qquad\qquad \vdots & \vdots \qquad\qquad \vdots \\
-b_{r(p),1}^{p-1} \cdots -b_{r(p),r(p)}^{p-1} & 0 \cdots\cdots\cdots 0 & 0 \cdots\cdots\cdots 0 \\[6pt]
d_{r(p)+1,1}^{p} \cdots d_{r(p)+1,r(p)}^{p} \; d_{r(p)+1,r(p)+1}^{p} \cdots d_{r(p)+1,s(p)}^{p} & 0 \cdots\cdots\cdots 0 \\
\vdots & \vdots \\
d_{s(p),1}^{p} \cdots\cdots\cdots\cdots\cdots\cdots d_{s(p),s(p)}^{p} & 0 \cdots\cdots 0 \\[6pt]
a_{11}^{p} \cdots\cdots\cdots\cdots\cdots a_{1,s(p)}^{p} & b_{11}^{p} \cdots\cdots b_{1,r(p+1)}^{p} \\
\vdots & \vdots \\
a_{r(p+1),1}^{p} \cdots\cdots\cdots a_{r(p+1),s(p)}^{p} & b_{r(p+1),1}^{p} \cdots b_{r(p+1),r(p+1)}^{p}
\end{array}
\right]
$$

FIGURE 1

from which we conclude that

$$
\mathrm{Tr}(h_p^{\#}) = \sum_{j=1}^{r(p)} (-b_{jj}^{p-1}) + \sum_{j=r(p)+1}^{s(p)} d_{jj}^{p} + \sum_{j=1}^{r(p+1)} b_{jj}^{p}.
$$

Thus

$$
\mathrm{Tr}(h^{\#}) = \sum_{p \in J} \mathrm{Tr}(h_p^{\#}) = \sum_{p \in J} \sum_{j=r'(p)+1}^{s(p)} d_{jj}^{p}.
$$

On the other hand, for $j = r(p) + 1, \ldots, s(p)$,

$$
h^*[z_j^p] = [h^{\#} z_j^p] = \left[\sum_{t=1}^{s(p)} d_{jt}^p z_t^p \right]
$$

$$
= \left[\sum_{t=1}^{r(p)} d_{jt}^p z_t^p \right] + \left[\sum_{t=r(p)+1}^{s(p)} d_{jt}^p z_t^p \right]
$$

$$
= \left[\sum_{t=r'(p)+1}^{s(p)} d_{jt}^p z_t^p \right],
$$

because $\sum_{t=1}^{r(p)} d_{jt}^p z_t^p \in B^p(C; F)$. Therefore

$$
\mathrm{Tr}(h^*) = \sum_{p \in J} \mathrm{Tr}(h_p^*) = \sum_{p \in J} \sum_{j=r(p)+1}^{s(p)} d_{jj}^p = \mathrm{Tr}(h^{\#})
$$

as required. ∎

If $h^*: H^*(C; F) \to H^*(C; F)$ is a morphism, write $L(h^*; F)$ for the Lefschetz number of h^* (see Section B). Let Q denote the rational numbers. Since we will usually be interested in the Lefschetz number $L(h^*; Q)$, we write $L(h^*; Q) = L(h^*)$. Since $\boldsymbol{h}^*$ is the alternating sign morphism of h^*, then $L(h^*; F) = \mathrm{Tr}(\boldsymbol{h}^*)$ by definition. Consequently we have

Corollary 3. *Let (C, ∂) be a finitary chain complex, let $h: C \to C$ be a chain map, and let F be a field, then $L(h^*; F) = \mathrm{Tr}(\boldsymbol{h})$ and therefore the Lefschetz number $L(h^*; F)$ is an integer.*

E. SIMPLICIAL COMPLEXES

A *simplicial complex K* is a finite collection of finite sets such that if s is a set in K and t is a subset of s, then t belongs to K. If $s \in K$ and s contains $p + 1$ elements, then s is called a *p-simplex* (or *simplex* of *dimension p*) of K. The 0-simplices are also known as *vertices* of K, so the elements of a simplex are vertices.

Consider collections $\{v_0, \ldots, v_p\}$ where each v_i is a vertex of K and $v_0, \ldots, v_p$ all belong to a single simplex of K. If the v_i are not all distinct, call the collection *degenerate*. An *oriented p-simplex* of K is a nondegenerate collection $\{v_0, \ldots, v_p\}$ (so $\{v_0, \ldots, v_p\}$ is a p-simplex of K) together with an equivalence class of orderings of the set $\{v_0, \ldots, v_p\}$, where two orderings are equivalent provided that they differ by an even permutation of the elements. An oriented p-simplex is denoted by $\langle v_0, \ldots, v_p \rangle$, where $v_0 < v_1 < \cdots < v_p$ in an ordering belonging to the equivalence class.

Let $C_p(K)$ denote the group generated by
(1) all degenerate collections $\{v_0, \ldots, v_p\} = \langle v_0, \ldots, v_p \rangle$
(2) all oriented p-simplices $v_0, \ldots, v_p$,
that is subject to the relations

$$\langle v_0, \ldots, v_p \rangle = 0$$

if $\{v_0, \ldots, v_p\}$ is degenerate and

$$\langle v_0, \ldots, v_p \rangle + \langle v_0', \ldots, v_p' \rangle = 0$$

if $\{v_0, \ldots, v_p\} = \{v_0', \ldots, v_p'\}$ as p-simplices, and the associated equivalence classes of orderings are different (i.e., their members differ by odd permutations). The group $C_p(K)$ is a free J-module with a basis consisting of as many elements as there are p-simplices in K. If $p < 0$, set $C_p(K) = 0$.

Define $\partial_p: C_p(K) \to C_{p-1}(K)$ as follows: For $\langle v_0, \ldots, v_p \rangle$ an oriented p-simplex, let

$$\partial_p \langle v_0, \ldots, v_p \rangle = \sum_{i=0}^{p} (-1)^i \langle v_0, \ldots, \hat{v}_i, \ldots, v_p \rangle,$$

where $\langle v_0, \ldots, \hat{v}_i, \ldots, v_p \rangle$ denotes the oriented $(p-1)$-simplex obtained by deleting v_i; then ∂_p extends to a homomorphism. Now $C(K) = \{C_p(K)\}_{p \in J}$ is a finitary graded J-module and $\{C(K), \partial\}$ is a chain complex. Denote its G-cohomology by $H^*(K; G)$.

For K and L simplicial complexes, a function $f: K \to L$ is said to be *simplicial* if

$$f\{v_0, \ldots, v_p\} = \{f(v_0), \ldots, f(v_p)\}$$

for any simplex $\{v_0, \ldots, v_p\}$ of K. A simplicial function $f: K \to L$ induces a chain map $C(f): C(K) \to C(L)$ by the following rule: Let $\langle v_0, \ldots, v_p \rangle \in C_p(K)$ be an oriented simplex, then let

$$C(f)\langle v_0, \ldots, v_p \rangle = \langle f(v_0), \ldots, f(v_p) \rangle.$$

F. BARYCENTRIC SUBDIVISION

Starting with a simplicial complex K, we are going to construct a new simplicial complex K_1 called its *barycentric subdivision*. The vertices of K_1 are in one-to-one correspondence with the elements of K, so denote a vertex of K_1 by $v(s)$ where $s \in K$. The simplices of K_1 consist of all sets $\{v(s_0), \ldots, v(s_p)\}$ such that, for all i and j, either $s_i \subset s_j$ or $s_j \subset s_i$. Since K_1 is a simplicial complex, we can form its barycentric subdivision $(K_1)_1 = K_2$ and, in general, we define the r-th *barycentric subdivision* K_r of K by $K_r = (K_{r-1})_1$.

Suppose that $c = \sum_i a_i \langle v(s_{i,0}), \ldots, v(s_{i,p-1}) \rangle$ is an element of $C_{p-1}(K_1)$ and suppose that $s \in K$ has the property that $s_{ij} \subset s$ for all i and j, then define

$$v(s) \cdot c = \sum_i a_i \langle v(s), v(s_{i,0}), \ldots, v(s_{i,p-1}) \rangle \in C_p(K_1).$$

Let $\varphi: C_0(K) \to C_0(K_1)$ have the property that $\varphi\langle v_0 \rangle = \langle v(v_0) \rangle$ for each vertex v_0 of K and extend φ to a homomorphism. Suppose that a homomorphism $\varphi: C_{p-1}(K) \to C_{p-1}(K_1)$ has been defined; then, for $\langle s \rangle$ an oriented p-simplex of K, let

$$\varphi\langle s \rangle = v(s) \cdot \varphi(\partial \langle s \rangle),$$

which produces a homomorphism $\varphi: C_p(K) \to C_p(K_1)$. We have inductively defined a chain map $\varphi: C(K) \to C(K_1)$. Iteration gives us a chain map $\varphi_r: C(K) \to C(K_r)$ for any $r \geq 1$.

G. THE EULER CHARACTERISTIC

For $M = \{M_p\}_{p \in J}$ a finitary graded Λ-module, define the *Euler characteristic* of M, written $\chi(M)$, to be the Lefschetz number of the identity function $1_M: M \to M$. Thus $\chi(M) = \sum (-1)^p \text{ rank } (M_p)$.

Let $\{C, \partial\}$ be a chain complex where C is a finitary graded J-module, then $H^*(C; Q)$ is a finitary graded vector space. It is clear that

$$1_C^*: H^*(C; Q) \to H^*(C; Q)$$

is the identity function; so, by D.3,

$$\chi(C) = L(1_C) = L(1_C^*) = \chi(H^*(C; Q)).$$

The matrix of the identity function $1^p: H^p(C; Q) \to H^p(C; Q)$ is the identity matrix $E(b_p)$ of rank b_p, the dimension of the vector space $H^p(C; Q)$. The matrix of $\mathbf{1}^p$ is therefore $(-1)^p E(b_p)$ and its trace is $(-1)^p b_p$. Since $L(\mathbf{1}) = \mathrm{Tr}(\mathbf{1})$, we have proved

Theorem 1. *Let $\{C, \partial\}$ be a chain complex where C is a finitary graded J-module, then*

$$\chi(C) = \sum_{p \in J} (-1)^p b_p$$

where $b_p = \dim(H^p(C; Q))$.

If K is a simplicial complex, then the matrix of the identity function $1_p: C_p(K) \to C_p(K)$ is the identity matrix whose rank is equal to the number of generators of the free J-module $C_p(K)$ which, we recall, is equal to the number of p-simplices in K. By the reasoning we used in Theorem 1, we obtain

Theorem 2. *Let K be a simplicial complex and let a_p denote the number of p-simplices in K, then*

$$\chi(C(K)) = \sum_{p \in J} (-1)^p a_p.$$

A classical consequence of Theorems 1 and 2 is

Corollary 3 (The Euler-Poincaré Formula). *If K is a simplicial complex, a_p is the number of p-simplices in K, and $b_p = \dim(H^p(K; Q))$, then*

$$\sum_{p \in J} (-1)^p a_p = \sum_{p \in J} (-1)^p b_p.$$

H. GEOMETRIC REALIZATION

Let K be a simplicial complex with vertices $v_1, \ldots, v_n$. Denote by $|K|$ the set of all symbols $\sum_{i=1}^{n} r_i v_i$ (r_i real) satisfying the conditions

(1) $r_i \geq 0$, $i = 1, \ldots, n$

(2) $\sum_{i=1}^{n} r_i = 1$

(3) $\{v_i \mid r_i \neq 0\}$ is a simplex of K.

A metric d can be defined on $|K|$ as follows: If $x = \sum\limits_{i=1}^{n} r_i v_i$ and $y = \sum\limits_{i=1}^{n} r'_i v_i$ are in $|K|$, then

$$d(x, y) = \left(\sum_{i=1}^{n} (r_i - r'_i)^2 \right)^{\frac{1}{2}}.$$

The space $|K|$ with the topology induced by d is a compact metric space called the *geometric realization* of K.

For a simplex $s \in K$, the set of all points $\sum\limits_{i=1}^{n} r_i v_i$ in $|K|$ with the property that $\{v_i \mid r_i \neq 0\} = s$ forms a subspace called the *geometric realization* of s and denoted by $|s|$.

A topological space X is a *polyhedron* if there exists a simplicial complex K such that $|K|$ is homeomorphic to X. A *triangulation* of a polyhedron X is a pair $T = (K, \tau)$, where K is a simplicial complex and $\tau: |K| \to X$ is a homeomorphism. A polyhedron X together with a specified triangulation T is called a *triangulated space*.

If K is a simplicial complex and L is a subcomplex, i.e., L is a simplicial complex and a subset of K, denote by St(L) the set of all simplices $s \in K$ with the property that there exists $t \in L$ such that $t \subseteq s$. On the geometric level, if A is a *subpolyhedron* of a polyhedron X, that means that there is a triangulation $T = (K, \tau)$ of X and a subcomplex L of K such that $\tau: |L| \to A$ is a homeomorphism. Let $|$St$(L)|$ be the union of the geometric realizations of all simplices in St(L) and define St$_T(A) = \tau\,|$St$(L)|$. Since $K - St(L)$ is a subcomplex of K, it follows that St$_T(A)$ is open in X.

For K a simplicial complex and K_1 its barycentric subdivision, there is a homeomorphism $\tau_1: |K_1| \to |K|$ which, customarily, is defined in the following way: Let $v(s)$ be a vertex of K_1 where $s = \{v_0, \ldots, v_p\} \in K$. Then define

$$\tau_1(v(s)) = \sum_{j=0}^{p} \frac{1}{p+1} v_j.$$

Now, for $x = \sum\limits_{i=1}^{m} r_i v(s_i) \in |K_1|$ any point, define

$$\tau_1(x) = \sum_{i=1}^{m} r_i \tau_1(v(s_i)) \in |K|.$$

An iteration of such homeomorphisms

$$|K_r| \xrightarrow{\tau_1} |K_{r-1}| \xrightarrow{\tau_1} \cdots \xrightarrow{\tau_1} |K_1| \xrightarrow{\tau_1} |K|$$

produces the *r-th barycentric homeomorphism* $\tau_r: |K_r| \to |K|$.

Let $T = (K, \tau)$ be a triangulation of a polyhedron X; then the triangulation $T_r = (K_r, \tau\tau_r)$ is called its *r-th barycentric subdivision*.

Let $\sigma(n)$ be the simplicial complex with $n + 1$ vertices $\{v_0, v_1, \ldots, v_n\}$, where the p-simplices of $\sigma(n)$ consist of all subsets of $\{v_0, v_1, \ldots, v_n\}$ which contain $p + 1$ elements. Thus $|\sigma(n)|$ is a closed n-cell. Let T be the triangulation $(\sigma(n)_1, \tau_1)$ of $|\sigma(n)|$. If K has $n + 1$ vertices, then K is a subcomplex of $\sigma(n)$ and $\mathrm{St}_T|K|$ is an open set in $|\sigma(n)|$ containing $|K|$ (called a *regular neighborhood* of $|K|$). There is a *strong deformation retraction* $r: \mathrm{St}_T|K| \to |K|$, that is, there is a map $H: \mathrm{St}_T|K| \times I \to |K|$ (where I is the interval $[0, 1]$) with the properties

$$H(x, 0) = x \qquad \text{for all } x \in \mathrm{St}_T |K|$$
$$H(k, t) = k \qquad \text{for all } k \in |K|, t \in I$$
$$r(x) = H(x, 1) \in |K| \quad \text{for all } x \in \mathrm{St}_T |K|.$$

For A a subset of a metric space X, $\mathrm{diam}(A)$ — the *diameter* of A — is the supremum of the set $\{d(x, y) \mid x, y \in A\}$ where d is the metric of X. If $T = (K, \tau)$ is a triangulation of a polyhedron X, define the *mesh* of T to be the maximum of the set $\{\mathrm{diam}(\tau |s|)\}$, where s ranges over all simplices of K. A standard result is

Lemma 1. *Given a triangulated space* (X, T) *and* $\epsilon > 0$, *there exists an integer* r *such that* $\mathrm{mesh}(T_r) < \epsilon$.

I. SIMPLICIAL APPROXIMATION

A simplicial function $h: K \to K'$ between simplicial complexes can be made to induce a map $|h|: |K| \to |K'|$ by defining, for $x = \sum_{i=1}^{n} r_i v_i \in |K|$,

$$|h| (x) = \sum_{i=1}^{n} r_i h(v_i).$$

Let (X, T) and (X', T') be triangulated spaces where $T = (K, \tau)$ and $T' = (K', \tau')$. A simplicial function $h: K \to K'$ induces a map, which we also call h, from X to X' so as to make the following diagram commute:

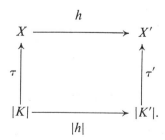

We write $h: (X, T) \to (X', T')$ and call the map h obtained in this way a *simplicial map* of triangulated spaces.

Given triangulated spaces (X, T) and (X, T'), where $T' = (K', \tau')$, and a map $f: X \to X'$, a simplicial map $h: (X, T) \to (X', T')$ is called a *simplicial approximation* to f if, for $x \in X$, the set $f(x) \cup h(x)$ is contained in the closure of $\tau' |s'|$ for some simplex s' of K'.

Theorem 1 (Simplicial Approximation Theorem).   *Let (X, T) and (X', T') be triangulated spaces and let $f: X \to X'$ be any map.   There exists a simplicial approximation $h: (X, T_r) \to (X', T')$ to f for some integer r.*

J. SINGULAR COHOMOLOGY THEORY

For each integer $n \geq 0$, we have the simplicial complex $\sigma(n)$ defined before such that $|\sigma(n)|$ is an n-cell. Let X be any topological space, define $C_n(X)$ to be the free J-module generated by all maps from $|\sigma(n)|$ to X for $n \geq 0$, and let $C_n(X) = 0$ for $n < 0$. Assuming that we have ordered the vertices of $\sigma(n)$ for all n, we can define, for $i = 1, \ldots, n + 1$, simplicial functions $\lambda_i: \sigma(n - 1) \to \sigma(n)$ by

$$\lambda_i(v_j) = \begin{cases} v_j & \text{if } j < i \\ v_{j+1} & \text{if } j \geq i. \end{cases}$$

Then each λ_i induces a map $|\lambda_i|: |\sigma(n - 1)| \to |\sigma(n)|$. Let $e: |\sigma(n)| \to X$ be a map and define

$$\partial(e) = \sum_{i=1}^{n+1} (-1)^i e \, |\lambda_i| \in C_{n-1}(X).$$

Thus we obtain a homomorphism $\partial: C_n(X) \to C_{n-1}(X)$. It is easy to check that $(C(X) = \{C_n(X)\}_{n \in J}, \partial)$ is a chain complex (see Section C). For G an abelian group, the G-cohomology of the chain complex is denoted by $H^*(X; G) = \{H^n(X; G)\}_{n \in J}$ and is called the *singular G-cohomology* of the space X.

Given topological spaces X and Y and a map $f: X \to Y$, we define a chain map

$$C(f): C(X) \to C(Y)$$

in the following manner: Let $e: |\sigma(n)| \to X$ be a map and define $C(f)(e) = fe: |\sigma(n)| \to Y$. Extend $C(f)$ to the required chain map. Consequently, $C(f)$ induces a morphism

$$f^*: H^*(Y; G) \to H^*(X; G).$$

We now list the properties of $H^*(X; G)$ and f^* that we will be using:

1. If X is pathwise connected then $H^0(X; G) \cong G$; and if $f \colon X \to X$ is any map, then $f^* \colon H^0(X; G) \to H^0(X; G)$ is the identity function.
2. If X is a point, then $H^n(X; G) = 0$ for $n \neq 0$.
3. The identity map on X induces the identity morphism on $H^*(X; G)$.
4. If the diagram

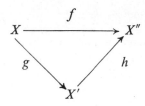

commutes, so does

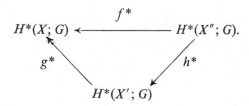

5. If $f, g \colon X \to Y$ are homotopic maps, then

$$f^* = g^* \colon H^*(Y; G) \to H^*(X; G).$$

K. THE CUP PRODUCT

Given Λ-modules M and M', one may form a new Λ-module $M \otimes M'$, their *tensor product*. The module $M \otimes M'$ is generated by all symbols $x \otimes x'$, where $x \in M$ and $x' \in M'$, subject to the relations

$$(\lambda_1 x_1 + \lambda_2 x_2) \otimes x' = \lambda_1(x_1 \otimes x') + \lambda_2(x_2 \otimes x')$$
$$x \otimes (\lambda_1 x_1' + \lambda_2 x_2') = \lambda_1(x \otimes x_1') + \lambda_2(x \otimes x_2')$$

where $\lambda_1, \lambda_2 \in \Lambda$, $x_1, x_2, x \in M$ and $x', x_1', x_2' \in M'$.

Let X be a space and define the *diagonal map* $\Delta \colon X \to X \times X$ by $\Delta(x) = (x, x)$; then Δ induces a morphism

$$\Delta^* \colon H^*(X \times X; G) \to H^*(X; G).$$

As a consequence of the Künneth Theorem it is known that, when F is a field, $H^n(X \times X; F)$ is isomorphic to $\bigoplus_{p+q=n} H^p(X; F) \otimes H^q(X; F)$ (direct sum) for each $n \in J$. Thus, by restriction, we have for each pair $p, q \in J$ a homomorphism

$$\Delta^* \colon H^p(X; F) \otimes H^q(X; F) \to H^{p+q}(X; F).$$

Given $x \in H^p(X; F), y \in H^q(X; F)$, we write $\Delta^*(x \otimes y) = x \cup y \in H^{p+q}(X; F)$, called the *cup product* of x and y.

The properties of the cup product that we will use are the following:

1. There is an element $1 \in H^0(X; F)$ such that $1 \cup x = x \cup 1 = x$ for any $x \in H^*(X; F)$.

2. Cup product is associative, so it makes sense to write $x \cup x = x^2$, $x \cup x^2 = x^2 \cup x = x^3$, and so on.

3. If $f: X \to X'$ is a map and $x_1', x_2' \in H^*(X'; F)$, then

$$f^*(x_1' \cup x_2') = f^*(x_1') \cup f^*(x_2').$$

L. THE IDENTIFICATION THEOREM

Given simplicial complexes K and K', a simplicial function $h: K \to K'$, and an abelian group G, we have two morphisms of graded G-modules. In Section E, we defined the chain map $C(h): C(K) \to C(K')$ which, by the material in Section C, induces a morphism

$$h^*: H^*(K'; G) \to H^*(K; G).$$

On the other hand, we have a map $|h|: |K| \to |K'|$ from Section I which, in the singular G-cohomology of Section J, gives us a morphism

$$|h|^*: H^*(|K'|; G) \to H^*(|K|; G).$$

Theorem 1. *If K is a simplicial complex and G is an abelian group, then there exists an isomorphism of graded G-modules*

$$\eta(K): H^*(K; G) \to H^*(|K|; G)$$

such that, if $h: K \to K'$ is a simplicial function, then the diagram

$$
\begin{array}{ccc}
 & h^* & \\
H^*(K'; G) & \longrightarrow & H^*(K; G) \\
\Big\downarrow{\scriptstyle \eta(K')} & & \Big\downarrow{\scriptstyle \eta(K)} \\
H^*(|K'|; G) & \longrightarrow & H^*(|K|; G) \\
 & |h|^* &
\end{array}
$$

commutes.

We will need one other identification of this sort. Let K be a simplicial complex and let K_r be its rth barycentric subdivision; then $|K|$ and $|K_r|$ may be considered to be the same topological space. Let $h: K_r \to K$ be a simplicial approximation to the identity map on $|K|$; then h induces a morphism $h^*: H^*(K; G) \to H^*(K_r; G)$. By Theorem 1, the diagram

$$
\begin{array}{ccc}
& h^* & \\
H^*(K; G) & \longrightarrow & H^*(K_r; G) \\
\eta(K) \downarrow & & \downarrow \eta(K_r) \\
H^*(|K|; G) & \longrightarrow & H^*(|K_r|; G) \\
& \text{id} &
\end{array}
$$

(where "id" denotes the identity function) commutes so h^* is an isomorphism. In Section F, we defined a chain map $\varphi_r: C(K) \to C(K_r)$. The identification result we need is that

$$\varphi_r^* = (h^*)^{-1}: H^*(K_r; G) \to H^*(K; G)$$

and, therefore, the diagram

$$
\begin{array}{ccc}
& \varphi_r^* & \\
H^*(K_r; G) & \longrightarrow & H^*(K; G) \\
\eta(K_r) \downarrow & & \downarrow \eta(K) \\
H^*(|K_r|; G) & \longrightarrow & H^*(|K|; G) \\
& \text{id} &
\end{array}
$$

commutes.

M. RELATIVE SINGULAR COHOMOLOGY

A (*topological*) *pair* (X, A) consists of a topological space X together with a subspace A. We will think of the single space X as the pair $(X, \varnothing)$.

For pairs (X, A) and (Y, B), the *cartesian product* is the pair defined by

$$(X, A) \times (Y, B) = (X \times Y, X \times B \cup A \times Y),$$

where $X \times Y$ is given the cartesian product topology. As an immediate consequence of the definition we have the following useful result — if $A \subseteq X$ and $B \subseteq Y$ then

$$(X, X - A) \times (Y, Y - B) = (X \times Y, X \times Y - A \times B).$$

A *map* of topological pairs $f: (X, A) \to (Y, B)$ is a map $f: X \to Y$ such that $f(A) \subseteq B$. Given maps $f: (X, A) \to (Y, B)$ and $f': (X', A') \to (Y', B')$

we can define the *product map*

$$f \times f' : (X, A) \times (X', A') \to (Y, B) \times (Y', B')$$

by letting $(f \times f')(x, x') = (f(x), f'(x'))$ for $x \in X$, $x' \in X'$. It is easy to check that the definition of the product map is compatible with the definition of the product of pairs and hence that the product map is really a map of pairs.

A map

$$H : (X \times I, A \times I) = (X, A) \times I \to (Y, B)$$

is called a *homotopy*. A homotopy H induces maps of pairs $f_t : (X, A) \to (Y, B)$ for each $t \in I$ defined by $f_t(x) = H(x, t)$. Maps $f, g : (X, A) \to (Y, B)$ are said to be *homotopic* if there exists a homotopy $H : (X, A) \times I \to (Y, B)$ such that $f = f_0$ and $g = f_1$.

From the material of Section J we have — for a pair (X, A) — two chain complexes $(C(X), \partial)$ and $(C(A), \partial)$, where the two morphisms ∂ are defined in exactly the same manner. Furthermore, $C(A)$ is a graded submodule of the graded J-module $C(X)$; so we can form the quotient graded module

$$\frac{C(X)}{C(A)} = C(X, A).$$

In addition, ∂ induces a morphism

$$\partial : C(X, A) \to C(X, A)$$

so that $(C(X, A), \partial)$ is a chain complex. As in Section C, for G an abelian group, we can define the G-cohomology of $(C(X, A), \partial)$, denote it by $H^*(X, A; G)$, and call it the (*singular*) G-*cohomology* of the pair (X, A).

A map of pairs $f : (X, A) \to (Y, B)$ induces chain maps $C(f) : C(X) \to C(Y)$ and $C(f) : C(A) \to C(B)$. The quotient morphism from $C(X, A)$ to $C(Y, B)$ induced by $C(f)$ is a chain map and therefore, again following Section C, gives rise to a morphism

$$f^* : H^*(Y, B; G) \to H^*(X, A; G).$$

Of course $C(\varnothing)$ is trivial, so $H^*(X; G) = H^*(X, \varnothing; G)$, and everything we have outlined is a direct generalization of the material of Sections C and J — when we identify a space X with the pair $(X, \varnothing)$ and a map $f : X \to Y$ with the map of pairs $f : (X, \varnothing) \to (Y, \varnothing)$.

The morphism $f^* : H^*(Y, B; G) \to H^*(X, A; G)$ induced by a map $f : (X, A) \to (Y, B)$ has the properties one would expect it to have. If $f : (X, A) \to (X, A)$ is the identity map, then $f^* : H^*(X, A; G) \to H^*(X, A; G)$ is the identity morphism. If the diagram

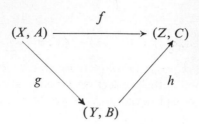

commutes, then the induced diagram

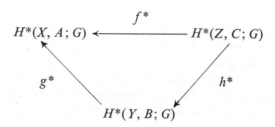

also commutes. If $f, g: (X, A) \to (Y, B)$ are homotopic maps, then

$$f^* = g^*: H^*(Y, B; G) \to H^*(X, A; G).$$

Let $M = \{M_p\}_{p \in J}$ be a graded Λ-module and $h: M \to M$ be a morphism of degree one. We call the pair (M, h) an *exact sequence* if $\mathrm{Im}(h_{p-1}) = \mathrm{Ker}(h_p)$ for all $p \in J$. It is customary to write that

$$\cdots \xrightarrow{h_{p-2}} M_{p-1} \xrightarrow{h_{p-1}} M_p \xrightarrow{h_p} M_{p+1} \xrightarrow{h_{p+1}} \cdots$$

is *exact*.

Given a pair (X, A), there are inclusions $i: A \to X$ and $j: (X, \varnothing) \to (X, A)$ inducing morphisms $i^*: H^*(X; G) \to H^*(A; G)$ and $j^*: H^*(X, A; G) \to H^*(X, \varnothing; G) = H^*(X; G)$. There exist homomorphisms

$$\delta: H^{p-1}(A; G) \to H^p(X, A; G)$$

for all $p \in J$ so that

$$\cdots \xrightarrow{i^*} H^{p-1}(A; G) \xrightarrow{\delta} H^p(X, A; G) \xrightarrow{j^*}$$

$$H^p(X; G) \xrightarrow{i^*} H^p(A; G) \xrightarrow{\delta} \cdots$$

is exact. The homomorphisms δ have the additional property of being *natural* in the following sense: Given a map of pairs $f: (X, A) \to (Y, B)$, the diagram

$$\begin{array}{ccc}
H^p(B;G) & \xrightarrow{\;\;\delta\;\;} & H^p(Y,B;G) \\[1mm]
\Big\downarrow{\scriptstyle f^*} & & \Big\downarrow{\scriptstyle f^*} \\[1mm]
H^p(A;G) & \xrightarrow[\;\;\delta\;\;]{} & H^p(X,A;G)
\end{array}$$

commutes for all $p \in J$.

If (X, A) is a pair and U is a subset of A, then we have an inclusion $j: (X - U, A - U) \to (X, A)$. If the closure of U is contained in the interior of A, the morphism

$$j^*: H^*(X, A; G) \to H^*(X - U, A - U; G)$$

is an isomorphism. This property of the cohomology of a pair is called *excision.*

Let R^n denote euclidean n-dimensional space. Recall that the unit sphere S^n in R^{n+1} is defined by

$$S^n = \left\{ (x_1, \ldots, x_{n+1}) \in R^{n+1} \,\middle|\, \sum_{j=1}^{n+1} x_j^2 = 1 \right\}.$$

Let $P = (1, 0, \ldots, 0) \in S^n$; then R^n is homeomorphic to $S^n - P$. In what follows we will identify R^n with $S^n - P$ so that a point of R^n is thought of as being also a point of S^n. Let 0 denote the origin in R^n. One fact about R^n that we will use is that

$$H^p(R^n, R^n - 0; Q) \cong \begin{cases} Q & \text{if } p = n \\ 0 & \text{otherwise.} \end{cases}$$

Another is the following application of excision: Let $C \subseteq R^n$ be a compact set and let $j: (R^n, R^n - C) \to (S^n, S^n - C)$ be inclusion. Then

$$j^*: H^*(S^n, S^n - C; Q) \to H^*(R^n, R^n - C; Q)$$

is an isomorphism of graded vector spaces.

If X and Y are spaces and we have points $x \in X$, $y \in Y$, define

$$X \vee Y = (X \times y) \cup (x \times Y) \subset X \times Y.$$

If

$$S^m \wedge S^n = \frac{S^m \times S^n}{S^m \vee S^n}$$

is given the quotient topology, then there is a homeomorphism $h: S^m \wedge S^n \to S^{m+n}$. Let $\pi': S^m \times S^n \to S^m \wedge S^n$ be the quotient map and define $\pi = h\pi': S^m \times S^n \to S^{m+n}$. Then the homomorphism

$$\pi^*: H^{m+n}(S^{m+n}; Q) \to H^{m+n}(S^m \times S^n; Q)$$

is an isomorphism.

Let $X_1, \ldots, X_n$ be disjoint open subsets of a space X, and for $j = 1, \ldots, n$, let $A_j \subseteq X_j$. Then it can be proved that

$$H^p\left(\bigcup_{j=1}^n X_j, \bigcup_{j=1}^n A_j; Q\right) \cong \bigoplus_{j=1}^n H^p(X_j, A_j; Q)$$

for all $p \in J$. Thus we can write an element $z \in H^p\left(\bigcup_{j=1}^n X_j, \bigcup_{j=1}^n A_j; Q\right)$ as

$z = (z_1, \ldots, z_n)$ where $z_j \in H^p(X_j, A_j; Q)$. Let $h_k \colon (X_k, A_k) \to \left(\bigcup_{j=1}^n X_j, \bigcup_{j=1}^n A_j\right)$

be inclusion. The morphism

$$(h_k)^* \colon H^*\left(\bigcup_{j=1}^n X_j, \bigcup_{j=1}^n A_j; Q\right) \to H^*(X_k, A_k; Q)$$

is characterized by the property that, if

$$z = (z_1, \ldots, z_n) \in H^*\left(\bigcup_{j=1}^n X_j, \bigcup_{j=1}^n A_j; Q\right),$$

then
$$(h_k)^*(z) = z_k \in H^*(X_k, A_k; Q).$$

Given homomorphisms $h_1 \colon M_1 \to M_1'$ and $h_2 \colon M_2 \to M_2'$ of Λ-modules, we can define their *tensor product*

$$h_1 \otimes h_2 \colon M_1 \otimes M_2 \to M_1' \otimes M_2'$$

by setting $h_1 \otimes h_2 \, (x_1 \otimes x_2) = h_1(x_1) \otimes h_2(x_2)$; then $h_1 \otimes h_2$ will again be a homomorphism of Λ-modules. Note that if $h_1 \colon M_1 \to M_1$ and $h_2 \colon M_2 \to M_2$ are identity functions, so is $h_1 \otimes h_2$.

If

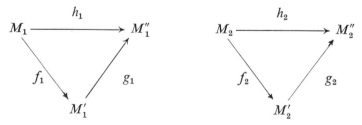

are commuting diagrams of Λ-modules and homomorphisms, then

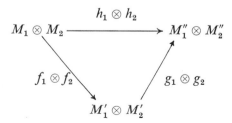

commutes. In particular, if $h_1: M_1 \to M_1'$ and $h_2: M_2 \to M_2'$ are isomorphisms, then $h_1 \otimes h_2$ is an isomorphism where $(h_1 \otimes h_2)^{-1} = h_1^{-1} \otimes h_2^{-1}$.

For "nice" pairs (X, A) and (Y, B), the Künneth Theorem relates the rational cohomology of the product $(X, A) \times (Y, B)$ to the cohomology of each factor in the following manner: For each $n \in J$ and any field F there is an isomorphism

$$\alpha: \quad \bigoplus_{p+q=n} H^p(X, A; F) \otimes H^q(Y, B; F) \to H^n((X, A) \times (Y, B); F)$$

called a *Künneth isomorphism.* Let $f: (X, A) \to (X', A')$ and $g: (Y, B) \to (Y', B')$ be maps. The Künneth isomorphism α is *natural* in the sense that the diagram (Figure 2) commutes.

$$\begin{array}{ccc}
H^n((X',A') \times (Y',B'); F) & \xrightarrow{\quad (f \times g)^* \quad} & H^n((X, A) \times (Y, B); F) \\
\alpha \uparrow & & \uparrow \alpha \\
\displaystyle\bigoplus_{p+q=n} H^p(X',A';F) \otimes H^q(Y',B';F) & \xrightarrow{\quad f^* \otimes g^* \quad} & \displaystyle\bigoplus_{p+q=n} H^p(X, A; F) \otimes H^q(Y, B; F)
\end{array}$$

FIGURE 2

We will adopt certain conventions throughout the book in order to simplify the notation. We will write $H^*(X, A)$ for $H^*(X, A; G)$ when it is not confusing to do so. In the rest of the present section, $H^*(X, A)$ will stand for F-cohomology where F is any field. If we have a set $\{G_j\}_{j \in J}$ of groups such that all but a finite number of the G_j are trivial, then we will write $\bigoplus_{j \in J} G_j$ to mean the *direct sum* of the nontrivial groups. We will replace the vector space $H^n((X, A) \times (Y, B))$ by $\bigoplus_{p+q=n} H^p(X, A) \otimes H^q(Y, B)$, without explicit mention of the fact that it is the Künneth Theorem that permits us to make the replacement, or that commutativity of diagrams is not destroyed because the Künneth isomorphism is natural. We will also replace $(f \times g)^*$ by $f^* \otimes g^*$ whenever it is convenient to do so. In the same spirit, if $f: A \to B \times C$ is a map, then we will write the induced homomorphism as

$$f^*: \quad \bigoplus_{p+q=n} H^p(B) \otimes H^q(C) \to H^n(A),$$

where it is understood that f^* here means the inverse of the Künneth isomorphism composed with the usual induced homomorphism.

We will be using some maps for which the behavior of the induced homomorphisms is well known. Let $t: (X, A) \times (Y, B) \to (Y, B) \times (X, A)$ be the map defined by $t(x, y) = (y, x)$. Consider the homomorphism

$$t^*: \quad \bigoplus_{p+q=n} H^p(Y, B) \otimes H^q(X, A) \to \bigoplus_{p+q=n} H^p(X, A) \otimes H^q(Y, B)$$

and let $z \in H^p(Y, B)$, $z' \in H^q(X, A)$. Then

$$t^*(z \otimes z') = (-1)^{pq}(z' \otimes z).$$

The *diagonal map* $\Delta: (X, A) \to (X, A) \times X$ is defined by $\Delta(x) = (x, x)$. It induces

$$\Delta^*: \bigoplus_{p+q=n} H^p(X, A) \otimes H^q(X) \to H^n(X, A).$$

We extend the definition of Δ^* to

$$\Delta^*: \bigoplus_{p,q \in J} H^p(X, A) \otimes H^q(X) \to H^n(X, A)$$

by setting

$$\Delta^*(H^p(X, A) \otimes H^q(X)) = 0 \in H^n(X, A)$$

if $p + q \neq n$. Define $\eta: R^n \to R^n$ by

$$\eta(x_1, \ldots, x_{j-1}, x_j, x_{j+1}, \ldots, x_n) = (x_1, \ldots, x_{j-1}, -x_j, x_{j+1}, \ldots, x_n).$$

Then η induces

$$\eta^*: H^n(R^n, R^n - 0) \to H^n(R^n, R^n - 0)$$

so that, for $z \in H^n(R^n, R^n - 0)$, $\eta^*(z) = -z$. Let B be a contractible space, choose $b \in B$, let S^n be the n-sphere, and define $i: S^n \to S^n \times B$ by $i(x) = (x, b)$. For v a generator of $H^n(S^n) \cong F$ and $1 \in H^0(B) \cong F$, then $i^*: H^n(S^n) \otimes H^0(B) \to H^n(S^n)$ has the property that $i^*(v \otimes 1) = v$.

Let $\sigma(n)$ be the simplicial complex from Section H such that $|\sigma(n)|$ is a closed n-cell. Define $\sigma(n)^r$ to be the subcomplex of all p-simplices of $\sigma(n)$, $p \leq r$, called the *r-skeleton* of $\sigma(n)$. Let $s_1, \ldots, s_m$ be the $(r + 1)$-simplices of $\sigma(n)$, and define S^r_p to be the boundary of the set $|s_p|$ — which is a subset of $|K|$ homeomorphic to the r-sphere. Choose generators $v_p \in H^r(S^r_p) \cong F$. It is known that $H^r(\sigma(n)^r)$ is an m-dimensional vector space and that there is a basis $v'_1, \ldots, v'_m$ for $H^r(\sigma(n)^r)$ with the following property: Let $i_p: S^r_p \to |\sigma(n)^r|$ be inclusion; then i_p induces $i_p^*: H^r(\sigma(n)^r) \to H^r(S^r_p)$. For any element $z = a_1 v'_1 + \cdots + a_m v'_m$ of $H^r(\sigma(n)^r)$, it is true that $i_p^*(z) = a_p v_p$.

N. THE FUNDAMENTAL GROUP

Let $I^n = I \times \cdots \times I$ (n factors). Given a space X and a point $x_0 \in X$, denote by $\text{Map}((I^n, \partial I^n), (X, x_0))$ the set of all maps of pairs from $(I^n, \partial I^n)$ to (X, x_0). Two such maps are homotopic if there is a homotopy of pairs connecting them. The relation "is homotopic to" partitions the elements of $\text{Map}((I^n, \partial I^n), (X, x_0))$ into equivalence classes. The set of equivalence classes is denoted by $\pi_n(X, x_0)$. The set $\pi_n(X, x_0)$ is given the structure of a group in the following manner: Write an element $r \in I^n$ as $r = (r_1, \ldots, r_n)$, $r_j \in I$. Given $\alpha, \beta \in \pi_n(X, x_0)$, let $g \in \alpha$, $h \in \beta$. Then define the product $\alpha\beta \in \pi_n(X, x_0)$ to be the equivalence class containing the map $gh: (I^n, \partial I^n) \to (X, x_0)$ where

$$gh(r) = \begin{cases} g(r_1, \ldots, r_{n-1}, 2r_n) & \text{if } 0 \leq r_n \leq \frac{1}{2} \\ h(r_1, \ldots, r_{n-1}, 2r_n - 1) & \text{if } \frac{1}{2} \leq r_n \leq 1. \end{cases}$$

The unit element of the group $\pi_n(X, x_0)$ is the equivalence class containing the constant map from I^n to x_0.

Let X and Y be spaces and take $x_0 \in X$, $y_0 \in Y$. For all $n \geq 1$, the group $\pi_n(X \times Y, (x_0, y_0))$ is isomorphic to the direct sum $\pi_n(X, x_0) \oplus \pi_n(Y, y_0)$.

We will, for the most part, be working with the group $\pi_1(X, x_0)$, the *fundamental group of X based at x_0*. In this case $\text{Map}((I^n, \partial I^n), (X, x_0))$ is just the set of paths $C: I \to X$ such that $C(0) = C(1) = x_0$, which paths are called the *loops* in X based at x_0.

The inverse of the equivalence class containing a loop C is the class containing the path C^{-1} defined by $C^{-1}(t) = C(1 - t)$ for $t \in I$. In symbols, $\{C\}^{-1} = \{C^{-1}\}$.

Given a map $f: X \to Y$ and a loop C in X based at x_0, define $f_\pi\{C\} = \{fC\}$, noting that fC is a loop in Y based at $f(x_0)$. The function f_π is a homomorphism $f_\pi: \pi_1(X, x_0) \to \pi_1(Y, f(x_0))$. If f is the identity map, then f_π is the identity isomorphism. If $f, f': (X, x_0) \to (Y, y_0)$ are homotopic maps of pairs, then the induced homomorphisms f_π, f_π' are identical.

Suppose x_0 and x_1 are points in X and P is a path in X from x_0 to x_1. For C a loop in X at x_0, define $P_\pi\{C\} = \{P^{-1}CP\}$, then $P_\pi: \pi_1(X, x_0) \to \pi_1(X, x_1)$ is an isomorphism. Therefore, when X is a pathwise connected space, $\pi_1(X, x_0)$ is independent, up to isomorphism, of the choice of the base point x_0.

If D is a loop in X based at x_0, then D induces an isomorphism $D_\pi: \pi_1(X, x_0) \to \pi_1(X, x_0)$. The isomorphism D_π is not, in general, the identity isomorphism. In fact, $D_\pi\{C\} = \{D\}^{-1}\{C\}\{D\}$, so $D_\pi\{C\} = \{C\}$ if and only if $\{D\}$ commutes with $\{C\}$ in $\pi_1(X, x_0)$. Another useful way of describing cases when an element of $\pi_1(X, x_0)$ stays fixed under D_π is given by the following result:

Lemma 1. *Let C and D be loops in X based at x_0. Then $D_\pi\{C\} = \{C\}$ if and only if there is a map $L: I \times I \to X$ such that $L(t, 0) = L(t, 1) = C(t)$ for all $t \in I$ and $L(0, u) = L(1, u) = D(u)$ for all $u \in I$.*

The proof is left to the reader.

NOTES

The general reference for this chapter is [49].*

The original proof of the Hopf Trace Theorem is in [26]. The Euler-Poincaré Formula was proved by Poincaré in [45].

EXERCISES

1. Prove that if M and N are Λ-modules, G is an abelian group, and $h\colon M \to N$ is a homomorphism, then the function

$$\mathrm{Hom}(h, G)\colon \mathrm{Hom}(N, G) \to \mathrm{Hom}(M, G),$$

defined by

$$\mathrm{Hom}(h, G)(\varphi)(x) = \varphi(h(x)) \qquad (\varphi \in \mathrm{Hom}(N, G),\ x \in M),$$

is a homomorphism of G-modules.

2. Prove B.1.

3. Prove B.2.

4. Consider the simplicial complex K consisting of all proper nonempty subsets of a set $\{x, y, z\}$. Let $f\colon K \to K$ be the simplicial function such that $f(x) = x$, $f(y) = z$, $f(z) = y$. Verify directly from the definitions that $C(f)\colon C(K) \to C(K)$ is a chain map. Prove that $\mathrm{Tr}(C(f)) = \mathrm{Tr}(C(f)^*)$ by going through the steps in the proof of the Hopf Trace Theorem for this special case.

5. For the complex K of Exercise 4, list the simplices of its barycentric subdivision K_1 and write out the definition of $\varphi\colon C(K) \to C(K_1)$.

6. Prove that for any simplicial complex K, if s is a p-simplex of K then $\varphi(\partial\langle s \rangle)$ is of the form

$$\sum_i a_i \langle v(s_{i0}), \ldots, v(s_{i, p-1}) \rangle,$$

where $s_{ij} \subset s$ for all i and j.

7. Verify that if L and M are subcomplexes of a simplicial complex K, so also are $L \cup M$ and $L \cap M$. Prove that

$$\chi(C(L \cup M)) = \chi(C(L)) + \chi(C(M)) - \chi(C(L \cap M)).$$

8. Verify the equation

$$(X, X - A) \times (Y, Y - B) = (X \times Y, X \times Y - A \times B).$$

9. Prove that $S^p \wedge S^q$ (see Section M) is homeomorphic to S^{p+q}.

10. Prove Lemma N.1.

* Bibliographic entries appear at the end of the volume.

Chapter II

The Lefschetz Theorem for Polyhedra

This chapter consists of a proof of the Lefschetz Fixed Point Theorem for polyhedra and also some geometric applications of the theorem.

A. THE LEFSCHETZ THEOREM

We consider a polyhedron X and a map $f: X \to X$. The *Lefschetz number* $L(f; F)$ of f, where F is a field, is defined to be the Lefschetz number (from Section I.B) of the morphism

$$f^*: H^*(X; F) \to H^*(X; F).$$

Let (K, τ) be a triangulation of X then, by I.L.1,

$$H^*(X; F) \cong H^*(|K|; F) \cong H^*(K; F).$$

Since $H^*(K; F)$ is clearly a finitary graded vector space, so also is $H^*(X; F)$, and we see that the Lefschetz number is well defined.

Since homotopic maps induce the same morphisms of $H^*(X; F)$, it is obvious that, if $f, g: X \to X$ are homotopic maps, then $L(f; F) = L(g; F)$.

A *fixed point* of a map $f: X \to X$ is a point $x \in X$ such that $f(x) = x$. A map without fixed points is said to be *fixed point free*.

Theorem 1 (The Lefschetz Fixed Point Theorem for Polyhedra). *Let X be a polyhedron and f a map from X to X. If $L(f; F) \neq 0$ for any field F, then every map homotopic to f has a fixed point.*

Proof The contrapositive statement of the theorem is: If there is a fixed point free map homotopic to f, then $L(f; F) = 0$ for every field F — and that is what we shall prove. Since homotopic maps have the same Lefschetz number, it suffices to prove that if f is fixed point free then $L(f; F) = 0$.

Define $f \times 1 : X \to X \times X$ by $(f \times 1)(x) = (f(x), x)$. Choose a metric $\boldsymbol{d} : X \times X \to R$ (the reals) which induces the topology of X. Hence $\boldsymbol{d}(f \times 1) : X \to R$ is a map and, since f is fixed point free, $\boldsymbol{d}(f(x), x) > 0$ for all $x \in X$; thus $\boldsymbol{d}(f \times 1)(X)$ is contained in $(0, \infty) \subset R$ as a compact subset. We conclude, therefore, that there exists $\epsilon > 0$ such that $\boldsymbol{d}(f(x), x) > \epsilon$ for all $x \in X$. Let $T = (K, \tau)$ be a triangulation of X of mesh less than $\epsilon/2$ (use I.H.1). Let $h : (X, T_r) \to (X, T)$ be a simplicial approximation to f, then for $x \in X$, $\boldsymbol{d}(f(x), h(x)) < \epsilon/2$. The key to the proof is the fact that for any $x \in X$,

$$\epsilon < \boldsymbol{d}(f(x), x) \leq \boldsymbol{d}(f(x), h(x)) + \boldsymbol{d}(h(x), x)$$
$$< \frac{\epsilon}{2} + \boldsymbol{d}(h(x), x),$$

so that

$$\boldsymbol{d}(h(x), x) > \frac{\epsilon}{2} > \text{mesh}(T).$$

Consequently, if $x \in |K_r|$ such that $\tau_r(x) \in |s| \subset |K|$, then $|h|(x) \notin |s|$, since otherwise we would have

$$\tau\tau_r(x) \cup \tau |h|(x) = \tau\tau_r(x) \cup h(\tau\tau_r(x)) \in \tau |s|$$

because the diagram

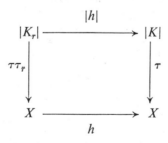

commutes. For $\langle s \rangle \in C(K)$ an oriented simplex, it is clear from the definitions that $\varphi_r \langle s \rangle = \sum a_j \langle s_j^r \rangle$ where $a_j = \pm 1$, $\langle s_j^r \rangle$ is an oriented simplex of K_r, and each s_j^r has the property that $\tau_r |s_j^r| \subset |s|$. The remark above therefore implies that $|h| \, |s_j{}^r| \cap |s| = \varnothing$ (the sets are disjoint). Certainly, then, $C(h)\langle s_j^r \rangle \neq \pm \langle s \rangle$ since otherwise $|h| \, |s_j^r| = |s|$. Looking at the row of the matrix of $C_p(h)\varphi_r$, the morphism $C_p(h)\varphi_r$ restricted to $C_p(K)$ corresponding to s we conclude that the entry at the element on the main diagonal is *zero*. Therefore $\mathrm{Tr}(C_p(h)\varphi_r) = 0$ for all p and so the trace of the alternating sign morphism corresponding to $C(h)\varphi_r$ is also zero. Thus, by the corollary to the Hopf Trace Theorem (I.D.3), $L(\varphi_r^* h^*) = L(C(h)\varphi_r) = 0$. Using the material of Section I.L, we have the commutative diagram

$$
\begin{array}{ccccc}
 & h^* & & \varphi_r^* & \\
H^*(K; F) & \longrightarrow & H^*(K_r; F) & \longrightarrow & H^*(K; F) \\
\eta(K) \downarrow \cong & & \cong \downarrow \eta(K_r) & & \cong \downarrow \eta(K) \\
H^*(|K|; F) & \longrightarrow & H^*(|K_r|; F) & \longrightarrow & H^*(|K|; F) \\
& |h|^* & & \mathrm{id} & \\
\| & & \| & & \| \\
H^*(X; F) & \longrightarrow & H^*(X; F) & \longrightarrow & H^*(X; F) \\
& f^* & & \mathrm{id} &
\end{array}
$$

Therefore, by I.B.2,

$$L(f; F) = L(f^*) = L(\varphi_r^* h^*) = 0. \quad \blacksquare$$

Our statement of the Lefschetz Theorem differs from the traditional one in which the conclusion is stated — "If $L(f) \neq 0$ then f has a fixed point" — where $L(f)$ is the Lefschetz number with respect to rational cohomology. We proved the theorem for $L(f; F)$, where F is any field, because it is often easier to compute $L(f; F)$; if the field is chosen properly, than it is to compute $L(f)$ (compare Section C below). We stated the conclusion for all maps homotopic to f rather than just for the map f itself partly because we want to emphasize that the Lefschetz Theorem is indeed a statement about an entire homotopy class of maps, rather than about a single map. A more important reason, however, was that the converse of the traditional statement is — "If $L(f) = 0$, then f is fixed point free" — and this is trivially false, e.g., let f be the identity map on $|K|$ where $\chi(C(K)) = 0$ (see Section I.G). On the other hand, the converse of our statement is — "If $L(f; F) = 0$ for all fields F, then there is a fixed point free map g homotopic to f". We shall prove in Chapter VIII that such a map g often does exist.

B. THE FIGURE-EIGHT

Although we will prove in Chapter VIII that, for a large class of polyhedra, the converse of the Lefschetz Fixed Point Theorem is true, nevertheless, for polyhedra in general, the converse is false. In this section we will define a map — which we will call e — from the figure-eight to itself such that $L(e) = 0$ and yet every map homotopic to e has a fixed point (and in fact has at least two of them). We will prove that $L(e) = 0$ now. The behavior of the maps homotopic to e will have to be considered later when we have more machinery to work with.

Let us begin with a simplicial complex K consisting of vertices $v_1, v_2, \ldots, v_7$ and the following 1-simplices:

$$\{v_1, v_2\}, \quad \{v_1, v_3\}, \quad \{v_2, v_4\}, \quad \{v_3, v_4\}$$
$$\{v_4, v_5\}, \quad \{v_5, v_6\}, \quad \{v_6, v_7\}, \quad \{v_4, v_7\}.$$

Next consider the barycentric subdivision K_1. Denote the vertex of K_1 corresponding to a vertex v_i of K by (i) and the vertex corresponding to a 1-simplex $\{v_i, v_j\}$ by (ij). In order to give a picture of what is going on, Figure 1 shows a subset of the plane homeomorphic to $|K_1|$ with the images of the geometric realizations of the vertices labeled.

Define a simplicial function $e': K_1 \rightarrow K$ to be the one which maps vertices according to the following table:

v	1	2	3	4	5	6	7	12	13	24	34	45	56	67	47
$e'(v)$	v_1	v_3	v_2	v_4	v_6	v_4	v_6	v_3	v_2	v_3	v_2	v_5	v_7	v_5	v_7

Our "figure-eight" space is $|K|$ and the map we will study is

$$e = |e'| \tau_1^{-1} : |K| \rightarrow |K|.$$

Roughly speaking, what e does is to "flip" the top of the figure-eight about the axis through (1) and (4) (see Figure 1) and to "wrap" the bottom half of the figure-eight around itself twice in the counter-clockwise direction. The map e does more than flip the top half of the figure-eight since two arcs collapse in the process, but the reversal of the two sides of the top is the essential idea.

We have defined e so that it is a simplicial map induced by the simplicial function $e' K:_1 \rightarrow K$. The observations of the previous section tell us that

$$L(e) = \mathrm{Tr}(C_0(e')\varphi) - \mathrm{Tr}(C_1(e')\varphi).$$

Since $\varphi\langle v_i \rangle = (i)$, then

$$C(e')\varphi\langle v_i \rangle = \langle e'(i) \rangle.$$

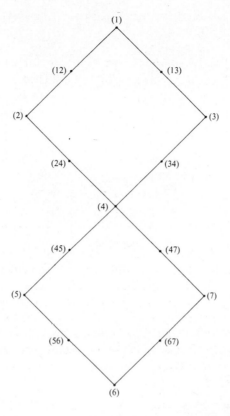

FIGURE 1

From the table above, we see that the matrix of $C_0(e')\varphi$ with respect to the basis $\langle v_1 \rangle, \ldots, \langle v_7 \rangle$ has ones on the main diagonal in the first and fourth rows and zeros at all other main diagonal locations, so $\text{Tr}(C_0(e')\varphi) = 2$.

Applying the definitions of φ and e' we find that

$$
\begin{aligned}
C(e')\varphi\langle v_1, v_2 \rangle &= C(e')((12) \cdot \varphi\partial\langle v_1, v_2 \rangle) \\
&= C(e')((12) \cdot (\langle 2 \rangle - \langle 1 \rangle)) \\
&= C(e')(\langle 12, 2 \rangle - \langle 12, 1 \rangle) \\
&= \langle e'(12), e'(2) \rangle - \langle e'(12), e'(1) \rangle \\
&= \langle v_3, v_3 \rangle - \langle v_3, v_1 \rangle \\
&= \langle v_1, v_3 \rangle.
\end{aligned}
$$

Similar computations for the other oriented 1-simplices of K produce the table below (see Ex. 10).

$\langle v_i, v_j \rangle$	$C(e')\varphi\langle v_i, v_j \rangle$
$\langle v_1, v_2 \rangle$	$\langle v_1, v_3 \rangle$
$\langle v_1, v_3 \rangle$	$\langle v_1, v_2 \rangle$
$\langle v_2, v_4 \rangle$	$\langle v_3, v_4 \rangle$
$\langle v_3, v_4 \rangle$	$\langle v_2, v_4 \rangle$
$\langle v_4, v_5 \rangle$	$\langle v_4, v_5 \rangle + \langle v_5, v_6 \rangle$
$\langle v_4, v_7 \rangle$	$\langle v_4, v_7 \rangle - \langle v_6, v_7 \rangle$
$\langle v_5, v_6 \rangle$	$-\langle v_4, v_7 \rangle + \langle v_6, v_7 \rangle$
$\langle v_6, v_7 \rangle$	$\langle v_4, v_5 \rangle + \langle v_5, v_6 \rangle$

FIGURE 2

Reading from the table, we see that $\langle v_4, v_5 \rangle$ contributes a "one" to the main diagonal of the matrix of $C_1(e')\varphi$, as does $\langle v_4, v_7 \rangle$, and that there is no other nonzero entry on the diagonal. Therefore $\mathrm{Tr}(C_1(e')\varphi) = 2$, so $L(e) = 2 - 2 = 0$ just as we claimed.

Another, more sophisticated, proof that $L(e) = 0$ can be obtained if one knows that $H^1(|K|; Q)$ is a two-dimensional vector space and that the matrix of $e^*: H^1(|K|; Q) \to H^1(|K|; Q)$, with respect to a properly chosen basis, looks like $\begin{bmatrix} -1 & 0 \\ 0 & 2 \end{bmatrix}$.

C. THE FIXED POINT PROPERTY

A space X has the *fixed point property* if every map $f: X \to X$ has a fixed point. The fixed point property is a topological invariant (Ex. 1). We will see that some polyhedra have the property that every map on them has a nonvanishing Lefschetz number which, by the Lefschetz Fixed Point Theorem, implies that they have the fixed point property.

A connected polyhedron X is said to be *Q-acyclic* if $H^p(X; Q) = 0$ for all $p \neq 0$. Let $f: X \to X$ be any map of a Q-acyclic polyhedron. Then, clearly, $L(f)$ is the trace of the identity function

$$f^*: H^0(X; Q) \to H^0(X; Q) \cong Q,$$

so $L(f) = 1$. We have proved that *a Q-acyclic polyhedron has the fixed point property*.

Examples of Q-acyclic polyhedra are not hard to find. If a polyhedron X is contractible to a point $x_0 \in X$, then this implies that, for $i: x_0 \to X$, the inclusion

$$i^*: H^*(X; Q) \to H^*(x_0; Q)$$

is an isomorphism, and thus X is Q-acyclic, because x_0 certainly is. Therefore, *a contractible polyhedron has the fixed point property.*

A very special case of this last result is a fixed point theorem that has been the motivation for a large number of results in this subject. Let D^n be the set of points of R^n whose distance from the origin 0 is less than or equal to one. Since D^n is a contractible polyhedron we have [the Brouwer Fixed Point Theorem]: *The n-cell D^n has the fixed point property.*

There are polyhedra which are not contractible but are nevertheless Q-acyclic. Define an equivalence relation on $R^{n+1} - 0$ by calling x and y equivalent if there exists $r \in R$ such that $x = ry$. The set of equivalence classes with the quotient topology is a polyhedron called *real projective n-space RP^n.* The J-cohomology of RP^n is

$$H^p(RP^n; J) = \begin{cases} J & \text{if } p = 0 \\ J_2 & \text{if } p \text{ is even and } 0 < p < n \\ J & \text{if } p = n \text{ and } n \text{ is odd} \\ 0 & \text{otherwise,} \end{cases}$$

where J_2 is the cyclic group of order 2. Since $H^*(RP^n; J) \not\cong H^*(x_0; J)$, then RP^n can not be contractible. We use the consequence of the Universal Coefficient Theorem that, if $H^p(X; J)$ is finite then $H^p(X; Q) = 0$, to see that RP^n is Q-acyclic when n is even. We have proved that *the real projective spaces RP^{2n} have the fixed point property.* On the other hand, when n is odd, RP^n is not Q-acyclic and, in fact, does not have the fixed point property (Ex. 4).

The use of the Lefschetz Fixed Point Theorem to prove that a polyhedron has the fixed point property is not restricted to Q-acyclic spaces. Let Γ denote either the complex numbers C or the quaternions H. Topologize Γ by identifying it with R^2 if $\Gamma = C$ or with R^4 if $\Gamma = H$. Let $\Gamma^n = \Gamma \times \Gamma \times \cdots \times \Gamma$ (n copies of Γ). Define an equivalence relation $\sim$ on $\Gamma^{n+1} - 0$ by setting $x \sim y$ if there exists $\gamma \in \Gamma$ such that $x = \gamma y$. The set of equivalence classes, denoted by ΓP^n, with the quotient topology, form a polyhedron which is called *complex* (respectively *quaternionic*) *projective n-space CP^n* (respectively *HP^n*). It is known that

$$H^p(\Gamma P^n; J_2) = \begin{cases} J_2 & \text{if } p = dk; k = 0, 1, \ldots, n \\ 0 & \text{otherwise,} \end{cases}$$

where $d = 2$ if $\Gamma = C$ and $d = 4$ if $\Gamma = H$. Let $\alpha \in H^d(\Gamma P^n; J_2)$ be the non-zero element; then α^k (cup product) is the nonzero element of $H^{dk}(\Gamma P^n; J_2)$ for $k = 1, \ldots, n$.

Let $f: \Gamma P^n \to \Gamma P^n$ be any map. Since ΓP^n is connected, $f^*(1) = 1 \in H^0(\Gamma P^n; J_2)$. Let $f^*(\alpha) = a\alpha$, where $a \in J_2$. Because f^* preserves cup products, $f^*(\alpha^k) = a^k\alpha^k = a\alpha^k$. Thus $L(f; J_2) = 1 + na$, so if n is even then $L(f, J_2)$ is odd and, by the Lefschetz Theorem, f has a fixed point. We have proved that *complex projective spaces CP^{2m} and quaternionic projective spaces HP^{2m} have the fixed point property.*

D. DEFORMATIONS

The identity map on a space X is denoted by 1_X. A *deformation* of X is a map homotopic to 1_X. Obviously there is no point in studying the fixed points of 1_X, but one would like to know whether a space admits a fixed point free deformation.

Let X be a polyhedron, then $L(1_X)$ is, by Section I.G, the Euler characteristic of $H^*(X, Q)$ which we write as $\chi(X)$ and call the *Euler characteristic* of X. By I.G.1, letting $b_p(X) = \dim(H^p(X; Q))$, we find that $\chi(X) = \sum_{p \in J} (-1)^p b_p(X)$. The Lefschetz Theorem tells us that a necessary condition for a polyhedron X to admit a fixed point free deformation is that $\chi(X) = 0$.

None of the spheres has the fixed point property, because we can define a fixed point free map $f: S^n \to S^n$, called the *antipodal map*, by $f(x) = -x$; but the question of the existence of fixed point free deformations does arise. Now

$$H^p(S^n; Q) = \begin{cases} Q & \text{if } p = 0 \text{ or } p = n \\ 0 & \text{otherwise} \end{cases}$$

so $b_0(S^n) = b_n(S^n) = 1$ and $b_p(S^n) = 0$ for all other $p \in J$. Thus

$$\chi(S^n) = 1 + (-1)^n 1 = \begin{cases} 0 & \text{if } n \text{ is odd} \\ 2 & \text{if } n \text{ is even.} \end{cases}$$

Therefore, the even-dimensional spheres do not admit fixed point free deformations.

Even though the fact that $\chi(X)$ vanishes does not, in general, guarantee that X admits a fixed point free deformation, it is possible in the case $X = S^{2n+1}$ to construct one. Choose a real number θ, $0 < \theta < \pi/2$, and define a linear transformation T_θ of the topological vector space R^{2n+2} to itself by specifying its matrix by Figure 3.

$$\begin{bmatrix} \sin\theta & \cos\theta & 0 & 0 & \cdots & 0 & 0 \\ -\cos\theta & \sin\theta & 0 & 0 & \cdots & 0 & 0 \\ 0 & 0 & \sin\theta & \cos\theta & \cdots & 0 & 0 \\ 0 & 0 & -\cos\theta & \sin\theta & \cdots & 0 & 0 \\ \cdot & \cdot & \cdot & \cdot & \cdots & \cdot & \cdot \\ \cdot & \cdot & \cdot & \cdot & \cdots & \cdot & \cdot \\ \cdot & \ddots & \cdot & \cdot & \cdots & 0 & 0 \\ 0 & 0 & 0 & 0 & \cdots & \sin\theta & \cos\theta \\ 0 & 0 & 0 & 0 & \cdots & -\cos\theta & \sin\theta \end{bmatrix}$$

FIGURE 3

Our transformation is seen to be orthogonal, so its restriction to S^{2n+1} is a map $T_\theta: S^{2n+1} \to S^{2n+1}$. If there exists $x \in S^{2n+1}$ such that $T_\theta(x) = x$, then for E the identity function on R^{2n+2}, we have $(T_\theta - E)(x) = 0$ (the zero vector) which, since $x \neq 0$, means that $T_\theta - E$ is a singular linear transformation. Abbreviate "determinant" to "det". Letting

$$M = \begin{bmatrix} \sin\theta - 1 & \cos\theta \\ -\cos\theta & \sin\theta - 1 \end{bmatrix},$$

then

$$\det(T_\theta - E) = (\det M)^{n+1} = 2^{n+1}(1 - \sin\theta)^{n+1},$$

which is not zero, because $0 < \theta < \pi/2$. We have established a contradiction which proves that T_θ cannot have any fixed points on S^{2n+1}. Finally, T_θ is a deformation because we can define a homotopy $H: S^{2n+1} \times I \to S^{2n+1}$ $(I = [0, 1] \subset R)$ between T_θ and the identity map on S^{2n+1} by setting $H(x, t) = T_{t\theta}(x)$ for all $x \in S^{2n+1}$, $t \in I$.

The real projective spaces of odd dimension not only admit fixed point free maps but, in fact, fixed point free deformations (Ex. 4). On the other hand, no complex or quaternionic projective space admits a fixed point free deformation, because $b_{dk}(\Gamma P^n) = 1$ for $k = 0, 1, \ldots, n$ (where $d = 2$ or $d = 4$), and $b_p(\Gamma P^n) = 0$ otherwise, so

$$\chi(\Gamma P^n) = n + 1 \neq 0.$$

NOTES

The first announcement of the Lefschetz Fixed Point Theorem (for a restricted class of polyhedra) was in 1923 [34], and the details appeared three years later [35]. Although Lefschetz managed to extend the class of polyhedra somewhat in [36], the first proof of the Lefschetz Theorem for all polyhedra was by Hopf [28]. Brouwer published the proof of the theorem that bears his name in [7].

EXERCISES

1. Prove that the fixed point property is a topological invariant.
2. Prove that, if X has the fixed point property and A is a retract of X, then A has the fixed point property.
3. Prove that every fixed point free map $f \colon S^n \to S^n$ is onto.
4. Find a fixed point free deformation of RP^{2n+1}.
5. Use the Intermediate Value Theorem to obtain a direct proof that D^1 has the fixed point property.

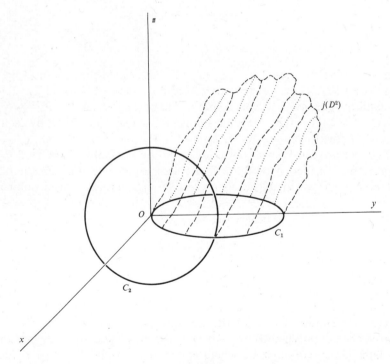

FIGURE 4

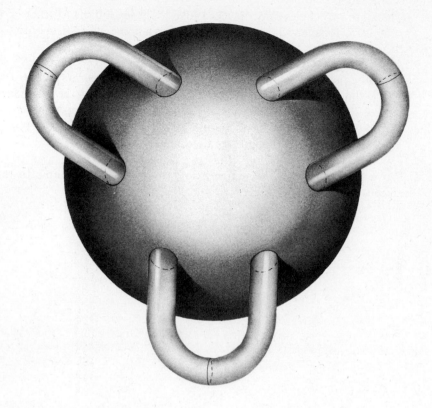

6. Prove that S^{n-1}, $n \geq 2$, is not a retract of D^n because, if it were, the retraction $r: D^n \to S^{n-1}$ would induce a one-to-one homomorphism

$$r^*: Q \cong H^{n-1}(S^{n-1}; Q) \to H^{n-1}(D^n; Q) = 0.$$

Show that this result implies the Brouwer Fixed Point Theorem for n-cells D^n, $n \geq 2$.

7. Prove that, if $f: D^n \to R^n$ is a map such that $f(S^{n-1}) \subseteq D^n$, then $f(x) = x$ for some $x \in D^n$.

8. Consider

$$C_1 = \{(x, \sqrt{2x - x^2}, 0) \in R^3 \mid 0 \leq x \leq 2\},$$

$$C_2 = \{(x, 0, \sqrt{1 - x^2}) \in R^3 \mid -1 \leq x \leq 1\},$$

which are two copies of S^1 in R^3. Prove that they link in R^3, that is, if $j: D^2 \to R^3$ is a map whose restriction to S^1 is a homeomorphism onto C_1, then $j(D^2)$ intersects C_2 (see Figure 4).

9. An *n-sphere with p handles*, written S_p^n, is formed in R^{n+1} from S^n by removing the interiors of $2p$ disjoint subsets, each homeomorphic to D^n, and adding p disjoint copies of $S^{n-1} \times I$ by attaching the boundary $S^{n-1} \times \{0, 1\}$ to the boundaries of two of the removed sets by homeomorphisms (see Figure 5). Compute $\chi(S_p^n)$. Prove that, if $\chi(S_p^{2n}) = 0$, then S_p^{2n} admits a fixed point free deformation.

10. Complete the computation of $C(e')\varphi\langle v_i, v_j\rangle$ in Section B.

11. Prove that every fixed point free map $f: S^n \to S^n$ is homotopic to the antipodal map.

Chapter III

The Lefschetz Theorem
for ANRs

The purpose of this chapter, as its title indicates, is to extend the Lefschetz Fixed Point Theorem so that it applies to maps on absolute neighborhood retracts. The key to the proof of the theorem is the fact that all absolute neighborhood retracts are dominated by polyhedra. It then becomes possible to use the already established Lefschetz Theorem for polyhedra to obtain the more general form of the result.

A. ABSOLUTE NEIGHBORHOOD RETRACTS

A subset A of a space X is called a *neighborhood retract* of X if there exists an open subset U of X containing A and a retraction of U onto A, i.e., a map $r: U \to A$ such that the restriction of r to A is the identity map.

A compact metric space X is a *compact absolute neighborhood retract* (compact ANR) if it has the following property: If A is a subspace of a separable metric space Y and A is homeomorphic to X, then A is a neighborhood retract of Y. Another way of stating the definition is to say that a compact metric space X is a compact ANR if it always imbeds in a separable metric space as a neighborhood retract. It is an immediate consequence of the definition that the ANR property is a topological invariant.

We will establish an equivalent definition of compact ANR which, in some cases, is easier to verify: Let I^∞ be the Hilbert cube, that is, all sequences of real numbers $(x_1, x_2, \ldots)$ such that $|x_i| < 1/i$ for all i, with the topology defined by the metric

$$d((x_1, x_2, \ldots), (x_1', x_2', \ldots)) = \left(\sum_{i=1}^{\infty} (x_i - x_i')^2 \right)^{1/2}.$$

A compact ANR can be imbedded in I^{∞} by the Urysohn Theorem and, since I^{∞} is separable metric, it imbeds as a neighborhood retract. Conversely, suppose that X is a compact metric space and that for some imbedding i of X into I^{∞}, the image $i(X)$ is a neighborhood retract of I^{∞}. Let $p_j: I^{\infty} \to [-1/j, 1/j]$ be the map which takes a sequence in I^{∞} to its j-th coordinate. Suppose that Y is a separable metric space, A is a subset of Y, and there is a homeomorphism h of A onto X. The map $p_j i h: A \to [-1/j, 1/j]$ can be extended to a map $h_j: Y \to [-1/j, 1/j]$ by Tietze's Extension Theorem. Define $H: Y \to I^{\infty}$ by $H(y) = (h_1(y), h_2(y), \ldots)$; then the restriction of H to A is the map ih. Since $ih(A) = i(X)$, there is an open set U in I^{∞} containing $ih(A)$ and a retraction $r: U \to ih(A)$. If we consider the open set $H^{-1}(U) \subseteq Y$ which contains A and the retraction $h^{-1}i^{-1}rH: H^{-1}(U) \to A$, we see that A is a neighborhood retract of Y and therefore X is a compact ANR. We have proved

Lemma 1.   *A compact space X is a compact ANR if and only if there exists an imbedding $i: X \to I^{\infty}$ such that $i(X)$ is a neighborhood retract of I^{∞}.*

It is an easy consequence of Lemma 1 that if A is a closed subset of X, X is a compact ANR, and if A is a neighborhood retract of X, then A is a compact ANR (Ex. 1).

We wish to show that the concept of ANR is more general than that of polyhedron. This means that we must prove that every polyhedron is a compact ANR and then exhibit a compact ANR which is not a polyhedron.

Let us begin with the simplicial complex $\sigma(n)$ consisting of a set $\{v_1, \ldots, v_{n+1}\}$ and all its nonempty subsets. Set

$$B^n = \left\{ x = (x_1, \ldots, x_n) \in R^n \,\middle|\, |x_i| \leq \frac{1}{i}, \quad i = 1, \ldots, n \right\}.$$

It is easy to construct a homeomorphism from $|\sigma(n)|$ to B^n. There is an imbedding $i: B^n \to I^{\infty}$ defined by

$$i(x_1, \ldots, x_n) = (x_1, \ldots, x_n, 0, 0, \ldots),$$

and a retraction $r: 1^{\infty} \to i(B^n)$, namely,

$$r(x_1, \ldots, x_n, x_{n+1}, \ldots) = (x_1, \ldots, x_n, 0, \ldots);$$

so B^n, and therefore $|\sigma(n)|$, is a compact ANR.

In order to prove that every polyhedron is an ANR, it is enough to prove that the geometric realization of a simplicial complex is an ANR. If K is a simplicial complex and K has $n + 1$ vertices, then $|K|$ can be considered to be a closed subset of $|\sigma(n)|$, which we have shown to be an ANR. As we remarked in Section I.H, there is a regular neighborhood of $|K|$ in $|\sigma(n)|$ which retracts onto $|K|$. Therefore,

Theorem 2. *A polyhedron is a compact* ANR.

Our candidate for an ANR which is not a polyhedron is the Hilbert cube I^∞. Certainly it is an ANR because it is compact metric and a retract of itself, so we must show that it cannot be triangulated. Let $T = (K, \tau)$ be a triangulation of I^∞. Then K has vertices $v_1, \ldots, v_n$ for some n. There is an imbedding $\eta : |K| \to R^n$ defined by sending the vertices to n linearly independent vectors and extending linearly. So $\eta\tau^{-1} : I^\infty \to R^n$ is an imbedding. Imbed B^{n+1} in I^∞ as before. Then the composition of that imbedding with $\eta\tau^{-1}$ imbeds B^{n+1} in R^n. Imbed R^n in R^{n+1}. Then the composition imbeds the interior of B^{n+1} in R^{n+1}. Since the imbedding factors through R^n, it cannot be that the interior of B^{n+1} imbeds as an open subset of R^{n+1}. Therefore, the assumption that I^∞ is a polyhedron has led to a contradiction of the Invariance of Domain Theorem.

Call a compact metric space X with metric $\boldsymbol{d}$ *uniformly locally contractible* (ULC) if, given $\epsilon > 0$, there exists $\delta > 0$ such that if

$$W = \{(x, x') \in X \times X \mid \boldsymbol{d}(x, x') < \delta\}$$

then there exists a map $\gamma : W \times I \to X$ such that

$$\gamma(x, x', 0) = x, \qquad \gamma(x, x', 1) = x'$$

$$\gamma(x, x, t) = x \quad \text{for all } t \in I$$

$$\operatorname{diam}(\gamma((x, x') \times I)) < \epsilon \quad \text{for all } (x, x') \in W$$

Theorem 3. *A compact* ANR *is* ULC.

Proof Let X be a compact ANR imbedded in I^∞, let U be an open subset of I^∞ containing X and let $r : U \to X$ be a retraction. Let $\eta > 0$ denote the distance from X to $I^\infty - V$, where V is an open subset of I^∞ containing X such that the closure of V is contained in U. By uniform continuity of r on V there exists $\delta > 0$, $\delta < \eta$, such that if $y, z \in V$ and $\boldsymbol{d}(y, z) < \delta$ ($\boldsymbol{d}$ is the metric of I^∞) then $\boldsymbol{d}(r(y), r(z)) < \epsilon$. For $x, x' \in X$ such that $\boldsymbol{d}(x, x') < \delta$, define

$$\gamma(x, x', t) = r((1 - t)x + tx'). \quad \blacksquare$$

Two maps $f,g\colon X \to X$ are said to be ϵ-*homotopic* for $\epsilon > 0$ if there exists a map $H\colon X \times I \to X$ such that

$$H(x, 0) = f(x) \quad \text{for all } x \in X$$
$$H(x, 1) = g(x) \quad \text{for all } x \in X$$
$$\text{diam}(H(x \times I)) < \epsilon \quad \text{for any } x \in X$$

Setting $H(x, t) = \gamma(f(x), g(x), t)$, we obtain

Corollary 4. *Let X be a compact* ANR *and let $\epsilon > 0$ be given. There exists $\delta > 0$ such that if $f,g\colon X \to X$ are maps and $d(f(x), g(x)) < \delta$ for all $x \in X$, then f and g are ϵ-homotopic.*

B. THE DOMINATION THEOREM

Let X be a compact metric space with metric d. If $x \in X$ and $A \subseteq X$ is a closed subset, then the *distance* from x to A, written $d(x, A)$, is defined to be the infimum of the set $\{d(x, a) \mid a \in A\}$. We observe that $d(x, A) = 0$ if and only if $x \in A$ since, if $x \notin A$, the function $d'\colon A \to R$ defined by $d'(a) = d(x, a)$ is continuous and $d'(a) > 0$ for all $a \in A$; so $d'(A)$ is bounded away from zero because of the compactness of A.

A *cover* of X will always mean a finite open cover, that is, a finite set $\{U_1, \ldots, U_n\}$ of open subsets of X such that $X = \bigcup\limits_{i=1}^{n} U_i$. Given a cover $\alpha = \{U_1, \ldots, U_n\}$ of X, we can construct a simplicial complex $K(\alpha)$, called the *nerve* of α, which depends on the structure of α in the following way: Denote the vertices of $K(\alpha)$ by $u_1, \ldots, u_n$ and define $s_j = \{u_{j(0)}, \ldots, u_{j(p)}\}$ to be a p-simplex of $K(\alpha)$ if and only if $\bigcap\limits_{k=0}^{p} U_{j(k)}$ is not empty. For $x \in X$, let $v(x) = \sum\limits_{i=1}^{n} d(x, X - U_i)$; then $v(x) > 0$ since $\alpha = \{U_1, \ldots, U_n\}$ is a cover and therefore $x \notin X - U_i$ for at least one $i = 1, \ldots, n$. Define a map $\varphi\colon X \to |K(\alpha)|$, called the *barycentric mapping*, by

$$\varphi(x) = \sum_{i=1}^{n} \frac{d(x, X - U_i)}{v(x)} u_i.$$

A space Y *dominates* a space X is there exist maps $\varphi\colon X \to Y$ and $\psi\colon Y \to X$ such that $\psi\varphi\colon X \to X$ is homotopic to the identity map. A space Y ϵ-*dominates* a space X for some $\epsilon > 0$ if there exist maps $\varphi\colon X \to Y$ and $\psi\colon Y \to X$ such that $\psi\varphi\colon X \to X$ is ϵ-homotopic to the identity map.

Having collected the concepts we require, we are now in a position to prove the result of this section.

Theorem 1 (The Domination Theorem).   *Given X, a compact* ANR, *and $\epsilon > 0$, there exists a polyhedron Y which ϵ-dominates X.*

Proof   Imbed X in I^∞ and call its image X also. We take the metric of X to be that of I^∞, which we call $\boldsymbol{d}$. For $p \in I^\infty$ and $\delta > 0$, define

$$N(p, \delta) = \{q \in I^\infty \mid \boldsymbol{d}(p, q) \mid < \delta\}.$$

Since X is a compact ANR, there is an open subset U of I^∞ containing X and a retraction $r: U \to X$. For $x \in X$, let

$$\eta(x) = \frac{1}{2}\,\boldsymbol{d}\!\left(x, I^\infty - \left[r^{-1}\!\left(N\!\left(x, \frac{\epsilon}{2}\right) \cap X\right)\right]\right)$$

The compactness of X assures us of the existence of a cover $\alpha = \{U_1, \ldots, U_n\}$ of X, where $U_i = N(x_i, \eta(x_i)) \cap X$. We will take $Y = |K(\alpha)|$. Now for

$$y = \sum_{k=0}^{p} a_k u_k \in Y, \, a_k > 0,$$ define $\psi'(y) = \sum_{k=0}^{p} a_k x_k$. We assume, without loss of generality, that $\eta(x_0) \geq \eta(x_k)$ for $k = 1, \ldots, p$. We know that $\{u_0, \ldots, u_p\}$ is a simplex of $K(\alpha)$, so there exists $z \in \bigcap_{k=0}^{p} U_k$ and, therefore,

$$\boldsymbol{d}(z, x_k) < \eta(x_k) \leq \eta(x_0)$$

for $k = 0, \ldots, p$. We conclude that $\boldsymbol{d}(x_0, x_k) < 2\eta(x_0)$ or, equivalently, that $x_k \in N(x_0, 2\eta(x_0))$ for $k = 0, \ldots, p$. But

$$N(x_0, 2\eta(x_0)) \subseteq r^{-1}\!\left[N\!\left(x_0, \frac{\epsilon}{2}\right) \cap X\right] \subseteq U,$$

and it is a convex set containing $x_0, \ldots, x_p$, so the convex hull of the x_k and, in particular, $\psi'(y)$ $\left(\text{recall that } \sum_{k=0}^{p} a_k = 1\right)$ is in U. Hence $\psi'(Y) \subseteq U$ and we define $\psi = r\psi': Y \to X$. For $\varphi: X \to Y$, we use the barycentric mapping defined above. For any $x \in X$, let $U_0, \ldots, U_p$ be the elements of α which contain x, ordered so that $\eta(x_k) \geq \eta(x_{k+1})$ for $k = 0, \ldots, p - 1$. By the argument we used to show that $\psi'(Y) \subseteq U$ we see that $\varphi(x) \in |\{u_0, \ldots, u_p\}|$ implies that $\psi'\varphi(x) \in N(x_0: 2\eta(x_0))$. Furthermore, $N(x_0, 2\eta(x_0))$ contains x because $x \in U_0$. Now $N(x_0, 2\eta(x_0))$ is convex, so, for $t \in I$,

$$(tx + (1 - t)\psi'\varphi(x)) \in N(x_0, 2\eta(x_0)) \subseteq U.$$

Define $H: X \times I \to X$ by

$$H(x, t) = r(tx + (1 - t)\psi'\varphi(x))$$

and note that $H(x, 0) = r\psi'\varphi(x) = \psi\varphi(x)$ while $H(x, 1) = r(x) = x$.

Finally,

$$H(x, t) \subset r(N(x_0, 2\eta(x_0))) \subseteq N\left(x_0, \frac{\epsilon}{2}\right)$$

and $\operatorname{diam}(H(x \times I)) < \epsilon$ as required. ∎

Recall that if X is a polyhedron, then $H^*(X; F)$ is finitary (see Sections I.B and I.L).

Corollary 2. *Let X be a compact* ANR *and F be any field, then $H^*(X; F)$ is a finitary graded vector space.*

Proof The Domination Theorem tells us that there is a polyhedron Y together with maps $\varphi: X \to Y$, $\psi: Y \to X$ such that $\psi\varphi$ is homotopic to the identity map 1_X. Therefore

$$\varphi^*\psi^* = (\psi\varphi)^* = (1_X)^*$$

which is the identity morphism on $H^*(X; F)$. Thus $\psi^*: H^*(X; F) \to H^*(Y; F)$ is an isomorphism from $H^*(X; F)$ to the graded vector subspace $\psi^*(H^*(X; F))$ of $H^*(Y; F)$. But Y is a polyhedron, so $H^*(Y; F)$ is finitary and, therefore, $H^*(X; F)$ is also finitary. ∎

C. THE LEFSCHETZ THEOREM

Let X be a compact ANR and $f: X \to X$ a map. By B.2, $f^*: H^*(X; F) \to H^*(X; F)$ is a morphism of a finitary graded vector space over a field F, so we define $L(f; F)$, the *Lefschetz number* of f, by $L(f; F) = L(f^*)$ which, we observe, is exactly the same as in the polyhedral case. Again, if $f, g: X \to X$ are homotopic maps, then $f^* = g^*$, so $L(f; F) = L(g; F)$ for such maps.

As an immediate consequence of I.B.2 we have

Lemma 1. *Let X be a compact* ANR. *Suppose that Y is a polyhedron which dominates X by means of maps $\varphi: X \to Y$ and $\psi: Y \to X$. If $f: X \to X$ is a map and we define $g = \varphi f \psi: Y \to Y$, then $L(f; F) = L(g; F)$ for any field F.*

We are now in a position to prove rather easily that the Lefschetz Theorem is true for maps on compact ANRs as well as for maps on polyhedra.

Theorem 2 (The Lefschetz Fixed Point Theorem for compact ANRs). *If X is a compact* ANR *and $f: X \to X$ is a map such that $L(f; F) \neq 0$ for any field F, then every map homotopic to f has a fixed point.*

Proof We begin just as we did in the proof of the Lefschetz Theorem in the polyhedral case. We assume that f is fixed point free, and our task is to prove that $L(f; F) = 0$ for any field F. Since X is compact metric, we still know that there exists $\epsilon > 0$ such that, for d the metric of X, $d(x, f(x)) > \epsilon$ for all $x \in X$. Let Y be a polyhedron which, by the Domination Theorem, ϵ-dominates X by means of maps $\varphi: X \to Y$ and $\psi: Y \to X$. We claim that the map $g = \varphi f \psi: Y \to Y$ is fixed point free. Suppose there exists $y \in Y$ such that $g(y) = y$, then

$$\psi g(y) = \psi \varphi f \psi(y) = \psi(y).$$

Now for $H: X \times I \to X$ — the ϵ-homotopy between $\psi \varphi$ and 1_X — we have that $\psi \varphi f \psi(y) = H(f \psi(y), 0)$ and $f \psi(y) = H(f \psi(y), 1)$; thus

$$d(\psi(y), f\psi(y)) = d(\psi \varphi f \psi(y), f \psi(y))$$
$$= d(H(f \psi(y), 0), H(f \psi(y), 1))$$
$$< \epsilon.$$

But letting $\psi(y) = x \in X$, the existence of a fixed point of g implies the existence of a point $x \in X$ such that $d(x, f(x)) < \epsilon$, which contradicts the definition of ϵ. Therefore g is fixed point free and, by the Lefschetz Fixed Point Theorem for Polyhedra, $L(g; F) = 0$. Lemma 1 states that $L(f; F) = L(g; F)$, so $L(f; F) = 0$. ∎

D. Q-ACYCLIC SPACES

A topological space X is Q-acyclic if $H^p(X; Q) = 0$ for all $p \neq 0$ and $H^0(X; Q) \cong Q$. An argument which is, word for word, identical to that of Section I.C proves that *a Q-acyclic compact ANR has the fixed point property* and that, in particular, *a contractible compact ANR has the fixed point property*.

As an application, we consider the Hilbert cube I^∞ which we have already proved is an ANR. A contraction $H: I^\infty \times I \to I^\infty$ is defined by $H(x, t) = tx$. Therefore, *the Hilbert cube has the fixed point property*. This may be viewed as a generalization of the Brouwer Fixed Point Theorem to the infinite-dimensional case. The Brouwer Theorem is an immediate consequence of this result because the n-cell D^n can be imbedded in I^∞ by sending $(x_1, \ldots, x_n) \in D^n$ to $\left(x_1, \frac{1}{2} x_2, \ldots, \frac{1}{n} x_n, 0, \ldots\right) \in I^\infty$, there is an obvious retraction of I^∞ onto the image of D^n, and we know that a retract of a space with the fixed point property has the fixed point property.

A mild generalization of the fact that a Q-acyclic compact ANR has the fixed point property states that if X is a connected ANR, if $f: X \to X$ is a map, and if there is a Q-acyclic subspace A of X such that $f(X) \subseteq A$, then f has a fixed point. The argument goes as follows: Since X is ULC (Theorem A.3) it is certainly locally pathwise connected and hence it is pathwise connected. Therefore, a connected ANR is pathwise connected. We know, then, that f^* is the identity function on $H^0(X; Q)$ and its trace is one. Let $f': X \rightarrow A$ be the map defined by $f'(x) = f(x)$ for all $x \in X$ and let $i: A \rightarrow X$ be inclusion. Clearly $f = if'$ so $f^* = f'^* i^*$. But for $p \neq 0$, $H^p(A; Q) = 0$, so i^* is the zero homomorphism on $H^p(X; Q)$ which implies that f^* is the zero homomorphism on $H^p(X; Q)$. Hence $L(f) = 1$ and the Lefschetz Theorem completes the argument.

We will give a more substantial generalization of the fixed point property of Q-acyclic ANRs. For $f: X \rightarrow X$, define $f^2: X \rightarrow X$ by $f^2(x) = f(f(x))$ and, in general, define $f^m(x) = f(f^{m-1}(x))$.

Theorem 1. *If X is a connected compact ANR, $f: X \rightarrow X$ is a map, and if, for some m, $f^m(X) \subseteq A$ where A is a Q-acyclic subspace of X, then f has a fixed point.*

Proof Let $g = f^m$, then since g maps X into the Q-acyclic subspace A, the argument above tells us that $g^*: H^p(X; Q) \rightarrow H^p(X; Q)$ is the zero homomorphism when $p \neq 0$. But $g^* = f^* \cdots f^*$ (composition m times) and so if we denote the matrix of f^* on $H^p(X; Q)$ by M, then the matrix of g^*, with respect to the same basis, is M^m. We know, then, that M^m is the zero matrix and therefore its eigenvalues are all zero. Let $\lambda_1, \ldots, \lambda_{b_p}$, where b_p is the dimension of $H^p(X; Q)$, be the eigenvalues of M. We have shown that $\lambda_i^m = 0$ for $i = 1, \ldots, b_p$, so since $\lambda_i \in C$, the complex numbers, we know that $\lambda_i = 0$ for $i = 1, \ldots, b_p$. Thus $\text{Tr}(f^*) = \text{Tr}(M) = \sum_{i=1}^{m} \lambda_i = 0$. Since X is a connected compact ANR, it is pathwise connected so that $L(f) = 1$. The result follows by the Lefschetz Theorem. ∎

E. FIXED POINTS OF HOMEOMORPHISMS

Lemma 1. *Let $s_k(x_1, \ldots, x_n)$ be the symmetric polynomial*

$$s_k(x_1, \ldots, x_n) = \sum_{i=1}^{n} x_i^k$$

and let $a_k \in C$ for $k = 1, \ldots, n$, then the system of equations $s_k(x_1, \ldots, x_n) = a_k$ for $k = 1, \ldots, n$ has a unique solution in C.

Proof Let $p_k(x_1, \ldots, x_n)$ be the elementary symmetric function

$$p_k(x_1, \ldots, x_n) = (-1)^k \sum x_{i(1)} x_{i(2)} \cdots x_{i(k)}$$

where the sum is taken over all sets of integers $i(1), i(2), \ldots, i(k)$ such that $1 \leq i(1) < i(2) < \cdots < i(k) \leq n$. Consider the polynomial

$$f(x) = \prod_{i=1}^{n} (x - x_i);$$

then, as is well known,

$$f(x) = x^n + p_1 x^{n-1} + \cdots + p_{n-1}x + p_n$$

where $p_k = p_k(x_1, \ldots, x_n)$. For $k = 1, \ldots, n$ there are *Newton's Formulas*

$$-kp_k = s_k + p_1 s_{k-1} + \cdots + p_{k-1}s_1$$

where $s_j = s_j(x_1, \ldots, x_n)$. In other words,

$$-p_1 = s_1$$
$$-2p_2 = s_2 + p_1 s_1$$
$$-3p_3 = s_3 + p_1 s_2 + p_2 s_1$$

and so on. Thus we can solve for the elementary symmetric functions p_i in terms of the polynomials s_i:

$$p_1 = -s_1$$
$$p_2 = -\tfrac{1}{2}(s_2 - s_1^2)$$
$$p_3 = -\tfrac{1}{3}(s_3 - s_1 s_2 - \tfrac{1}{2}(s_2 - s_1^2)s_1)$$

and so on. We were given a system of equations $s_k(x_1, \ldots, x_n) = a_k$ for $k = 1, \ldots, n$ which now gives us a new system

$$p_1(x_1, \ldots, x_n) = -a_1$$
$$p_2(x_1, \ldots, x_n) = -\tfrac{1}{2}(a_2 - a_1^2)$$
$$p_3(x_1, \ldots, x_n) = -\tfrac{1}{3}(a_3 - a_1 a_2 - \tfrac{1}{2}(a_2 - a_1^2)a_1)$$

and so on. Since we now know the values of the coefficients in the polynomial

$$f(x) = x^n + p_1 x^{n-1} + \cdots + p_{n-1}x + p_n$$

then, by the Fundamental Theorem of Algebra, the roots $x_1, \ldots, x_n$ of f are uniquely defined. ∎

Let X be a compact ANR and define $b_p(X)$, the pth *Betti number* of X, to be the dimension of $H^p(X; Q)$. The *Euler characteristic* $\chi(X)$ is defined to be the Euler characteristic of $H^*(X; Q)$ so

$$\chi(X) = L(1_X) = \sum_{p \in J}(-1)^p b_p(X)$$

(see I.G.1).

Theorem 2. *Let X be a compact ANR such that $\chi(X) \neq 0$. Let $N(X)$ be the larger of the two integers $\sum_{p \text{ odd}} b_p(X)$ and $\sum_{p \text{ even}} b_p(X)$. If $f: X \to X$ is any homeomorphism, then f^k has a fixed point for some $k \leq N(X)$.*

Proof We will show that $L(f^k) \neq 0$ for some $k \leq N(X)$ and then apply the Lefschetz Theorem to obtain the result. Suppose that

$$L(f) = L(f^2) = \cdots = L(f^{N(K)}) = 0. \tag{1}$$

Then we will prove that $\chi(X) = 0$, contrary to the hypothesis of the theorem. Choose a basis for each vector space $H^p(X; Q)$ and let M_p be the matrix of $f^*: H^p(X; Q) \to H^p(X; Q)$. By the definition of the Lefschetz number, (1) can be written as the system of equations

$$\sum_{p \in J} (-1)^p \operatorname{Tr}(M_p^k) = 0 \qquad k = 1, \ldots, N(X)$$

or

$$\sum_{p \text{ odd}} \operatorname{Tr}(M_p^k) = \sum_{p \text{ even}} \operatorname{Tr}(M_p^k) \qquad k = 1, \ldots, N(X).$$

(We understand $\operatorname{Tr}(M_p^k) = 0$ if $H^p(X; Q) = 0$.) Let $\lambda_{p,1}, \ldots, \lambda_{p,b_p(X)}$ be the eigenvalues of the matrix M_p. Then the eigenvalues of M_p^k are $\lambda_{p,1}^k, \ldots, \lambda_{p,b_p(X)}^k$, and

$$\operatorname{Tr}(M_p^k) = \lambda_{p,1}^k + \cdots + \lambda_{p,b_p(X)}^k.$$

Thus (1) can be rewritten as the system

$$\sum_{p \text{ odd}} \sum_{i=1}^{b_p(X)} \lambda_{p,i}^k = \sum_{p \text{ even}} \sum_{j=1}^{b_p(X)} \lambda_{p,j}^k \qquad k = 1, \ldots, N(X).$$

Let us assume, without loss of generality, that $N(X) = \sum_{p \text{ odd}} b_p(X)$ and relabel the eigenvalues $\lambda_{p,i}$, where p is odd, as $\lambda_1, \ldots, \lambda_{N(X)}$. Since f is a homeomorphism, f^* is an isomorphism and M_p is nonsingular, so $\lambda_i \neq 0$ for $i = 1, \ldots, N(X)$. Let $P = \sum_{p \text{ even}} b_p(X)$ and relabel the eigenvalues $\lambda_{p,j}$, where p is even, as $\mu_1, \ldots, \mu_P$. If $P < N(X)$, set $\mu_{P+1} = \ldots = \mu_{N(X)} = 0$, then (1) can be further rewritten as

$$\sum_{i=1}^{N(X)} \lambda_i^k = \sum_{i=1}^{N(X)} \mu_i^k \qquad k = 1, \ldots, N(X)$$

or, in the notation of Lemma 1,

$$s_k(\lambda_1, \ldots, \lambda_{N(X)}) = s_k(\mu_1, \ldots, \mu_{N(X)}) \qquad k = 1, \ldots, N(X).$$

But, by Lemma 1, the sets $\lambda_1, \ldots, \lambda_{N(X)}$ and $\mu_1, \ldots, \mu_{N(X)}$ must be identical. Since $\lambda_i \neq 0$ for $i = 1, \ldots, N(X)$, then $\mu_i \neq 0$ for $i = 1, \ldots, N(X)$, and it must have been true that $P = N(X)$ or

$$\sum_{p \text{ odd}} b_p(X) = \sum_{p \text{ even}} b_p(X).$$

Therefore, the assumption (1) implies that $\chi(X) = 0$. ∎

To see that the hypothesis $\chi(X) \neq 0$ is needed in order to be certain that every homeomorphism on X has an iterate with a fixed point, consider the circle S^1. We know that $\chi(S^1) = 0$; we will define a homeomorphism h on S^1 such that h^k is fixed point free for all $k \geq 1$. Identify R^2 with the complex numbers C and consider S^1 as the unit circle in C, that is, as all complex numbers $\exp(\theta 2\pi i)$ where $0 \le \theta < 1$. For x a real number, define $\{x\} = x - [x]$, where $[x]$ is the largest integer smaller than or equal to x. Now define $h: S^1 \to S^1$ by

$$h(\exp(\theta 2\pi i)) = \exp\left(\left\{\theta + \frac{1}{\sqrt{2}}\right\}2\pi i\right).$$

Clearly, h is a homeomorphism because it is just a rotation of S^1. Furthermore,

$$h^k(\exp(\theta 2\pi i)) = \exp\left(\left\{\theta + \frac{k}{\sqrt{2}}\right\}2\pi i\right).$$

We can have $h^k(\exp(\theta 2\pi i)) = \exp(\theta 2\pi i)$ only if $\{\theta + k/\sqrt{2}\} = \theta$, that is, only if $k/\sqrt{2}$ were an integer for some integer k, so h^k has no fixed point for all $k \ge 1$.

Theorem 2 also fails if f does not induce an isomorphism of $H^*(X; Q)$, even if $\chi(X) \ne 0$. For example, define $f: S^1 \vee S^2 \to S^1 \vee S^2$ (see Section I.M) by $f(x, y) = (h(x), \bar{y})$ where $S^1 \vee S^2 = (S^1 \times \bar{y}) \cup (\bar{x} \times S^2)$ and $h: S^1 \to S^1$ is the homeomorphism defined in the paragraph above. We note that $\chi(S^1 \vee S^2) = 1$, but f^k is fixed point free for all k.

Thus $S^1 \vee S^2$ certainly does not have the fixed point property, although by Theorem 2 it does have the fixed point property for homeomorphisms, that is, every homeomorphism from $S^1 \vee S^2$ to itself has a fixed point.

F. TOPOLOGICAL GROUPS

If G is a group, where the group operation is written as multiplication, then G is called *divisible* if, given any integer $k \ge 2$ and any $a \in G$, there is a solution x in G to the equation $x^k = a$. In other words, every element in G has a "k-th root" in G for each $k \ge 2$.

Let G be a topological group which is a connected compact ANR. Define $p_k: G \to G$ by $p_k(x) = x^k$ for each integer $k \ge 2$, $\mu: G \times G \to G$ by $\mu(x, y) = xy$, and let $\Delta: G \to G \times G$ be the diagonal map $\Delta(x) = (x, x)$. Then the diagram

$$
\begin{array}{ccc}
G & \xrightarrow{\ \ p_{k+1}\ \ } & G \\
\Delta \downarrow & & \uparrow \mu \\
G \times G & \xrightarrow{\ \ p_k \times 1_G\ \ } & G \times G
\end{array}
$$

commutes, where $(p_k \times 1_G)(x, y) = (p_k(x), y)$.

If $x \in H^p(G; Q)$, then say that x is of *degree* p and write $\deg(x) = p$. The Leray-Samelson Theorem states that there are elements $x_1, \ldots, x_\lambda$ in $H^*(G; Q)$ of odd degree with the property that $H^*(G; Q)$ is generated as a graded vector space over Q by $1 \in H^0(G; Q) \cong Q$ and all monomials

$$y_i = x_{i(1)} \cup x_{i(2)} \cup \cdots \cup x_{i(r)},$$

where $1 \le i(1) < i(2) < \cdots < i(r) \le \lambda$. It further states that if we consider, when $n > 0$,

$$\mu^*: H^n(G; Q) \to H^n(G \times G; Q) \cong \bigoplus_{p+q=n} H^p(G; Q) \otimes H^q(G; Q)$$

then, for any $x \in H^n(G; Q)$, it is true that

$$\mu^*(x) = x \otimes 1 + 1 \otimes x.$$

Now, choosing any element $x \in H^*(G; Q)$ of positive degree, since

$$p_2(a) = a^2 = \mu(a, a) = \mu\Delta(a) \qquad \text{for } a \in G,$$

we have

$$(p_2)^*(x) = \Delta^*\mu^*(x) = \Delta^*(x \otimes 1 + 1 \otimes x)$$
$$= x \cup 1 + 1 \cup x = 2x.$$

Proceeding by induction, suppose that $(p_k)^*(x) = kx$; then from the preceding commutative diagram we obtain

$$(p_{k+1})^*(x) = \Delta^*((p_k)^* \otimes 1_H)\mu^*(x)$$
$$= \Delta^*((p_k)^* \otimes 1_H)(x \otimes 1 + 1 \otimes x)$$
$$= \Delta^*((p_k)^*(x) \otimes 1 + (p_k)^*(1) \otimes x)$$
$$= \Delta^*(kx \otimes 1 + 1 \otimes x)$$
$$= kx \cup 1 + 1 \cup x$$
$$= (k + 1)x,$$

where 1_H denotes the identity function on $H^*(G; Q)$. By induction we have proved that, for any $x \in H^*(G; Q)$ of positive degree and for any integer $k \ge 2$, $(p_k)^*(x) = kx$.

Let $x_{i(1)} \cup \cdots \cup x_{i(r)}$ be a generating monomial for $H^*(G; Q)$. Then for any $k \ge 2$,

$$(p_k)^*(x_{i(1)} \cup \cdots \cup x_{i(r)}) = (p_k)^*(x_{i(1)}) \cup \cdots \cup (p_k)^*(x_{i(r)})$$
$$= kx_{i(1)} \cup \cdots \cup kx_{i(r)}$$
$$= k^r(x_{i(1)} \cup \cdots \cup x_{i(r)}).$$

In other words, if $y_i = x_{i(1)} \cup \cdots \cup x_{i(r)}$ and we let $r = \text{len}(y_i)$ (the *length* of the monomial y_i), then $(p_k)^*(y_i) = k^{\text{len}(y_i)}y_i$.

We have shown that the matrix of $(p_k)^*: H^n(G; Q) \to H^n(G; Q)$ is a diagonal matrix (for any n such that $H^n(G; Q) \ne 0$) with diagonal entry

$k^{\text{len}(y_i)}$ corresponding to each $y_i \in H^n(G; Q)$. Therefore, by the definition of the Lefschetz number,

$$L(p_k) = \sum (-1)^{\deg(y_i)} k^{\text{len}(y_i)} + 1,$$

where the sum is taken over all monomials y_i generating $H^*(G; Q)$. Note that the "one" is the contribution of $(p_k)^* \colon H^0(G; Q) \to H^0(G; Q)$.

Recall that each of the elements $x_1, \ldots, x_\lambda$ was of odd degree, so

$$(-1)^{\deg(y_i)} = (-1)^{\text{len}(y_i)}.$$

An elementary combinatorial result tells us that there are precisely $\binom{\lambda}{r}$ (binomial coefficient) monomials of length r and so, rearranging terms in the sum,

$$L(p_k) = \sum (-1)^{\text{len}(y_i)} k^{\text{len}(y_i)} + 1$$
$$= \sum_{r=1}^{\lambda} \binom{\lambda}{r} (-1)^r k^r + 1$$
$$= \sum_{r=0}^{\lambda} \binom{\lambda}{r} (-1)^r k^r = (1 - k)^\lambda$$

by the binomial formula.

Theorem 1. *Let G be a topological group which is a connected compact ANR, then G is divisible.*

Proof Given an integer $k \geq 2$ and an element $a \in G$, define $p_{k+1}^a \colon G \to G$ by $p_{k+1}^a(x) = x^{k+1} a^{-1}$. Denote the identity element of G by e; then, since G is pathwise connected, there is a map $C \colon I \to G$ such that $C(0) = a^{-1}$ and $C(1) = e$. Define $H \colon G \times I \to G$ by $H(x, t) = x^{k+1} C(t)$. Then it is clear that p_{k+1}^a is homotopic to $p_{k+1} = p_{k+1}^e$. Thus by the computation above,

$$L(p_{k+1}^a) = L(p_{k+1}) = (-k)^\lambda \neq 0.$$

By the Lefschetz theorem for ANRs, there exists $x_0 \in G$ such that $p_{k+1}^a(x_0) = x_0^{k+1} a^{-1} = x_0$, which means that $x_0^k = a$. ∎

NOTES

Lefschetz introduced ANRs (under a different name) in his book of 1930 [38] and proved his fixed point theorem for these spaces. He also claimed the result for all compact metric spaces, but Borsuk found a counterexample [3]. Lefschetz gave another proof in the compact ANR case later [37], and then extended the result in [33]. There have been many generalized Lefschetz theorems discovered — for example, by Leray [40], Browder [10], Knill [32] and Granas [23]. The Domination Theorem is the work of Hanner

[25]. Theorem D.1 was first proved by Browder [8], while E.2 is due to Fuller [21]. Hopf proved in 1940 that all compact connected Lie groups are divisible [27], and this was generalized in 1945 to Theorem F.1 by Leray [39]. It has since been shown by Mycielski, using quite different methods, that all compact connected topological groups are divisible [42]. However, methods like those of Section H have also led to a divisibility result (by Brown [11]) not included in Mycielski's. For a different development of E.2 and for other material on fixed points of the iterates of a map, see E. Fadell, *Recent results in the fixed point theory of continuous maps*, Bull. Amer. Math. Soc. 76 (1970), 10–29.*

EXERCISES

1. Prove that a closed neighborhood retract of a compact ANR is a compact ANR.
2. A compact metric space X is said to be of *dimension* $\leq n$ if, given any cover $\alpha = \{U_i\}$ of X, there is a refinement $\beta = \{V_j\}$ of α (for each $V_j \in \beta$ there exists $U_i \in \alpha$ so that $V_j \subseteq U_i$) which is a cover of X such that, if $V_{j(1)}, \ldots, V_{j(n+2)} \in \beta$, then $\bigcap_{k=1}^{n+2} V_{j(k)}$ is empty. Prove that, given X, a compact ANR of dimension $\leq n$, and $\epsilon > 0$, there exists a simplicial complex K of dimension $\leq n$ (there is no p-simplex in K for $p > n$) such that $|K|$ ϵ-dominates X.
3. Let X be a compact ANR with metric d. Prove that there exists $\epsilon > 0$ such that if $f, g: X \to X$ are maps with $d(f(x), g(x)) < \epsilon$ for all $x \in X$, then f and g are homotopic.
4. Prove that a space with the fixed point property is connected.
5. Let $T = (K, \tau)$ be a triangulation of a polyhedron X, let L be a sub-complex of K, and let $f: (X, T) \to (X, T)$ be a simplicial map such that $P = \tau |L| \subseteq \bigcap_{j=0}^{m-1} f^j(X)$. Suppose there exists a Q-acyclic subset A of P such that $\bigcup_{j=m}^{2m-1} f^j(P) \subseteq A$. Prove that f has a fixed point.
6. Prove that a retract of a locally pathwise connected space is locally pathwise connected.
7. Let X and Y be compact ANRs and let $f: X \to Y$, $g: Y \to X$ be maps. Prove that $L(fg) = L(gf)$.
8. Prove that the bound $N(X)$ of Theorem E.2 cannot be improved in the case $X = S^n$, n even. What does E.2 imply about homeomorphisms of CP^n, n odd?

---

* This reference added by author at time of proofreading.

Chapter IV

Index Theory for Polyhedra

Early in the history of fixed point theory it was discovered that, if X is a polyhedron and $f: X \to X$ is a map with only a finite number of fixed points satisfying an additional technical requirement, it is possible to associate to each fixed point an integer, called the "index," which describes the way in which the map "winds around" the point. Furthermore, the sum of all the indices was found to equal the *Lefschetz number* $L(f)$. If U is an open subset of X without fixed points of f on its boundary, then the *index* of f on U was defined to be the sum of the indices of the fixed points of f which lie in U. In this way, index theory was a generalization of Lefschetz fixed point theory.

Subsequently, the restrictions on the behavior of the fixed points were dropped. In other words to a polyhedron X, a map $f: X \to X$, and an open subset U of X without fixed points of f on its boundary it is possible to associate a number $i(X, f, U)$, the index of f on U, which is a generalization of the index described above.

The modern development of index theory is different from that of Lefschetz theory. An index is first defined abstractly as a function satisfying five axioms, which were inspired by properties of the classical index. One then proves an existence theorem, that is, one exhibits a function which satisfies all the axioms. An axiomatic definition of a concept in topology is often used because it is possible to prove a uniqueness theorem. We will show in Appendix II that the index is such a concept.

A. THE AXIOMS FOR AN INDEX

Let $\mathscr{C}_F$ denote the collection of all connected spaces X with the property that $H^*(X; Q)$ is finitary. If $X \in \mathscr{C}_F$ and $f: X \to X$ is a map, then the *Lefschetz number* $L(f)$ can be defined, just as in the ANR case, to be the Lefschetz number of $f^*: H^*(X; Q) \to H^*(X; Q)$. The fact that we can define a Lefschetz number for maps of spaces in $\mathscr{C}_F$ does not, of course, imply that the Lefschetz Fixed Point Theorem holds for all spaces in $\mathscr{C}_F$.

Let $\mathscr{C}$ be a subcollection of $\mathscr{C}_F$. A triple (X, f, U) will be called $\mathscr{C}$-*admissible* if

(1) $X \in \mathscr{C}$

(2) $f: X \to X$ is a map

(3) U is open in X

(4) there are no fixed points of f on the boundary of U.

Observe that if $X \in \mathscr{C}$ and $f: X \to X$ is a map, then (X, f, X) and $(X, f, \varnothing)$, where $\varnothing$ denotes the empty set, are $\mathscr{C}$-admissible because condition (4) is vacuously satisfied. The symbol $\mathscr{C}'$ will be used to denote the collection of all $\mathscr{C}$-admissible triples.

For $\mathscr{C}$ a subcollection of $\mathscr{C}_F$, a *(fixed point) index* on $\mathscr{C}$ is a function $i: \mathscr{C}' \to Q$ which satisfies the following axioms:

AXIOM 1 (LOCALIZATION).   *If $(X, f, U) \in \mathscr{C}'$ and $g: X \to X$ is a map such that $g(x) = f(x)$ for all $x \in \mathrm{cl}(U)$ (the closure of U), then*

$$i(X, f, U) = i(X, g, U).$$

AXIOM 2 (HOMOTOPY).   *For $X \in \mathscr{C}$ and $H: X \times I \to X$ a homotopy, define $f_t: X \to X$ by $f_t(x) = H(x, t)$. If $(X, f_t, U) \in \mathscr{C}'$ for all $t \in I$, then*

$$i(X, f_0, U) = i(X, f_1, U).$$

AXIOM 3 (ADDITIVITY).   *If $(X, f, U) \in \mathscr{C}'$ and $U_1, \ldots, U_s$ is a set of mutually disjoint open subsets of U such that $f(x) \neq x$ for all $x \in \left[U - \bigcup_{j=1}^{s} U_j \right]$, then*

$$i(X, f, U) = \sum_{j=1}^{s} i(X, f, U_j).$$

AXIOM 4 (NORMALIZATION).   *If $X \in \mathscr{C}$ and $f: X \to X$ is a map, then*

$$i(X, f, X) = L(f).$$

AXIOM 5 (COMMUTATIVITY).   *If $X, Y \in \mathscr{C}$ and $f: X \to Y$, $g: Y \to X$ are maps such that $(X, gf, U) \in \mathscr{C}'$, then*

$$i(X, gf, U) = i(Y, fg, g^{-1}(U)).$$

There may be some question in the reader's mind as to whether the last axiom makes sense. That is, does $(X, gf, U) \in \mathscr{C}'$ imply that $(Y, fg, g^{-1}(U)) \in \mathscr{C}'$? The reader is invited to check that indeed it does. (Ex. 1).

The localization axiom obviously makes the definition of the index "local" in the sense that $i(X, f, U)$ is not affected by the behavior of f outside of $cl(U)$. The normalization axiom connects the index to Lefschetz theory. The homotopy and commutativity axioms are generalizations of properties of the Lefschetz number (compare III. Ex. 7).

Motivation for the additivity axiom is supplied by the following result:

Corollary 1. *If there is an index i for a subcollection $\mathscr{C}$ of $\mathscr{C}_F$ and if $(X, f, U) \in \mathscr{C}'$ such that $i(X, f, U) \neq 0$, then f has a fixed point in U.*

Proof Suppose that f has no fixed points on $cl(U)$. We must prove that $i(X, f, U) = 0$. First apply the additivity axiom for $U = U_1 = U_2 = \varnothing$; then

$$i(X, f, \varnothing) = i(X, f, \varnothing) + i(X, f, \varnothing)$$
$$= 2i(X, f, \varnothing).$$

So $i(X, f, \varnothing) = 0$ since it is rational. Now, apply the additivity axiom for U the given open set and for $U_1 = \varnothing$. The axiom applies because there are no fixed points of f on $U - U_1 = U$. Thus

$$i(X, f, U) = i(X, f, \varnothing) = 0. \quad \blacksquare$$

Corollary 2. *Let $\mathscr{C}$ be a subcollection of $\mathscr{C}_F$ on which an index i can be defined. If X is in $\mathscr{C}$ and $f: X \to X$ is a map such that $L(f) \neq 0$ then every map homotopic to f has a fixed point.*

Proof Let g be any map homotopic to f; then $L(g) = L(f) \neq 0$. By the normalization axiom, $i(X, g, X) = L(g) \neq 0$, so, g has a fixed point by Theorem 1. $\blacksquare$

The last result is obvious, but it makes the important point that Index Theory is more powerful than Lefschetz Theory in the sense that the existence of a function on $\mathscr{C}'$ satisfying just two of the axioms of an index: additivity and normalization — is enough to imply that the Lefschetz Fixed Point Theorem is true for all maps on spaces in $\mathscr{C}$. Thus the results of this chapter may be viewed as a generalization of the results in Chapter II, and the proof in the next chapter that the collection of connected ANRs admits an index will generalize the work of Chapter III.

B. THE INDEX

Throughout this chapter, $H^*(X, A)$ will mean $H^*(X, A; Q)$.

Recall that we think of R^n as a subset $S^n - P$ of S^n. For a point $x \in R^n$ let $|x|$ denote its distance to the origin. Observe that if $f: R^n \to R^n$ is a map with the property that, for any sequence $x_1, x_2, \ldots$ in R^n such that if $\lim_{n \to \infty} |x_n| = \infty$ then $\lim_{n \to \infty} |f(x_n)| = \infty$ we can extend f to a map $f: S^n \to S^n$ by setting $f(P) = P$.

Choose, once and for all, a generator $\mu_1 \in H^1(R^1, R^1 - 0) \cong Q$. We define generators $\mu_n \in H^n(R^n, R^n - 0)$ inductively as follows: Having obtained μ_{n-1}, we have the Künneth isomorphism (page 38)

$$\alpha: H^{n-1}(R^{n-1}, R^{n-1} - 0) \otimes H^1(R^1, R^1 - 0) \to H^n(R^n, R^n - 0),$$

and we define $\mu_n = \alpha(\mu_{n-1} \otimes \mu_1)$. It is a consequence of the associativity of the tensor product that for

$$\alpha: H^p(R^p, R^p - 0) \otimes H^q(R^q, R^q - 0) \to H^{p+q}(R^{p+q}, R^{p+q} - 0)$$

we have the formula $\alpha(\mu_p \otimes \mu_q) = \mu_{p+q}$.

Let $x_0 \in R^n$ and define $d: (R^n, R^n - x_0) + (R^n, R^n - 0)$ by $d(x) = x - x_0$. Let $j: (R^n, R^n - x_0) \to (S^n, S^n - x_0)$ and $k: S^n \to (S^n, S^n - x_0)$ be inclusions. Note that d^* is an isomorphism because d is a homeomorphism, j^* is an isomorphism by excision, and k^* is an isomorphism by exactness because $S^n - x_0$ is contractible.

Consider the composition

$$H^n(R^n, R^n - 0) \xrightarrow{d^*} H^n(R^n, R^n - x_0) \xrightarrow{j^{*-1}} H^n(S^n, S^n - x_0) \xrightarrow{k^*} H^n(S^n),$$

and define

$$v_n = k^* j^{*-1} d^*(\mu_n) \in H^n(S^n) \cong Q.$$

Since the composition is an isomorphism, v_n is a generator of $H^n(S^n)$.

Lemma 1. *The definition of v_n is independent of the choice of the point $x_0 \in R^n$.*

Proof Choose any point $x_0' \in R^n$ and define $h: R^n \to R^n$ by $h(x) = x + (x_0 - x_0')$. Then h is a homeomorphism taking x_0' to x_0. We extend h to S^n by setting $h(P) = P$. Define $H: S^n \times I \to S^n$ by

$$H(x, t) = \begin{cases} x + t(x_0 - x_0') & \text{if } x \neq P \\ P & \text{if } x = P. \end{cases}$$

Then we see that h is homotopic to the identity map on S^n and therefore $h^*: H^n(S^n) \to H^n(S^n)$ is the identity isomorphism. The commutative diagram (Figure 1), where $d'(x) = x - x_0'$ and j' and k' are the obvious inclusions, completes the argument. ∎

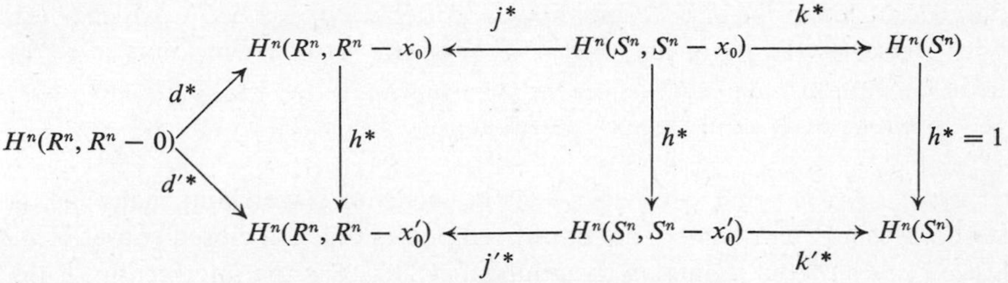

$$
\begin{array}{ccccc}
 & & H^n(R^n, R^n - x_0) \xleftarrow{\quad j^* \quad} H^n(S^n, S^n - x_0) \xrightarrow{\quad k^* \quad} H^n(S^n) \\
\end{array}
$$

FIGURE 1

The μ's were related by the formula $\alpha(\mu_p \otimes \mu_q) = \mu_{p+q}$. We next show that a similar relationship holds among the generators $v_n \in H^n(S^n)$. Consider the diagram (Figure 2).

The homomorphisms d^*, j^*, k^* are as before. The symbol α denotes a Künneth isomorphism and π is the quotient map defined in Section I.M. Subdiagrams (1) and (2) commute because they are induced by commutative diagrams of spaces and maps. All the other diagrams commute by the naturality of the Künneth isomorphism. The diagram tells us that $v_{p+q} = \pi^{*-1}\alpha(v_p \otimes v_q)$.

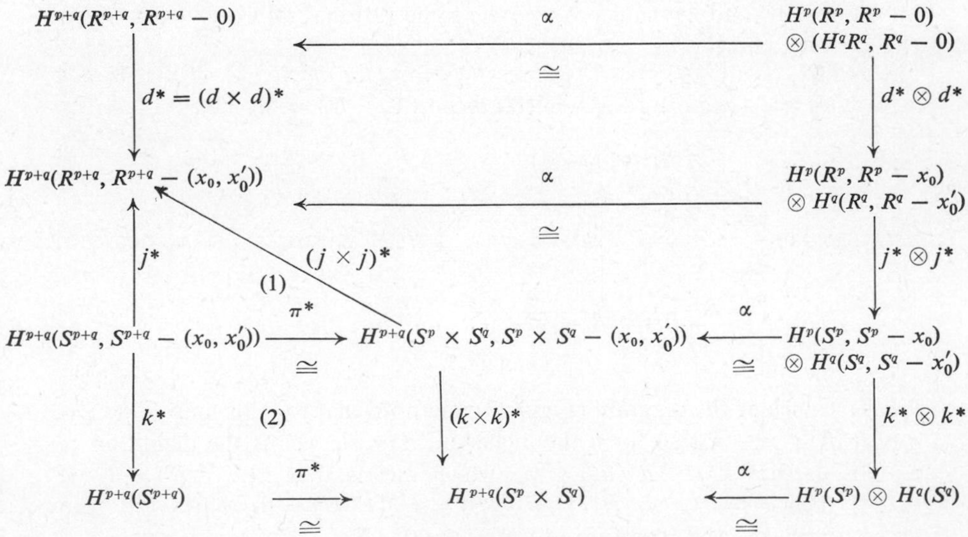

FIGURE 2

Let X be a polyhedron and $T = (K, \tau)$ a triangulation of X. Recall that we can imbed $|K|$ in R^n for n equal to the number of vertices of K, so we can imbed X in $R^n \subset S^n$. Since X is an ANR and R^n is separable metric, there is an open subset W of R^n containing X and a retraction $r: W \to X$.

Given $(X, f, U) \in \mathscr{C}'_P$ where $\mathscr{C}_P$ denotes the collection of all connected polyhedra, let $r: W \to X$ be as above and define $V = r^{-1}(U)$, which is an open subset of W and hence of S^n. Let F be the set of fixed points of f that lie in U. Define $d: V \to R^n$ by $d(x) = x - fr(x)$. If $d(x) = 0$ then $fr(x) = x$, so x must be in U, and since r is a retraction, $f(x) = x$. Thus $d(V - F) \subseteq R^n - 0$.

Let $j: (V, V - F) \to (S^n, S^n - F)$ be inclusion; we claim that $j*$ is an isomorphism by excision. The set of fixed points of f is a closed subset of X. Since f has no fixed points on the boundary of U, F is the intersection of the set of fixed points of f and the closure of U. Therefore, F is closed in the compact space X and we see that F is closed in S^n. Since $S^n - V$ is a closed set in the open set $S^n - F$, the excision can be performed.

Consider the composition

$$H^n(R^n, R^n - 0) \xrightarrow{d*} H^n(V, V - F) \xrightarrow{j*^{-1}} H^n(S^n, S^n - F) \xrightarrow{k*} H^n(S^n)$$

where $k: S^n \to (S^n, S^n - F)$ is inclusion; then $k*j*^{-1}d*(\mu_n) = qv_n$ for some $q \in Q$. Define $q = i_r(X, f, U)$. We use the notation i_r to indicate that the definition appears to depend on the choice of the imbedding of X in R^n, the open set W, and the retraction r because the definitions of the map d and open set V depend on r and W. We will prove later that, in fact, any such imbedding, W and r would produce the same rational number.

Theorem 2.   Let $(X, f, U) \in \mathscr{C}'_P$ where $f(x) = x_0$ for all $x \in X$. If $x_0 \in U$ then $i_r(X, f, U) = 1$, and if $x_0 \in X - \mathrm{cl}(U)$ then $i_r(X, f, U) = 0$.

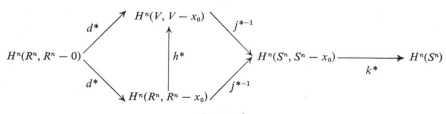

FIGURE 3

Proof   Consider the diagram (Figure 3) and note that for this map f, $d(x) = x - fr(x) = x - x_0$, so for h the inclusion, $d = dh$. Thus the definition of v_n tells us that $k*j*^{-1} d*(\mu_n) = v_n$, which means that $i_r(X, f, U) = 1$. If $x_0 \notin U$ then $F = \varnothing$, so $H^n(V, V - F) = H^n(V, V) = 0$, $d*$ is the zero homomorphism, and therefore $i_r(X, f, U) = 0$. ∎

The next result permits us to replace F by a larger closed set and V by a smaller open set in defining $i_r(X, f, U)$.

Lemma 3. *Let* $(X, f, U) \in \mathscr{C}'_P$, *let* $F \subseteq \tilde{F} \subseteq \tilde{V} \subseteq V$ *where* $\tilde{F}$ *is closed,* $\tilde{V}$ *is open, and* $S^n - \tilde{V}$ *is in the interior of* $S^n - \tilde{F}$. *Let* $\tilde{d}: (\tilde{V}, \tilde{V} - \tilde{F}) \to (R^n, R^n - 0)$ *be the restriction of* d. *If* $\tilde{j}: (S^n, S^n - \tilde{F}) \to (\tilde{V}, \tilde{V} - \tilde{F})$ *and* $\tilde{k}: S^n \to (S^n, S^n - \tilde{F})$ *are inclusions, then*

$$\tilde{k}*\tilde{j}*^{-1}\tilde{d}*(\mu_n) = i_r(X, f, U) \cdot \nu_n.$$

Proof The proof can be read off the commutative diagram (Figure 4) where $h: (S^n, S^n - \tilde{F}) \to (S^n, S^n - F)$ is inclusion. ∎

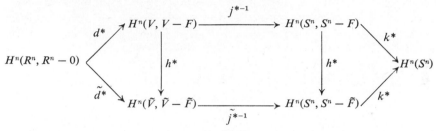

FIGURE 4

Corresponding to the additivity axiom for an index, we have the following result:

Theorem 4. *If* $(X, f, U) \in \mathscr{C}'_P$, *and* $U_1, \ldots, U_s$ *are disjoint open subsets of* U *such that* $F \subset \bigcup_{j=1}^{s} U_j$, *then*

$$i_r(X, f, U) = \sum_{j=1}^{s} i_r(X, f, U_j).$$

Proof Let $F_j = F \cap U_j$ and $V_j = r^{-1}(U_j)$. By Lemma 3, for the composition

$$H^n(R^n, R^n - 0) \xrightarrow{d*} H^n\left(\bigcup_{j=1}^{s} V_j, \left(\bigcup_{j=1}^{s} V_j\right) - F\right)$$

$$\xrightarrow{j*^{-1}} H^n(S^n, S^n - F) \xrightarrow{k*} H^n(S^n)$$

we know that $k*j*^{-1} d*(\mu_n) = i_r(X, f, U) \cdot \nu_n$. By definition, if we consider, for $k = 1, \ldots, s$,

$$H^n(R^n, R^n - 0) \xrightarrow{d_k^*} H^n(V_k, V_k - F_k)$$

$$\xrightarrow{j_k^{*-1}} H^n(S^n, S^n - F_k) \xrightarrow{k_k^*} H^n(S^n),$$

then $k_k^* j_k^{*-1} d_k^*(\mu_n) = i_r(X, f, U_k) \cdot v_n$, where d_k is the restriction of d to V_k and j_k and k_k are inclusions. Since the V_j are disjoint open sets and $F_j \subset V_j$, then

$$H^n\left(\bigcup_{j=1}^{s} V_j, \left(\bigcup_{j=1}^{s} V_j\right) - F\right) = H^n\left(\bigcup_{j=1}^{s} V_j, \bigcup_{j=1}^{s}(V_j - F_j)\right)$$

$$\cong \bigoplus_{j=1}^{s} H^n(V_j, V_j - F_j),$$

so we can write $d^*(\mu_n) = (u_1, \ldots, u_s)$, where $u_k \in H^n(V_k, V_k - F_k)$. Let $h_k: (V_k, V_k - F_k) \to \left(\bigcup_{j=1}^{s} V_j, \bigcup_{j=1}^{s}(V_j - F_j)\right)$ be inclusion; then $dh_k = d_k$. Furthermore, $h_k^*(u_1, \ldots, u_s) = u_k$, so

$$h_k^* d^*(\mu_n) = h_k^*(u_1, \ldots, u_s) = u_k = d_k^*(\mu_n),$$

and thus $d^*(\mu_n) = (d_1^*(\mu_n), \ldots, d_s^*(\mu_n))$. Diagrams

$$\begin{array}{c} H^n\left(\bigcup_{j=1}^{s} V_j, \left(\bigcup_{j=1}^{s} V_j\right) - F\right) \\ \downarrow h_j^* \\ H^n(V_j, V_j - F_j) \xleftarrow[j_j^*]{} H^n(S^n, S^n - F_k) \end{array} \quad m_k'^*$$

commute for $j = 1, \ldots, s$ when all homomorphisms are inclusion-induced. For $x \in H^n(S^n, S^n - F_k)$, write $m_k'^*(x) = (u_1', \ldots, u_s')$, then $h_j^* m_k'^*(x) = u_j' = j_j'^*(x)$. When $j \neq k$ we have $V_j \subseteq S^n - F_k$, so j_j' can be written as the composition of inclusions

$$(V_j, V_j - F_j) \to (S^n - F_k, S^n - F_k) \to (S^n, S^n - F_k),$$

and $j_j'^*$ is the zero homomorphism. Therefore, since $j_k' = j_k$,

$$m_k'^*(x) = (0, \ldots, 0, j_k^*(x), 0, \ldots, 0).$$

Let $m_k: (S^n, S^n - F) \to (S^n, S^n - F_k)$ be inclusion. Then the diagram (Figure 5) commutes, because all homomorphisms are induced by inclusions.

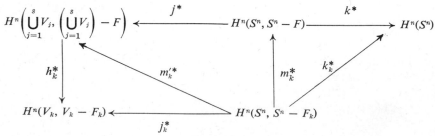

FIGURE 5

Therefore, for $x \in H^n(S^n, S^n - F_k)$,

$$m_k^*(x) = j^{*-1}m_k'^*(x) = j^{*-1}(0, \ldots, 0, j_k^*(x), 0, \ldots, 0)$$

and

$$k_k^*(x) = k^*m_k^*(x) = k^*j^{*-1}(0, \ldots, 0, j_k^*(x), 0, \ldots, 0).$$

In the first part of the proof we were able to write

$$d^*(\mu_n) = (u_1, \ldots, u_s) = (d_1^*(\mu_n), \ldots, d_s^*(\mu_n)),$$

so

$$
\begin{aligned}
k_k^* j_k^{*-1} d_k^*(\mu_n) &= k_k^* j_k^{*-1}(u_k) \\
&= k^*j^{*-1}(0, \ldots, 0, j_k^*(j_k^{*-1}(u_k)), 0, \ldots, 0) \\
&= k^*j^{*-1}(0, \ldots, 0, u_k, 0, \ldots, 0).
\end{aligned}
$$

By the definition of direct sum,

$$
\begin{aligned}
k^*j^{*-1}d^*(\mu_n) &= k^*j^{*-1}(u_1, \ldots, u_s) \\
&= k^*j^{*-1}(u_1, 0, \ldots, 0) + \cdots + k^*j^{*-1}(0, \ldots, 0, u_s) \\
&= k_1^* j_1^{*-1} d_1^*(\mu_n) + \cdots + k_s^* j_s^{*-1} d_s^*(\mu_n).
\end{aligned}
$$

Applying the definitions of the i_r, we have

$$i_r(X, f, U) \cdot \nu_n = \sum_{j=1}^{s} [i_r(X, f, U_j) \cdot \nu_n] = \left(\sum_{j=1}^{s} i_r(X, f, U_j) \right) \cdot \nu_n$$

which completes the proof. ∎

The next result corresponds to the homotopy axiom.

Theorem 5. *Let $H: X \times I \to X$ be a homotopy and define $f_t: X \to X$ by $f_t(x) = H(x, t)$. If $(X, f_t, U) \in \mathscr{C}_P'$ for all $t \in I$, then*

$$i_r(X, f_0, U) = i_r(X, f_1, U).$$

Proof Theorem 4 depended on the fact, proved in Lemma 3, that in defining $i_r(X, f, U)$ we could make use of an open set smaller than $V = r^{-1}(U)$. The present result depends on the other part of Lemma 3 — that the set of fixed points F of f in U can be replaced by a larger closed set. Let $\tilde{F}$ be the set of points $x \in U$ such that $H(x, t) = x$ for some $t \in I$. In order to apply Lemma 3 we must prove that $\tilde{F}$ is closed in S^n, so $S^n - V$ is in the interior of $S^n - \tilde{F}$. It is clearly sufficient to show that $\tilde{F}$ is closed in X. Let $\{x_j\}$ be a sequence of points in $\tilde{F}$ converging to a point x in the closure of U. There is a sequence $\{t_j\}$ in I such that $H(x_j, t_j) = x_j$. Since I is compact, there is no loss of generality in assuming that the sequence $\{t_j\}$ converges to a point $t \in I$. By the continuity of H, we have $H(x, t) = x$ so $x \in \tilde{F}$, and this completes the argument.

Now we can apply Lemma 3 to state that, for the composition

$$H^n(R^n, R^n - 0) \xrightarrow{d_t^*} H^n(V, V - \tilde{F}) \xrightarrow{\tilde{j}*-1} H^n(S^n, S^n - \tilde{F}) \xrightarrow{\tilde{k}*} H^n(S^n),$$

where $d_t(x) = x - f_t r(x)$, it is true that $\tilde{k}^* \tilde{j}^{*-1} d_t^*(\mu_n) = i_r(X, f_t, U) \cdot \nu_n$. Define $D: (V, V - \tilde{F}) \times I \to (R^n, R^n - 0)$ by $D(x, t) = x - f_t r(x)$. Then D is a homotopy between d_0 and d_1, so $d_0^* = d_1^*$ and $i_r(X, f_0, U) = i_r(X, f_1, U)$. ∎

Given polyhedra X, X' and maps $f: X \to X, f': X' \to X'$, we have a map of polyhedra $f \times f': X \times X' \to X \times X'$. If, after imbedding, $X \subset R^n$ and $X' \subset R^{n'}$ then X and $W' \subset R^n \times R^{n'} = R^{n+n'}$. Furthermore we have open sets $W \subseteq R^{n'}$ containing X and $w' \subseteq R^{n'}$ containing X' and retractions $r: W \to X, r': W' \to X'$. Thus $W \times W'$ is an open subset of $R^{n+n'}$ containing $X \times X'$, and $r \times r': W \times W' \to X \times X'$ is a retraction. If (X, f, U) and (X', f', U') are in $\mathscr{C}'_P$, then $f \times f'$ has no fixed points on $\partial(U \times U') = (U \times \partial U') \cup (\partial U \times U')$, where ∂ denotes the boundary. Note also that $(r \times r')^{-1}(U \times U') = V \times V'$ and that the set of fixed points of $f \times f'$ on $U \times U'$ is $F \times F'$. Therefore if we consider the composition (Figure 6) where $d'_\times = d \times d'$, and $j_\times, k_\times$ are inclusions, then

$$k_\times^* j_\times^{*-1} d_\times^*(\mu_{n+n'}) = i_{r \times r'}(X \times X', f \times f', U \times U') \cdot \nu_{n+n'}.$$

$$
\begin{array}{ccc}
H^{n+n'}(R^{n+n'}, R^{n+n'} - 0) & & H^{n+n'}(S^{n+n'}) \\
\Big\downarrow d_\times^* & & \Big\uparrow k_\times^* \\
H^{n+n'}(V \times V', V \times V' - F \times F') & \xrightarrow{\ \ j_\times^{*-1}\ \ } & H^{n+n'}(S^{n+n'}, S^{n+n'} - F \times F')
\end{array}
$$

FIGURE 6

Theorem 6. *If (X, f, U) and (X', f', U') are in $\mathscr{C}'_P$, then*

$$i_{r \times r'}(X \times X', f \times f', U \times U') = i_r(X, f, U) \cdot i_{r'}(X', f', U').$$

Proof The argument depends on the diagram (Figure 7). The α's denote the appropriate Künneth homomorphisms or their restrictions to subgroups. Note that the formula $(X, X - A) \times (Y, Y - B) = (X \times Y, X \times Y - A \times B)$ has been used several times. By definition, $d_\times = d \times d'$ and $j_\times = j \times j'$. All subdiagrams except (1) and (2) commute by the naturality of the Künneth homomorphism. We observe that $F \subset R^n, F' \subset R^{n'}$, so subdiagrams (1) and (2) commute because they were induced by commutative diagrams of spaces and maps. Since the diagram commutes,

$$\alpha_4^{-1} \pi^* k_\times^* j_\times^{*-1} d_\times^* \alpha_1 = (k^* \otimes k'^*)(j^* \otimes j'^*)^{-1}(d^* \otimes d'^*).$$

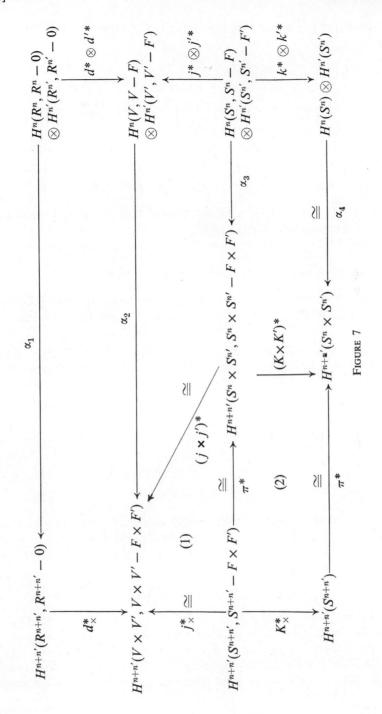

FIGURE 7

We defined the μ's and ν's so that $\alpha_1(\mu_n \otimes \mu_{n'}) = \mu_{n+n'}$ and $\pi^{*-1}\alpha_4(\nu_n \otimes \nu_{n'}) = \nu_{n+n'}$; hence

$i_{r \times r'}(X \times X', f \times f', U \times U') \cdot \nu_{n+n'}$

$$
\begin{aligned}
&= k_X^* j_X^{*-1} d_X^*(\mu_{n+n'}) \\
&= \pi^{*-1}\alpha_4(k^* \otimes k'^*)(j^* \otimes j'^*)^{-1}(d^* \otimes d'^*)(\mu_n \otimes \mu_{n'}) \\
&= \pi^{*-1}\alpha_4[k^*j^{*-1}d^*(\mu_n) \otimes k'^*j'^{*-1}d'^*(\mu_{n'})] \\
&= \pi^{*-1}\alpha_4[i_r(X, f, U) \cdot \nu_n \otimes i_{r'}(X', f', U') \cdot \nu_{n'}] \\
&= [i_r(X, f, U) \cdot i_{r'}(X', f', U')]\pi^{*-1}\alpha_4(\nu_n \otimes \nu_{n'}) \\
&= [i_r(X, f, U) \cdot i_{r'}(X', f', U')] \cdot \nu_{n+n'}. \quad \blacksquare
\end{aligned}
$$

The reader will not be surprised to find that we have a result corresponding to the commutativity axiom.

Theorem 7. *If $X, X' \in \mathscr{C}_P$ and $f: X \to X'$, $g: X' \to X$ are maps such that $(X, gf, U) \in \mathscr{C}'_P$, then $i_r(X, gf, U) = i_{r'}(X', fg, g^{-1}(U))$.*

Proof Let $V = r^{-1}(U)$, $V' = r'^{-1}g^{-1}(U)$, F be the set of fixed points of gf on U, and let F' be the set of fixed points of fg on $g^{-1}(U)$. Define a map $\gamma: X \times X' \to X \times X'$ by $\gamma(x, x') = (g(x'), f(x))$ for $x \in X$, $x' \in X'$. If $\gamma(x, x') = (x, x')$ then $g(x') = x$ and $f(x) = x'$, which implies $gf(x) = g(x') = x$ and $fg(x') = f(x) = x'$. Hence γ has no fixed points on $\delta(U \times g^{-1}(U))$.

$H^{n+n'}(R^{n+n'}, R^{n+n'} - 0)$ $H^{n+n'}(S^{n+n'})$

$\downarrow d_0^*$ $\uparrow k_X^*$

$H^{n+n'}(V \times V', V \times V' - F \times F') \xrightarrow{\quad j_X^{*-1} \quad} H^{n+n'}(S^{n+n'}, S^{n+n'} - F \times F')$

FIGURE 8

We observe that the set of fixed points of δ in $U \times g^{-1}(U)$ is $F \times F'$. Thus $i_{r \times r'}(X \times X', \gamma, U \times g^{-1}(U))$ can be defined from the composition (Figure 8) where $d_0(x, x') = (x, x') - \gamma(r \times r')(x, x')$. Define maps $\gamma_t: X \times X' \to R^{n+n'}$ by

$$\gamma_t(x, x') = (tgf(x) + (1 - t)g(x'), f(x)),$$

and note that $\gamma_0 = \gamma$ while $\gamma_1(x, x') = (gf(x), f(x)) \in X \times X'$. If $\gamma(x, x') = (x, x')$ then $\gamma_t(x, x') = (x, x')$ for all $t \in I$, while if $\gamma_t(x, x') = (x, x')$ for some $t \in I$ then $tgf(x) + (1 - t)g(x') = x$ and $f(x) = x'$, so $tg(x') + (1 - t)g(x') = g(x') = x$ and therefore $\gamma(x, x') = (x, x')$. We conclude that, for all $t \in I$, the set of fixed points of γ_t on $U \times g^{-1}(U)$ is precisely

$$H^{n+n'}(R^{n+n'}, R^{n+n'} - 0) \qquad\qquad\qquad\qquad H^{n+n'}(S^{n+n'})$$

$$\downarrow d_1^* \qquad\qquad\qquad\qquad\qquad\qquad\qquad \uparrow k_\times^*$$

$$H^{n+n'}(V \times V', V \times V' - F \times F') \xrightarrow{\;\;j_\times^{*-1}\;\;} H^{n+n'}(S^{n+n'}, S^{n+n'} - F \times F')$$

FIGURE 9

$F \times F'$. Therefore, since $\gamma_1 \colon X \times X' \to X \times X'$ is a map, $i_{r \times r'}(X \times X', \gamma_1, U \times g^{-1}(U))$ can be defined using the composition (Figure 9) where $d_1(x, x') = (x, x') - \gamma_1(r \times r')(x, x')$. Define a homotopy $H \colon (V \times V', V \times V' - F \times F') \times I \to (R^{n+n'}, R^{n+n'} - 0)$ by $H((x, x'), t) = (x, x') - \gamma_t(r \times r')(x, x')$. Then clearly d_0 and d_1 are homotopic, so $d_0^* = d_1^*$ and hence

$$i_{r \times r'}(X \times X', \gamma, U \times g^{-1}(U)) = i_{r \times r'}(X \times X', \gamma_1, U \times g^{-1}(U)). \qquad (1)$$

Look at the fixed points of γ_1 on $U \times X'$. If $\gamma_1(x, x') = (x, x')$ then $gf(x) = x$ and $f(x) = x'$. Now if $x' \notin g^{-1}(U)$, but $\gamma_1(x, x') = (x, x')$, we would have $f(x) \notin g^{-1}(U)$ or $gf(x) \notin U$. However, if $x \in U$ then $gf(x) = x$ would be in U. Hence, if $(x, x') \in U \times X'$ and $x' \notin g^{-1}(U)$, then $\gamma_1(x, x') \neq (x, x')$ and we conclude that the set of fixed points of γ_1 on $U \times X'$ is again $F \times F'$. By Theorem 4, therefore,

$$i_{r \times r'}(X \times X', \gamma_1, U \times g^{-1}(U)) = i_{r \times r'}(X \times X', \gamma_1, U \times X'). \qquad (2)$$

Next define $\delta_t \colon X \times X' \to R^{n+n'}$ by

$$\delta_t(x, x') = (gf(x), (1 - t)f(x) + tx_0')$$

after choosing, once and for all, $x_0' \in X'$. If $\delta_t(x, x') = (x, x')$ then $gf(x) = x$ and $x' = (1 - t)f(x) + tx_0'$. Define a map from $F \times I$ to $R^{n'}$ by sending (x, t) to $(1 - t)f(x) + tx_0'$. Then the image is compact and its intersection with X' — call it $\tilde{F}'$ — is also compact. For each $t \in I$, the fixed points of δ_t in $U \times X'$ are contained in $F \times \tilde{F}'$. Define $d_t' \colon (V \times W', V \times W' - F \times \tilde{F}') \to (R^{n+n'}, R^{n+n'} - 0)$ by $d_t'(x, x') = (x, x') - \delta_t(r \times r')(x, x')$ (W' is the open subset of $R^{n'}$ retracted onto X' by r'). Now $\delta_0 = \gamma_1$, so by Lemma 3

$$H^{n+n'}(R^{n+n'}, R^{n+n'} - 0) \qquad\qquad\qquad\qquad H^{n+n'}(S^{n+n'})$$

$$\downarrow d_0'^* \qquad\qquad\qquad\qquad\qquad\qquad\qquad \uparrow k'^*$$

$$H^{n+n'}(V \times W', V \times W' - F \times \tilde{F}') \xrightarrow{\;\;j'^{*-1}\;\;} H^{n+n'}(S^{n+n'}, S^{n+n'} - F \times \tilde{F}')$$

FIGURE 10

$i_{r \times r'}(X \times X', \gamma_1, U \times X')$ can be defined by the composition (Figure 10) where j' and k' are inclusions. Now $\delta_1(x, x') = (gf(x), x'_0) \in X \times X'$, so $i_{r \times r'}(X \times X', \delta_1, U \times X')$ is defined, and by Lemma 3,

$$k'^* j'^{*-1} d_1'^*(\mu_{n+n'}) = i_{r \times r'}(X \times X', \delta_1, U \times X') \cdot \nu_{n+n'}.$$

But d_0' and d_1' are homotopic maps; so $d_0'^* = d_1'^*$ and we have

$$i_{r \times r'}(X \times X', \gamma_1, U \times X') = i_{r \times r'}(X \times X', \delta_1, U \times X'). \tag{3}$$

Let $c': X' \to X'$ be the map taking X' to x'_0. Then since $\delta_1 = gf \times c'$ Theorems 6 and 2 imply

$$i_{r \times r'}(X \times X', \delta_1, U \times X') = i_r(X, gf, U) \cdot i_{r'}(X', c', X')$$
$$= i_r(X, gf, U). \tag{4}$$

Equations (1) through (4) imply

$$i_{r \times r'}(X \times X', \gamma, U \times g^{-1}(U)) = i_r(X, gf, U). \tag{5}$$

Define $\Gamma_t : X \times X' \to R^{n+n'}$ by

$$\Gamma_t(x, x') = (g(x'), tfg(x') + (1 - t)f(x)).$$

Then $\Gamma_0 = \gamma$ and $\Gamma_1(x, x') = (g(x'), fg(x')) \in X \times X'$. For each $t \in I$ the fixed points of Γ_t on $U \times g^{-1}(U)$ are $F \times F'$, so we can use an argument like the one in the first part of the proof to conclude that

$$i_{r \times r'}(X \times X', \gamma, U \times g^{-1}(U)) = i_{r \times r'}(X \times X', \Gamma_1, U \times g^{-1}(U)). \tag{1'}$$

Suppose that $\Gamma_1(x, x') = (x, x')$ for $(x, x') \in X \times g^{-1}(U)$. Then $g(x') = x \in U$, so Γ_1 has no fixed points on $X \times g^{-1}(U)$ other than $F \times F'$, and by Theorem 4,

$$i_{r \times r'}(X \times X', \Gamma_1, U \times g^{-1}(U)) = i_{r \times r'}(X \times X', \Gamma_1, X \times g^{-1}(U)). \tag{2'}$$

Now choose $x_0 \in X$ and define $\Delta_t : X \times X' \to R^{n+n'}$ by

$$\Delta_t(x, x') = ((1 - t)g(x') + tx_0, fg(x')).$$

Then $\Delta_0 = \Gamma_1$ and $\Delta_1(x, x') = (x_0, fg(x'))$. As in the first part of the proof, we can find a compact set $\tilde{F} \subset X$ such that all fixed points of Δ_t on $X \times g^{-1}(U)$ are in $\tilde{F} \times F'$ and then conclude that

$$i_{r \times r'}(X \times X', \Gamma_1, X \times g^{-1}(U)) = i_{r \times r'}(X \times X', \Delta_1, X \times g^{-1}(U)). \tag{3'}$$

For $c: X \to X$ the constant map at x_0, $\Delta_1 = c \times fg$. So by Theorems 6 and 2

$$i_{r \times r'}(X \times X', \Delta_1, X \times g^{-1}(U)) = i_r(X, c, X) \cdot i_{r'}(X', fg, g^{-1}(U))$$
$$= i_{r'}(X', fg, g^{-1}(U)). \tag{4'}$$

Equations (5) and (1′) through (4′) imply that

$$i_r(X, gf, U) = i_{r \times r'}(X \times X', \gamma, U \times g^{-1}(U))$$
$$= i_{r'}(X', fg, g^{-1}(U)). \quad \blacksquare$$

Theorem 7 has an easy, but most significant, consequence:

Theorem 8. *For* $(X, f, U) \in \mathscr{C}'_P$, *the rational number* $i_r(X, f, U)$ *is independent of choice of the imbedding of* X *in* R^n, *of the open set* W *in* R^n *containing* X, *and of the retraction* $r : W \to X$

Proof Let $h : X \to R^n$ be an imbedding and let $r : W \to h(X)$ be a retraction from an open set; then, strictly speaking, by i_r (X, f, U) we mean $i_r(h(X), hfh^{-1}, h(U))$ since, in the definition, X was identified with its image in R^n. Similarly, for another imbedding $h' : X \to R^{n'}$ and retraction $r' : W' \to h'(X)$, the index $i_{r'}(X, f, U)$ means $i_{r'}(h'(X), h'fh'^{-1}, h'(U))$. Now it is easy to see that Theorem 7 implies our result because

$$i_r(h(X), hfh^{-1}, h(U)) = i_r(h(X), (hh'^{-1})h'fh^{-1}, h(U))$$
$$= i_{r'}(h'(X), h'fh^{-1}(hh'^{-1}), (h'h^{-1})h(U))$$
$$= i_{r'}(h'(X), h'fh'^{-1}, h'(U)). \quad \blacksquare$$

Theorem 8 permits us to define the *index* $i(X, f, U)$ for $(X, f, U) \in \mathscr{C}'_P$ by

$$i(X, f, U) = i_r(X, f, U),$$

where $r : W \to X$ is any retraction from an open subset of R^n containing an imbedded image of X.

The localization axiom is satisfied by this index. The only ways the map f comes into the definition of $i_r(X, f, U)$ is in defining the map $d : V \to R^n$, which only makes use of the behavior of f on U, and in the definition of F, the fixed points of f on U. Thus if $g : X \to X$ agrees with f at each point of $\mathrm{cl}(U)$, then $(X, g, U) \in \mathscr{C}'_P$ and we can use the same d and F in defining $i_r(X, g, U)$.

We have already verified the additivity axiom (Theorem 4), the homotopy axiom (Theorem 5), and the commutativity axiom (Theorem 7). Therefore it remains to prove the normalization axiom. This task will be carried out in the next two sections.

C. THE LEFSCHETZ NUMBER

The *dual* of a graded vector space $V = \{V_p\}_{p \in J}$ over Q is defined to be the graded vector space $\hat{V} = \{\hat{V}_p\}_{p \in J}$ where $\hat{V}_p = \mathrm{Hom}(V_p, Q)$. It is clear that if V is finitary, so is $\hat{V}$.

For a vector space W over Q, define a homomorphism $\theta_p \colon \hat{W} \otimes W \to \text{Hom}(W, W)$ by letting

$$[\theta_p(\varphi \otimes w)](w') = (-1)^p \varphi(w') \cdot w$$

for $\varphi \in \hat{W}$, $w, w' \in W$, and extending to all of $\hat{W} \otimes W$.

Lemma 1. *If the vector space W is finite-dimensional, then θ_p is an isomorphism.*

Proof Let $w_1, \ldots, w_r$ be a basis for W; and let $w \in W$ and $\varphi \in \hat{W}$ where, with respect to the dual basis $\hat{w}_1, \ldots, \hat{w}_r$ for $\hat{W}$,

$$\varphi = a_1 \hat{w}_1 + \cdots + a_r \hat{w}_r.$$

If $\theta_p(\varphi \otimes w) = 0$ then

$$[\theta_p(\varphi \otimes w)](w_j) = (-1)^p \sum_{k=1}^{r} (a_k \hat{w}_k)(w_j) \cdot w = a_j w = 0$$

for all $j = 1, \ldots, r$; so either $w = 0$ or $a_j = 0$ for all j, which implies $\varphi = 0$. In either case, $\theta_p(\varphi \otimes w) = 0$ implies $\varphi \otimes w = 0$, so θ_p is one-to-one. To prove that θ_p is onto, let $\psi \in \text{Hom}(W, W)$ Then we can write $\psi(w_j) = \sum_{k=1}^{r} a_{jk} w_k$ for $j = 1, \ldots, r$. Let

$$x = (-1)^p \sum_{k=1}^{r} \left(\sum_{m=1}^{r} a_{mk} \hat{w}_m \otimes w_k \right) \in \hat{W} \otimes W.$$

For each $j = 1, \ldots, r$ we see that

$$[\theta_p(x)](w_j) = (-1)^{2p} \sum_{k=1}^{r} \left[\left(\sum_{m=1}^{r} a_{mk} \hat{w}_m \right)(w_j) \right](w_k)$$

$$= \sum_{k=1}^{r} a_{jk} w_k = \psi(w_j).$$

So ψ and $\theta_p(x)$ agree on a basis for W, which implies that $\theta_p(x) = \psi$ and θ_p is onto. ∎

Define $e \colon \hat{W} \otimes W \to Q$ to be the evaluation homomorphism $e(\varphi \otimes w) = \varphi(w)$ for $\varphi \in \hat{W}$, $w \in W$.

Lemma 2. *If W is a finite-dimensional vector space over Q and $h \colon W \to W$ is a homomorphism, then $e\theta_p^{-1}(h) = (-1)^p \text{Tr}(h)$.*

Proof Take a basis $w_1, \ldots, w_r$ for W and write $h(w_j) = \sum\limits_{k=1}^{r} a_{jk}w_k$ for $j = 1, \ldots, r$. From the proof of Lemma 1 we know that

so

$$\theta_p^{-1}(h) = (-1)^p \sum_{k=1}^{r} \left(\sum_{m=1}^{r} a_{mk}\hat{w}_m \otimes w_k \right),$$

$$e\theta_p^{-1}(h) = (-1)^p \sum_{k=1}^{r} \sum_{m=1}^{r} a_{mk}\hat{w}_m(w_k)$$

$$= (-1)^p \sum_{k=1}^{r} a_{kk}. \quad \blacksquare$$

Let $V = \{V_p\}_{p \in J}$ be a finitary graded vector space. Define

$$\theta^{-1} \colon \{\mathrm{Hom}(V_p, V_p)\}_{p \in J} \to \bigoplus_{p \in J} \hat{V}_p \otimes V_p$$

by $\theta^{-1}(\psi_p) = \theta_p^{-1}(\psi_p)$ for $\psi_p \in \mathrm{Hom}(V_p, V_p)$, and

$$e \colon \bigoplus_{p \in J} \hat{V}_p \otimes V_p \to Q$$

by $e\{\varphi_p \otimes v_p\} = \sum \varphi_p(v_p)$. In the next section we will want to define e on $\bigoplus\limits_{p,q \in J} \hat{V}_p \otimes V_q$, which we do by setting $e(\hat{V}_p \otimes V_q) = 0$ if $p \neq q$.

It is immediate from Lemma 2 that

Theorem 3. *If $h \colon V \to V$ is a morphism of degree zero on a finitary graded vector space over Q, then $e\theta^{-1}(h) = L(h)$.*

D. THE NORMALIZATION AXIOM

If W is a finite-dimensional vector space over Q and $w_1, \ldots, w_r$ is a basis for W, recall that we denoted the dual basis for $\hat{W}$ by $\hat{w}_1, \ldots, \hat{w}_r$. Given $w = a_1w_1 + \cdots + a_rw_r \in W$, define

$$\hat{w} = a_1\hat{w}_1 + \cdots + a_r\hat{w}_r \in \hat{W}.$$

Given a homomorphism $h \colon W_1 \to W_2$ of vector spaces over Q, we set

$$\hat{h} = \mathrm{Hom}(h, Q) \colon \hat{W}_2 \to \hat{W}_1.$$

Note that if $h \colon V \to V$ is a morphism of degree zero on a finitary graded vector space, then $L(h) = L(\hat{h})$ by I.B.1.

Denote the dual of the vector space $H^n(X, A) = H^n(X, A; Q)$ by $H_n(X, A)$ (see Section I.C). Let $f \colon X \to X \subseteq R^n$ be a map on a polyhedron, $r \colon U \to X$ a retraction of an open subset of R^n onto X, and $d \colon (U, U - F) \to (R^n, R^n - 0)$ the map defined by $d(x) = x - fr(x)$, where F is the set of fixed points of f. Consider the composition

$$H_n(S^n) \xrightarrow{k_*} H_n(S^n, S^n - X) \xrightarrow[\cong]{j_*^{-1}} H_n(U, U - X) \xrightarrow{d_*} H_n(R^n, R^n - 0),$$

where j and k are inclusions. By the definition of the index and Lemma B.3,

$$d_* j_*^{-1} k_*(\hat{v}_n) = i(X, f, X) \cdot \hat{\mu}_n.$$

The map f induces a morphism of degree zero, $f_* : H_*(X) \to H_*(X)$, and by what we just noted about the Lefschetz number we see that the normalization axiom states that $i(X, f, X) = L(f_*)$.

The map $a : (U, U - X) \times X \to (R^n, R^n - 0)$, defined by $a(u, x) = u - x$ for $u \in U$, $x \in X$, induces a homomorphism

$$a_* : \bigoplus_{p+q=n} H_p(U, U - X) \otimes H_q(X) \to H_n(R^n, R^n - 0),$$

For $j \in J$ define

$$a' : H_j(U, U - X) \to H^{n-j}(X)$$

in the following manner: Identity $H_n(R^n, R^n - 0)$ with Q so that $\hat{\mu}_n$ corresponds to $1 \in Q$. Think of $H^{n-j}(X)$ as the dual of its dual, that is,

$$H^{n-j}(X) = \mathrm{Hom}(H_{n-j}(X), H_n(R^n, R^n - 0)).$$

For $u \in H_j(U, U - X)$, let $a'(u)$ be the homomorphism such that if $z \in H_{n-j}(X)$, then $a'(u)(z) = a_*(u \otimes z)$.

Consider the composition

$$H_n(U, U - X) \xrightarrow{\Delta_*} \bigoplus_{p+q=n} H_p(U, U - X) \otimes H_q(U) \xrightarrow{a' \otimes (fr)_*}$$

$$\bigoplus_{q \in J} H^q(X) \otimes H_q(X),$$

where Δ is the diagonal map. Let

$$\beta = (a' \otimes (fr)_*) \Delta_* j_*^{-1} k_*(\hat{v}_n).$$

We wish to prove two statements:

STATEMENT 1. $e(\beta) = i(X, f, X)$,

STATEMENT 2. $\theta(\beta) = f_*$.

Together, these statements imply the normalization axiom because, by C.3, we would have

$$L(f) = L(f_*) = e\theta^{-1}(f_*) = e(\beta) = i(X, f, X).$$

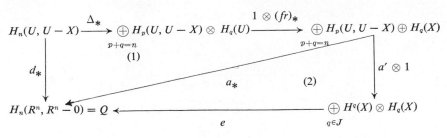

FIGURE 11

In order to prove Statement 1 we look at the first diagram (Figure 11). Clearly $a(1 \times fr)\Delta = d$, so subdiagram (1) commutes. To see that (2) commutes, let $u \otimes z \in H_p(U, U - X) \otimes H_q(X)$, then

$$e(a' \otimes 1)(u \otimes z) = a'(u)(z) = a_*(u \otimes z).$$

Since the diagram commutes, $i(X, f, X) \cdot \hat{\mu}_n = e(\beta) \cdot \hat{\mu}_n$ where $e(\beta) \in Q$ has been identified with $e(\beta) \cdot \hat{\mu}_n \in H_n(R^n, R^n - 0)$. We have proved Statement 1.

The dual of the commutative diagram in the statement of Dold's Lemma (Appendix I) is Figure 12. Note that the homomorphisms ϵ and ϵ^{-1} are

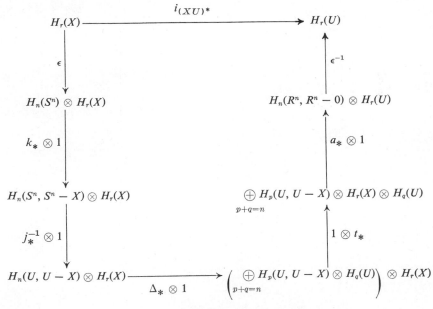

FIGURE 12

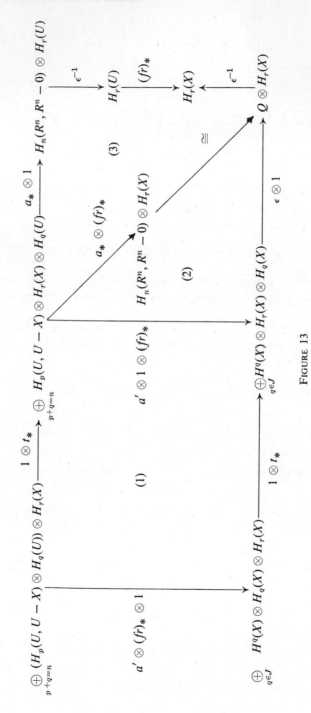

FIGURE 13

defined by $\epsilon(z) = \hat{v}_n \otimes z$ and by $\epsilon^{-1}(\hat{\mu}_n \otimes u) = u$, where $z \in H_r(X)$ and $u \in H_r(U)$. It makes sense to write

$$\bigoplus_{p+q=n} H_p(U, U - X) \otimes H_r(X) \otimes H_q(U) \xrightarrow{\ a_* \otimes 1\ } H_n(R^n, R^n - 0) \otimes H_r(U),$$

because $a_*(H_p(U, U - X) \otimes H_r(X)) = 0$ unless $r = q = p - n$. For the same reason, the inclusion of the extra terms in the direct sums (i.e., those terms that we dropped in constructing the diagram of Dold's Lemma) does not affect the fact that the diagram commutes.

To prove Statement 2 we consider the last diagram (Figure 13). Note that we can write

$$\bigoplus_{q \in J} H^q(X) \otimes H_r(X) \otimes H_q(X) \xrightarrow[\ e \otimes 1\ ]{} Q \otimes H_r(X),$$

because $e(H^q(X) \otimes H_r(X)) = 0$ unless $q = r$. Subdiagram (1) commutes because it comes from a commutative diagram of spaces and maps. The commutativity of subdiagram (2) follows from subdiagram (2) of Figure 11. Obviously subdiagram (3) commutes. Let $z \in H_r(X)$; then by Dold's Lemma and the fact that $fri_{(XU)} = f$ we compute that

$$\begin{aligned}
f_*(z) &= (fr)_* i_{(XU)*}(z) \\
&= (fr)_* \epsilon^{-1}(a_* \otimes 1)(1 \otimes t_*)[\Delta_* j_*^{-1} k_*(\hat{v}_n) \otimes z] \\
&= \epsilon^{-1}(e \otimes 1)(1 \otimes t_*)(a' \otimes (fr)_* \otimes 1)[\Delta_* j_*^{-1} k_*(\hat{v}_n) \otimes z] \\
&= \epsilon^{-1}(e \otimes 1)(1 \otimes t_*)(\beta \otimes z).
\end{aligned}$$

Since e is the trivial homomorphism, except when $q = r$, we can (for the present purpose) write $\beta = \varphi \otimes x$, where $\varphi \in H^r(X) = \mathrm{Hom}(H_r(X), Q)$ and $x \in H_r(X)$ (we are only interested in the r level of the graded vector spaces). Now

$$\begin{aligned}
\epsilon^{-1}(e \otimes 1)(1 \otimes t_*)(\beta \otimes z) &= \epsilon^{-1}(e \otimes 1)(1 \otimes t_*)(\varphi \otimes x \otimes z) \\
&= \epsilon^{-1}(e \otimes 1)(-1)^{r^2}(\varphi \otimes z \otimes x) \\
&= (-1)^r \epsilon^{-1}(\varphi(z) \otimes x) \\
&= \theta_r(\beta)(z).
\end{aligned}$$

We have proved that, for each $r \in J$,

$$\theta_r(\beta) = f_* : H_r(U) \to H_r(X),$$

and therefore $\theta(\beta) = f_*$ as morphisms of graded vector spaces. This completes the proof of Statement 2 and, therefore, the verification of the normalization axiom.

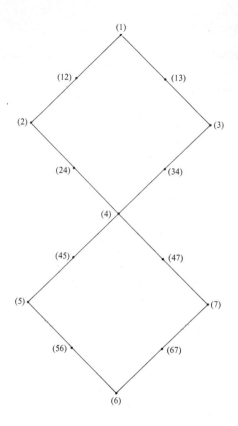

FIGURE 14

E. THE FIGURE-EIGHT AGAIN

In Section B of Chapter II we defined a "figure-eight" polyhedron X which was represented by a subset of the plane (Figure 14). We also had a map $e: X \to X$, defined by the table below on the labeled points and then extended over line segments to all of X.

x	1	2	3	4	5	6	7	12	13	24	34	45	56	67	47
$e(x)$	1	3	2	4	6	4	6	3	2	3	2	5	7	5	7

For points $a, b \in R^n$, denote by $[a, b]$ the line segment connecting them.

Let
$$U = [(1), (12)] \cup [(1), (13)] - \{(12), (13)\}.$$

Then U is an open subset of X containing the fixed point (1) of e.

We define a map $f: X \to X$ which will agree with e except on $A = [(2), (24)] \cup [(1), (2)]$ and $B = [(3), (34)] \cup [(1), (3)]$. Let $f: A \to [(1), (3)]$ such that

$$f(1) = (1), \quad f(12) = (1), \quad f(2) = (13), \quad f(24) = (3)$$

and extend f linearly over the various segments. Similarly $f: B \to [(1), (2)]$ is determined by

$$f(13) = (1), \quad f(3) = (12), \quad f(34) = (2).$$

The map $H: X \times I \to X$ given by $H(x, t) = tf(x) + (1 - t)e(x)$ is a homotopy between f and e. Furthermore, $H((12), t) \in [(1), (3)]$ and $H((13), t) \in [(1), (12)]$ for all $t \in I$, so H is a homotopy without fixed points on $\partial U = \{(12), (13)\}$, and by the homotopy axiom, $i(X, e, U) = i(X, f, U)$.

Since $f(\text{cl}(U)) = (1)$ then, by the localization axiom, $i(X, f, U) = i(X, c, U)$, where $c: X \to X$ is the map such that $c(X) = (1)$. Theorems B.2 and B.8 imply that $i(X, c, U) = 1$, so $i(X, e, U) = 1$.

Let V be a neighborhood of (4) disjoint from U. We computed in Section II.B that $L(e) = 0$. The additivity and normalization axioms tell us that

$$0 = L(e) = i(X, e, U) + i(X, e, V) = 1 + i(X, e, V)$$

and thus that $i(X, e, V) = -1$.

In conclusion, let U be any open subset of X containing (1) such that (4) $\notin \text{cl}(U)$, and let V be any open subset containing (4) such that (1) $\notin \text{cl}(V)$. Then (by the additivity axiom) $i(X, e, U) = 1$ and $i(X, e, V) = -1$.

NOTES

Hopf made very effective use of an index in 1929 in order to prove the Lefschetz Theorem for polyhedra [28]. The first formal axiom system (for an index on polyhedra) was stated by O'Neill [44]. The one presented here is due to Browder [9]. Both O'Neill and Browder defined indices for polyhedra, as Leray had done earlier [40]. The index given in this chapter is the work of Dold [18].

An easier verification of the normalization axiom, based on VIII.A.2 and the identification of the index in section VIII.B, has been discovered by D. McCord (*The converse of the Lefschetz fixed point theorem for surfaces and higher dimensional manifolds*, Doctoral Dissertation, University of Wisconsin, 1970). For the verification of the normalization axiom in a setting more general than that presented here, see M. Nakaoka, *Note on the Lefschetz fixed point theorem*, Osaka J. Math. **6** (1969), 135–142.*

EXERCISES

1. Prove that if X and X' are spaces in a collection $\mathscr{C}$ and if $f: X \to X'$, $g: X' \to X$ are maps so that (X, gf, U) is $\mathscr{C}$-admissible for some $U \subseteq X$, then $(X', fg, g^{-1}(U))$ is also $\mathscr{C}$-admissible.

2. Let X be a Hausdorff space and $f: X \to X$ a map, prove that the set of fixed points of f is closed in X.

3. Given a map $F: A \times X \to X$ where A is a connected topological space and X is a polyhedron, define $f_a: X \to X$, for $a \in A$, by $f_a(x) = F(a, x)$. Prove that if $(X, f_a, U) \in \mathscr{C}'_P$ for all $a \in A$, then $i(X, f_a, U) = i(X, f_{a'}, U)$ for all $a, a' \in A$.

4. Let X be a Q-acyclic polyhedron such that $(X, f, U) \in \mathscr{C}'_P$. If $g: X \to X$ is a map such that $g(x) = f(x)$ for all $x \in \partial U$, prove that $i(X, f, U) = i(X, g, U)$.

5. Let $f: [-1, 1] \to [-1, 1]$ be a map differentiable at 0 such that $f(0) = 0$ and $f'(0) < 1$. Prove that there exists $\epsilon > 0$ such that 0 is the only fixed point of f on $[-\epsilon, \epsilon]$.

6. For the map f of exercise 5, let $U = (-\epsilon, \epsilon)$ and prove that $i([-1, 1], f, U) = 1$.

7. Show that the inclusion of J into Q induces a natural homomorphism $H^*(X, A; J) \to H^*(X, A; Q)$ for any pair (X, A) and use this observation to prove that $i(X, f, U)$ is an integer for any $(X, f, U) \in \mathscr{C}'_P$.

* These references added by author at time of proofreading.

Chapter V

Index Theory for ANRs

After establishing the existence of an index on the collection $\mathscr{C}_P$ of connected polyhedra, we turn next to a proof of the existence of an index on the collection $\mathscr{C}_A$ of connected compact ANRs. The relationship between this chapter and Chapter IV is analogous to the relationship between Chapters II and III. In both cases we establish the results we need for the collection $\mathscr{C}_P$ and then make use of the fact that, for arbitrary $\epsilon > 0$, a compact ANR can be ϵ-dominated by a polyhedron in order to extend the results to $\mathscr{C}_A$.

The only information we need from Chapter IV is the fact that the existence of an index i on $\mathscr{C}_P$ has been proved. We will at no point make use of the way in which the index on $\mathscr{C}_P$ was defined. The symbol i will stand both for the index on $\mathscr{C}_P$ and for the index to be defined on $\mathscr{C}_A$ because, when the new index is restricted to $\mathscr{C}_P$, it is the original index.

A. THE INDEX FOR ANRs

Our first preliminary result is obtained by generalizing one of the arguments in the proof of the Lefschetz Theorem (II.A.1).

Lemma 1. *Let X be a compact metric space with metric d, let A be a closed subset of X, and let $f: X \to X$ be a map without fixed points on A. There exists $\delta > 0$ such that if $d(x, A) < \delta$ then $d(x, f(x)) > \delta$.*

Proof The function $d(f \times 1): X \to R$ is continuous and A is compact so the set $d(f \times 1)(A) \subset (0, \infty)$ is bounded below by some $\eta > 0$. Since X is compact, f is uniformly continuous and therefore there exists $\delta > 0$ such that $d(x_1, x_2) < \delta$ implies $d(f(x_1), f(x_2)) < \eta/3$ for all $x_1, x_2 \in X$. We may assume that $\delta < \eta/3$. This is the δ we require. To prove it, first note that since A is compact, for $x \in X$ there exists $a_x \in A$ such that $d(x, a_x) = d(x, A)$. Now let $x \in X$ such that $d(x, A) < \delta$, then

$$\eta \le d(f(a_x), a_x)$$
$$\le d(f(a_x), f(x)) + d(f(x), x) + d(x, a_x)$$
$$< \frac{\eta}{3} + d(f(x), x) + \delta,$$

so $d(f(x), x) > \eta/3 > \delta$ as required. ∎

Let X be a compact ANR with metric d and let $\epsilon > 0$ be given. By the Domination Theorem III.B.1 there is a polyhedron Y which ϵ-dominates X by means of maps $\varphi : X \to Y$ and $\psi : Y \to X$. Suppose $(X, f, U) \in \mathscr{C}'_A$; then f has no fixed points on ∂U. Taking $A = \partial U$ in Lemma 1, we obtain $\delta = \delta(f, U) > 0$ such that $d(x, \partial U) < \delta(f, U)$ implies $d(x, f(x)) > \delta(f, U)$.

Lemma 2. *Let $(X, f, U) \in \mathscr{C}'_A$ and let Y be a polyhedron which ϵ-dominates X by means of maps $\varphi : X \to Y$ and $\psi : Y \to X$. If $\epsilon < \delta(f, U)$, then $(Y, \varphi f \psi, \psi^{-1}(U)) \in \mathscr{C}'_P$.*

Proof Suppose $y \in \partial(\psi^{-1}(U))$ such that $\varphi f \psi(y) = y$. Therefore $\psi \varphi f \psi(y) = \psi(y)$. By the definition of ϵ-domination, $d(\psi \varphi f \psi(y), f \psi(y)) < \epsilon$ which means that $d(\psi(y), f \psi(y)) < \epsilon$. But $y \in \partial(\psi^{-1}(U))$ implies that $\psi(y) \in \partial U$ so, by Lemma 1, $d(\psi(y), f \psi(y)) > \delta(f, U) > \epsilon$. We have arrived at a contradiction and, hence, $\varphi f \psi(y) \ne y$ for all $y \in \partial(\psi^{-1}(U))$, which is all we need in order to see that $(Y, \varphi f \psi, \psi^{-1}(U)) \in \mathscr{C}'_P$. ∎

Theorem 3. *Let $(X, f, U) \in \mathscr{C}'_A$ and, for $j = 1, 2$, let Y_j ϵ_j-dominate X by means of maps $\varphi_j : X \to Y_j$ and $\psi_j : Y_j \to X$. If both ϵ_1 and ϵ_2 are smaller than $\frac{1}{4}\delta(f, U)$, then*

$$i(Y_1, \varphi_1 f \psi_1, \psi_1^{-1}(U)) = i(Y_2, \varphi_2 f \psi_2, \psi_2^{-1}(U)).$$

We will devote the next section to the proof of Theorem 3. Assuming this result, we define the *index* i on $\mathscr{C}_A$ by defining, for $(X, f, U) \in \mathscr{C}'_A$,

$$i(X, f, U) = i(Y, \varphi f \psi, \psi^{-1}(U)),$$

where Y is any polyhedron ϵ-dominating X by means of maps $\varphi : X \to Y$ and $\psi : Y \to X$, and $0 < \epsilon < \frac{1}{4}\delta(f, U)$ for some $\delta(f, U)$ satisfying the conclusion of Lemma 1. (Note that $\delta(f, U)$ is not uniquely defined.) Lemma 2 tells us that $i(X, f, U)$ is well-defined, and Theorem 3 assures us that $i(X, f, U)$

depends only on f and U and not on the choice of Y, φ, ψ, or ϵ, so long as ϵ is small enough.

B. PROOF OF THE INVARIANCE THEOREM

We have $(X, f, U) \in \mathscr{C}'_A$ and, for $j = 1$, 2, polyhedra Y_j which ϵ_j-dominate X by maps $\varphi_j \colon X \to Y_j$ and $\psi_j \colon Y_j \to X$, where ϵ_1 and ϵ_2 are smaller than $\frac{1}{4}\delta(f, U)$. Our job is to prove that

$$i(Y_1, \varphi_1 f \psi_1, \psi_1^{-1}(U)) = i(Y_2, \varphi_2 f \psi_2, \psi_2^{-1}(U)).$$

Here, in outline, is how the proof will go: The argument consists of establishing four equations by making use of the fact, proved in Chapter IV, that the function $i \colon \mathscr{C}'_P \to Q$ satisfies the axioms of a fixed point index. The homotopy axiom will show that

$$i(Y_2, \varphi_2 f \psi_2, \psi_2^{-1}(U)) = i(Y_2, \varphi_2 \psi_1 \varphi_1 f \psi_1 \varphi_1 \psi_2, \psi_2^{-1}(U)). \tag{1}$$

Next, the additivity axiom will be invoked to prove

$$i(Y_2, \varphi_2 \psi_1 \varphi_1 f \psi_1 \varphi_1 \psi_2, \psi_2^{-1}(U)) = i(Y_2, \varphi_2 \psi_1 \varphi_1 f \psi_1 \varphi_1 \psi_2, \psi_2^{-1}\varphi_1^{-1}\psi_1^{-1}(U)). \tag{2}$$

Then we will use the commutativity axiom to establish the equation

$$i(Y_2, \varphi_2 \psi_1 \varphi_1 f \psi_1 \varphi_1 \psi_2, \psi_2^{-1}\varphi_1^{-1}\psi_1^{-1}(U)) = (Y_1, \varphi_1 \psi_2 \varphi_2 \psi_1 \varphi_1 f \psi_1, \psi_1^{-1}(U)). \tag{3}$$

A final application of the homotopy axiom finishes the argument by proving that

$$i(Y_1, \varphi_1 \psi_2 \varphi_2 \psi_1 \varphi_1 f \psi_1, \psi_1^{-1}(U)) = i(Y_1, \varphi_1 f \psi_1, \psi_1^{-1}(U)). \tag{4}$$

We know that there is a homotopy $H \colon X \times I \to X$ such that $H(x, 0) = x$, $H(x, 1) = \psi_1 \varphi_1(x)$, and $d(H(x, t), x) < \epsilon_1$ for all $x \in X$, $t \in I$. In order to prove (1) by invoking the homotopy axiom we have to show that, for any $t \in I$,

$$\varphi_2 H_t f H_t \psi_2 \colon Y_2 \to Y_2$$

has no fixed points on $\partial(\psi_2^{-1}(U))$, where $H_t \colon X \to X$ is defined by $H_t(x) = H(x, t)$. In order to use the same material to handle equation (2) later, we will do more than this. Noting that $\partial(\psi_2^{-1}(U)) \subseteq \psi_2^{-1}(\partial U)$, we will prove that $\varphi_2 H_t f H_t \psi_2(y) \neq y$ for any $y \in Y$ with the property $d(\psi_2(y), \partial U) < \frac{1}{4}\delta(f, U)$. Let y be such a point, then there is a point $x \in \partial U$ such that $d(\psi_2(y), \partial U) = d(\psi_2(y), x)$. Now

$$d(H_t \psi_2(y), \partial U) \leq d(H_t \psi_2(y), x)$$
$$\leq d(H_t \psi_2(y), \psi_2(y)) + d(\psi_2(y), x)$$
$$< \epsilon_1 + \tfrac{1}{4}\delta(f, U)$$
$$< \tfrac{1}{2}\delta(f, U)$$

so, by A.1,

$$d(fH_t\psi_2(y), H_t\psi_2(y)) > \delta(f, U).$$

Since

$$d(H_t\psi_2(y), \psi_2(y)) < \epsilon_1 < \tfrac{1}{4}\delta(f, U)$$

then

$$d(fH_t\psi_2(y), \psi_2(y)) > \tfrac{3}{4}\delta(f, U).$$

Applying the property of H_t again,

$$d(H_t fH_t\psi_2(y), fH_t\psi_2(y)) < \epsilon_1 < \tfrac{1}{4}\delta(f, U)$$

which implies that

$$d(H_t fH_t\psi_2(y), \psi_2(y)) > \tfrac{1}{2}\delta(f, U).$$

Now let us suppose that, for some point y such that $d(\psi_2(y), \partial U) < \tfrac{1}{4}\delta(f, U)$, it were true that if $\varphi_2 H_t fH_t\psi_2(y) = y$ then $\psi_2\varphi_2 H_t fH_t\psi_2(y) = \psi_2(y)$. But

$$d(\psi_2\varphi_2(H_t fH_t\psi_2(y)), H_t fH_t\psi_2(y)) < \epsilon_2 < \tfrac{1}{4}\delta(f, U),$$

while we have already proved that

$$d(H_t fH_t\psi_2(y), \psi_2(y)) > \tfrac{1}{2}\delta(f, U),$$

which together imply that

$$d(\psi_2\varphi_2 H_t fH_t\psi_2(y), \psi_2(y)) > \tfrac{1}{4}\delta(f, U) > 0,$$

thus establishing a contradiction. Since $H': Y_2 \times I \to Y_2$, defined by $H'(y, t) = \varphi_2 H_t fH_t\psi_2(y)$ for $y \in Y_2$, $t \in I$, is a homotopy between $\varphi_2 f\psi_2$ and $\varphi_2\psi_1\varphi_1 f\psi_1\varphi_1\psi_2$, which we have just hroved is without fixed points on $\partial(\psi_2^{-1}(U))$, the homotopy axiom implies

$$i(Y_2, \varphi_2 f\psi_2, \psi_2^{-1}(U)) = i(Y_2, \varphi_2\psi_1\varphi_1 f\psi_1\varphi_1\psi_2, \psi_2^{-1}(U)). \tag{1}$$

In order to prove (2), we first show that the map $\varphi_2\psi_1\varphi_1 f\psi_1\varphi_1\psi_2: Y_2 \to Y_2$ fails to have fixed points on

$$A = \psi_2^{-1}(U) - (\psi_2^{-1}(U) \cap \psi_2^{-1}\varphi_1^{-1}\psi_1^{-1}(U)).$$

Let $y \in A$; then by definition $\psi_2(y) \in U$, but $\psi_1\varphi_1\psi_2(y) \notin U$. Consider the map $C: I \to X$, defined by $C(t) = H(\psi_2(y), t)$; then $C(I)$ intersects U at $C(0)$ and $X - U$ at $C(1)$, so for some $t' \in I$, $C(t') \in \partial U$. But

$$d(\psi_2(y), H(\psi_2(y), t')) < \epsilon_1 < \tfrac{1}{4}\delta(f, U),$$

so $d(\psi_2(y), \partial U) < \tfrac{1}{4}\delta(f, U)$, and by the argument in the proof of equation (1), $\varphi_2\psi_1\varphi_1 f\psi_1\varphi_1\psi_2(y) \neq y$. The additivity axiom therefore applies to prove

$$i(Y_2, \varphi_2\psi_1\varphi_1 f\psi_1\varphi_1\psi_2, \psi_2^{-1}(U))$$
$$= i(Y_2, \varphi_2\psi_1\varphi_1 f\psi_1\varphi_1\psi_2, \psi_2^{-1}(U) \cap \psi_2^{-1}\varphi_1^{-1}\psi_1^{-1}(U)). \tag{2a}$$

Let

$$B = \psi_2^{-1}\varphi_1^{-1}\psi_1^{-1}(U) - (\psi_2^{-1}(U) \cap \psi_2^{-1}\varphi_1^{-1}\psi_1^{-1}(U))$$

and take $y \in B$. The argument we used in the proof of (2a) shows us that $d(\psi_2(y), \partial U) < \frac{1}{4}\delta(f, U)$, and so again we know that $\varphi_2\psi_1\varphi_1 f \psi_1\varphi_1\psi_2(y) \neq y$. Thus applying the additivity axiom we get

$$i(Y_2, \ \varphi_2\psi_1\varphi_1 f \psi_1\varphi_1\psi_2, \ \psi_2^{-1}\varphi_1^{-1}\psi_1^{-1}(U))$$
$$= i(Y_2, \ \varphi_2\psi_1\varphi_1 f \psi_1\varphi_1\psi_2, \ \psi_2^{-1}(U) \cap \psi_2^{-1}\varphi_1^{-1}\psi_1^{-1}(U)). \quad (2b)$$

Equations (2a) and (2b) together imply equation (2).

In order to establish the other two equations, let K be the ϵ_2-homotopy on X such that $K(x, 0) = x$ and $K(x, 1) = \psi_2\varphi_2(x)$. We wish to show that for any $t \in I$, $\varphi_1 K_t H_t f \psi_1$ is without fixed points on $\partial(\psi_1^{-1}(U))$. Let $y \in Y_1$ such that $\psi_1(y) \in \partial U$; consequently, $d(\psi_1(y), f\psi_1(y)) > \delta(f, U)$. Now

$$d(K_t H_t f \psi_1(y), f\psi_1(y))$$
$$\leq d(K_t H_t f \psi_1(y), H_t f \psi_1(y)) + d(H_t f \psi_1(y), f\psi_1(y))$$
$$< \epsilon_2 + \epsilon_1 < \frac{1}{2}\delta(f, U)$$

so

$$d(K_t H_t f \psi_1(y), \psi_1(y)) > \frac{1}{2}\delta(f, U).$$

If, for $y \in \psi_1^{-1}(\partial U)$, we had $\varphi_1 K_t H_t f \psi_1(y) = y$ then $\psi_1\varphi_1 K_t H_t f \psi_1(y) = \psi_1(y)$. But

$$d(\psi_1\varphi_1 K_t H_t f \psi_1(y), K_t H_t f \psi_1(y)) < \epsilon_1 < \frac{1}{4}\delta(f, U).$$

Using the last inequality, for such points y, we have

$$d(\psi_1\varphi_1 K_t H_t f \psi_1(y), \psi_1(y)) > \frac{1}{4}\delta(f, U) > 0,$$

which establishes the desired contradiction. In particular, taking $t = 1$, we have shown that the map $\varphi_1\psi_2\varphi_2\psi_1\varphi_1 f \psi_1$ has no fixed points on the set $\partial(\psi_1^{-1}(U))$.

Let $h: Y_1 \to Y_2$ be the composition

$$Y_1 \xrightarrow{\psi_1} X \xrightarrow{f} X \xrightarrow{\varphi_1} Y_1 \xrightarrow{\psi_1} X \xrightarrow{\varphi_2} Y_2$$

and let $k = \varphi_1\psi_2: Y_2 \to Y_1$. Note that $kh = \varphi_1\psi_2\varphi_2\psi_1\varphi_1 f \psi_1$; so, by the last paragraph, $(Y_1, kh, \psi_1^{-1}(U)) \in \mathscr{C}'_P$ and the commutativity axiom applies in proof of

$$i(Y_1, \ \varphi_1\psi_2\varphi_2\psi_1\varphi_1 f \psi_1, \ \psi_1^{-1}(U)) = i(Y_1, kh, \psi_1^{-1}(U))$$
$$= i(Y_2, hk, k^{-1}\psi_1^{-1}(U))$$
$$= i(Y_2, \ \varphi_2\psi_1\varphi_1 f \psi_1\varphi_1\psi_2, \ \psi_2^{-1}\varphi_1^{-1}\psi_1^{-1}(U)). \quad (3)$$

For the final equation, we define a homotopy $L: Y_1 \times I \to Y_1$ by $L(y, t) = \varphi_1 K_t H_t f \psi_1(y)$. We have already proved that $L(y, t) \neq y$ for all $y \in \partial(\psi_1^{-1}(U))$ and $t \in I$, so the homotopy axiom implies

$$i(Y_1, \ \varphi_1\psi_2\varphi_2\psi_1\varphi_1 f \psi_1, \ \psi_1^{-1}(U)) = i(Y_1, \ \varphi_1 f \psi_1, \ \psi_1^{-1}(U)), \quad (4)$$

and this completes the proof of Theorem A.3.

C. VERIFICATION OF THE AXIOMS*

Localization (Axiom 1).

We have two maps $f, g \colon X \to X$ such that $f(x) = g(x)$ for all $x \in \mathrm{cl}(U)$ and such that $(X, f, U) \in \mathscr{C}'_A$. From A.1 we have two positive numbers $\delta(f, U)$ and $\delta(g, U)$. Let δ be the smaller of the two. Choose $\epsilon < \delta/4$. Then by III.B.1 there is a polyhedron Y which ϵ-dominates X by means of maps $\varphi \colon X \to Y$ and $\psi \colon Y \to X$. Since $\epsilon < \frac{1}{4}\delta(f, U)$ and $\epsilon < \frac{1}{4}\delta(g, U)$, then

$$i(X, f, U) = i(Y, \varphi f \psi, \psi^{-1}(U))$$
$$i(X, g, U) = i(Y, \varphi g \psi, \psi^{-1}(U)).$$

Since $\psi^{-1}(\mathrm{cl}(U))$ is a closed set containing $\psi^{-1}(U)$,

$$\mathrm{cl}(\psi^{-1}(U)) \subseteq \psi^{-1}(\mathrm{cl}(U)).$$

Thus if $y \in \mathrm{cl}(\psi^{-1}(U))$ then $\psi(y) \in \mathrm{cl}(U)$ so $g\psi(y) = f\psi(y)$ and therefore $\varphi g \psi(y) = \varphi f \psi(y)$. The function i on $\mathscr{C}'_P$ satisfies the localization axiom, so

$$i(Y, \varphi g \psi, \psi^{-1}(U)) = i(Y, \varphi f \psi, \psi^{-1}(U)),$$

which completes the proof.

Homotopy (Axiom 2).

Let $H \colon X \times I \to X$ be a homotopy. Recall the maps $f_t \colon X \to X$ defined by $f_t(x) = H(x, t)$. We are given that $(X, f_t, U) \in \mathscr{C}'_A$ for all $t \in I$. Note that $X \times I$ is compact metric and that the cartesian product topology permits us to define the metric d' by

$$d'((x, t), (x', t')) = ((d(x, x'))^2 + (t - t')^2)^{\frac{1}{2}},$$

where d is the metric of X. Define

$$H' \colon X \times I \to X \times I \qquad \text{by} \qquad H'(x, t) = (H(x, t), t).$$

If $x \in \partial U$, then $H'(x, t) = (x, t)$ means that $H(x, t) = f_t(x) = x$, which is contrary to hypothesis, so H' has no fixed points on $\partial U \times I$. Applying A.1 to the map H' and the closed set $\partial U \times I$, we obtain $\delta > 0$ such that $d'((x, t), \partial U \times I) < \delta$ implies $d'((x, t), H'(x, t)) > \delta$. But from the way d' was defined, we see that $d'((x, t), \partial U \times I) = d(x, \partial U)$ and

$$d'((x, t), H'(x, t)) = d(x, H(x, t)) = d(x, f_t(x)).$$

Therefore we may take $\delta(f_t, U) = \delta$ for all $t \in I$. For $\epsilon < \delta/4$, we have a polyhedron Y dominating X by means of maps $\varphi \colon X \to Y$ and $\psi \colon Y \to X$.

* Section IV.A, pages 97–98.

By definition,

$$i(X, f_t, U) = i(Y, \varphi f_t \psi, \psi^{-1}(U))$$

for all $t \in I$. Since, by A.2, $(Y, \varphi f_t \psi, \psi^{-1}(U)) \in \mathscr{C}'_P$ for all t, the homotopy axiom for the index on $\mathscr{C}_P$ implies that $i(X, f_0, U) = i(X, f_1, U)$, as we require.

Additivity (Axiom 3).

This time we are given $(X, f, U) \in \mathscr{C}'_A$ and a set $U_1, \ldots, U_s$ of mutually disjoint open subsets of U such that $f(x) \neq x$ for $x \in \left[U - \bigcup_{j=1}^{s} U_j \right]$. Applying A.1 to the map f and the closed set $A = \mathrm{cl}(U) - \bigcup_{j=1}^{s} U_j$, we get $\delta > 0$, so that $d(x, A) < \delta$ implies $d(x, f(x)) > \delta$. Note that $d(x, B) < \delta$ implies $d(x, A) < \delta$ for B any closed subset of A, and thus we may take $\delta(f, U) = \delta$ and $\delta(f, U_j) = \delta$ as well, for all $j = 1, \ldots, s$. Therefore, if Y is a polyhedron which ϵ-dominates X by maps $\varphi: X \to Y$ and $\psi: Y \to X$, and $\epsilon < \delta/4$, then $i(X, f, U) = i(Y, \varphi f \psi, \psi^{-1}(U))$ while, for $j = 1, \ldots, s$, $i(X, f, U_j) = i(Y, \varphi f \psi, \psi^{-1}(U_j))$. If we can show that $\varphi f \psi$ is without fixed points on $\psi^{-1}(U) - \bigcup_{j=1}^{s} \psi^{-1}(U_j)$, then the additivity axiom on $\mathscr{C}_A$ will follow from the corresponding property of the index on $\mathscr{C}_P$. But

$$\psi^{-1}(U) - \bigcup_{j=1}^{s} \psi^{-1}(U_j) = \psi^{-1}\left(U - \bigcup_{j=1}^{s} U_j \right),$$

so if $y \in \psi^{-1}(U) - \bigcup_{j=1}^{s} \psi^{-1}(U_j)$ then $\psi(y) \in U - \bigcup_{j=1}^{s} U_j$. Hence, if $\varphi f \psi(y) = y$ so that

$$\psi \varphi f \psi(y) = \psi(y) \in U - \bigcup_{j=1}^{s} U_j,$$

we arrive at a contradiction due to the fact that

$$d(\psi(y), f\psi(y)) = d(\psi \varphi f \psi(y), f\psi(y)) < \epsilon < \frac{\delta}{4},$$

contrary to A.1 (since $\psi(y) \in A$).

Normalization (Axiom 4).

For $X \in \mathscr{C}_A$ and $f: X \to X$, by definition, $i(X, f, X) = i(Y, \varphi f \psi, Y)$ for any polyhedron Y which dominates X by maps $\varphi: X \to Y$ and $\psi: Y \to X$.

We know that $i(Y, \varphi f \psi, Y) = L(\varphi f \psi)$ by the normalization axiom of the index on $\mathscr{C}_P$, and $L(\varphi f \psi) = L(f)$ by III.C.1, so the argument is complete.

Commutativity (Axiom 5).

We are presented with $X, X' \in \mathscr{C}_A$ and maps $f: X \to X'$, $g: X' \to X$ such that $(X, gf, U) \in \mathscr{C}'_A$. Our job is to prove that $i(X, gf, U) = i(X', fg, g^{-1}(U))$.

From A.1 we have two positive numbers $\delta(gf, U)$ and $\delta(fg, g^{-1}(U))$; let δ be the smaller. By the uniform continuity of g there exists $\epsilon' > 0$, $\epsilon' < \delta/2$, such that if $x'_1, x'_2 \in X'$ and $d(x'_1, x'_2) < \epsilon'$ then $d(g(x'_1), g(x'_2)) < \delta/4$. (We will use d to denote the metric of all spaces that appear in the proof.) The uniform continuity of f implies that there exists $\epsilon > 0$, $\epsilon < \delta/2$, such that if $x_1, x_2 \in X$ and $d(x_1, x_2) < \epsilon$ then $d(f(x_1), f(x_2)) < \epsilon'/2$. Let Y be a polyhedron $(\epsilon/2)$-dominating X by means of maps $\varphi: X \to Y$ and $\psi: Y \to X$, and let Y' be a polyhedron which $(\epsilon'/2)$-dominates X' by maps $\varphi': X' \to Y'$ and $\psi': Y' \to X'$. Since

$$\frac{\epsilon}{2} < \frac{\delta}{4} \leq \frac{1}{4}\delta(gf, U), \text{ then } i(X, gf, U) = i(Y, \varphi g f \psi, \psi^{-1}(U))$$

and since

$$\frac{\epsilon'}{2} < \frac{\delta}{4} \leq \frac{1}{4}\delta(fg, g^{-1}(U)),$$

then $i(X', fg, g^{-1}(U)) = i(Y', \varphi' fg\psi', \psi'^{-1}g^{-1}(U))$.

The proof that

$$i(Y, \varphi g f \psi, \psi^{-1}(U)) = i(Y', \varphi' fg\psi', \psi'^{-1}g^{-1}(U))$$

is similar to Section B but differs considerably in detail. Again we must establish four equations, which are:

$$i(Y, \varphi g f \psi, \psi^{-1}(U)) = i(Y, \varphi g \psi' \varphi' f \psi, \psi^{-1}(U)) \qquad (1)$$

$$i(Y, \varphi g \psi' \varphi' f \psi, \psi^{-1}(U)) = i(Y', \varphi' f \psi \varphi g \psi', \psi'^{-1}g^{-1}\varphi^{-1}\psi^{-1}(U)) \qquad (2)$$

$$i(Y', \varphi' f \psi \varphi g \psi', \psi'^{-1}g^{-1}\varphi^{-1}\psi^{-1}(U)) = i(Y', \varphi' f \psi \varphi g \psi', \psi'^{-1}g^{-1}(U)) \qquad (3)$$

$$i(Y', \varphi' f \psi \varphi g \psi', \psi'^{-1}g^{-1}(U)) = i(Y', \varphi' fg\psi', \psi'^{-1}g^{-1}(U)). \qquad (4)$$

Since we are working with the index on $\mathscr{C}_P$, we have all the axioms available to us. Equations (1) and (4) will follow from the homotopy axiom, equation (2) depends on the commutativity axiom, and equation (3) is a consequence of the additivity axiom.

In order to verify equation (1), let $H': X' \times I \to X'$ be an $(\epsilon'/2)$-homotopy such that $H'(x', 0) = x'$ and $H'(x', 1) = \psi'\varphi'(x')$ for $x' \in X'$. Define $H'_t: X' \to X'$ by $H'_t(x') = H'(x', t)$. In order to apply the homotopy axiom, we will prove that $\varphi g H'_t f \psi$ has no fixed points on $\psi^{-1}(\partial U)$. Let

$y \in \psi^{-1}(\partial U)$ such that $\varphi g H'_t f \psi(y) = y$ for some $t \in I$, then $\psi \varphi g H'_t f \psi(y) = \psi(y)$. Thus $d(\psi(y), g H'_t f \psi(y)) < \epsilon/2$. We know that $d(H'_t f \psi(y), f \psi(y)) < \epsilon'/2$, so, by the definition of ϵ', we have $d(g H'_t f \psi(y), g f \psi(y)) < \delta/4$. We conclude that

$$d(\psi(y), g f \psi(y)) < \frac{\epsilon}{2} + \frac{\delta}{4} < \frac{\delta}{2}.$$

But $d(\psi(y), \partial U) = 0 < \delta(gf, U)$, so

$$d(\psi(y), g f \psi(y)) > \delta(gf, U) \geq \delta,$$

which establishes a contradiction, and $\varphi g H'_t f \psi(y) \neq y$ for all $y \in \psi^{-1}(\partial U)$, $t \in I$.

Equation (2) is seen to be an immediate consequence of the commutativity axiom if we observe that $\psi'^{-1} g^{-1} \varphi^{-1} \psi^{-1}(U) = (\varphi g \psi')^{-1}(\psi^{-1}(U))$.

We will obtain equation (3) from the additivity axiom as soon as we verify that $\varphi' f \psi \varphi g \psi'$ has no fixed points on either

$$S = \psi'^{-1} g^{-1} \varphi^{-1} \psi^{-1}(U) - [\psi'^{-1} g^{-1}(U) \cap \psi'^{-1} g^{-1} \varphi^{-1} \psi^{-1}(U)]$$

or

$$T = \psi'^{-1} g^{-1}(U) - [\psi'^{-1} g^{-1}(U) \cap \psi'^{-1} g^{-1} \varphi^{-1} \psi^{-1}(U)].$$

If $y' \in S \cup T$, then exactly one of the points $\psi \varphi g \psi'(y')$ and $g \psi'(y')$ is in U. Let $H_t : X \to X$ be obtained from the $(\epsilon/2)$-homotopy H between $\psi \varphi$ and the identity on X. There exists $t \in I$ such that $H_t g \psi'(y') \in \partial U$ (compare Section B), so $d(g \psi'(y'), \partial U) < \epsilon/2$. Suppose $y' \in S \cup T$ and yet $\varphi' f \psi \varphi g \psi'(y') = y'$. Then this, as usual, tells us that

$$\psi' \varphi' f \psi \varphi g \psi'(y') = \psi'(y').$$

Therefore $d(\psi'(y'), f \psi \varphi g \psi'(y')) < \epsilon'/2$. Since

$$d(\psi \varphi g \psi'(y'), g \psi'(y')) < \frac{\epsilon}{2},$$

then by the definition of ϵ, $d(f \psi \varphi g \psi'(y'), f g \psi'(y')) < \epsilon'/2$, so $d(f g \psi'(y'), \psi'(y')) < \epsilon'$. The definition of ϵ' then implies that $d(g f g \psi'(y'), g \psi'(y')) < \delta/4$. On the other hand, we have seen that $y' \in S \cup T$ implies

$$d(g \psi'(y'), \partial U) < \frac{\epsilon}{2} < \delta(gf, U),$$

so

$$d(g f g \psi'(y'), g \psi'(y')) > \delta$$

in contradiction to what we just proved.

If we can show that, for all $t \in I$, $\varphi' f H_t g \psi'$ is without fixed points on $\psi'^{-1} g^{-1}(\partial U)$, then we can apply the homotopy axiom to verify equation (4). If $y' \in \psi'^{-1} g^{-1}(\partial U)$, then $\psi'(y') \in g^{-1}(\partial U)$ and thus

$$d(f g \psi'(y'), \psi'(y')) > \delta(fg, g^{-1}(U)) \geq \delta.$$

Suppose $\varphi' f H_t g \psi'(y') = y'$ for some $t \in I$, then $d(\psi'(y'), f H_t g \psi'(y')) < \epsilon'/2$. We know that $d(H_t g \psi'(y'), g \psi'(y')) < \epsilon/2$, so $d(f H_t g \psi'(y'), f g \psi'(y')) < \epsilon'/2$, and therefore $d(\psi'(y'), f g \psi'(y')) < \epsilon' < \delta/4$, which establishes the contradiction.

NOTES

The extension of index theory to the ANR case was first accomplished by Browder [10] who subsequently obtained an index on much more general kinds of spaces [9]. Other general index theories have been worked out by Leray [40] (extended further by Deleanu in [17]), Bourgin [4], and Lefschetz [33]. There are also a number of "indices" for the study of problems related to fixed point theory: Lefschetz [33], Brooks [5], Fadell [19], and Fuller [20], [22] have defined some of these.

EXERCISES

1. Prove that, if $(X, f, U) \in \mathscr{C}'_P$, then the value of $i(X, f, U)$ is the same whether we use the index on $\mathscr{C}_P$ or the index on $\mathscr{C}_A$.

2. If $(X, f, U) \in \mathscr{C}'_A$, where f is a constant map, prove that

$$i(X, f, U) = \begin{cases} 0 & \text{if } f(X) \notin U \\ 1 & \text{if } f(X) \in U. \end{cases}$$

3. Given maps $f: X \to X$ and $g: X' \to X'$, prove that if $(X, f, U) \in \mathscr{C}'_A$ and $(X', g, U') \in \mathscr{C}'_A$, then

$$i(X \times X', f \times g, U \times U') = i(X, f, U) \cdot i(X', g, U').$$

4. Give an example of an ANR X and maps $f, g: X \to X$ such that, for $x \in X$, $f(x) = x$ if and only if $g(x) = x$, and yet $L(f) \neq L(g)$.

5. Let X and Y be ANRs, let A be a closed subset of X and let $f, g: X \to Y$ be maps such that $f(a) = g(a)$ for all $a \in A$. Prove that there exists an open subset V of X containing A such that the maps $f', g': V \to V$ are homotopic, where the prime denotes restriction to V.

6. Let X and X' be ANRs and $f: X \times X' \to X$ a map. Prove that the set

$$A = \{(x, x') \in X \times X' \mid f(x, x') = x\}$$

is closed in $X \times X'$.

7. Let X and X' be ANRs, $f: X \times X' \to X$ and $g: X \times X' \to X'$ maps, and define $f \star g: X \times X' \to X \times X'$ by

$$f \star g(x, x') = (f(x, x'), g(x, x')).$$

Let A be defined as in the previous exercise. Prove that, if $h: X \times X' \to X'$ is a map such that $h(x, x') = g(x, x')$ for all $(x, x') \in A$, then $L(f \star g) = L(f \star h)$.

Chapter VI

The Nielsen Number

For X, a compact ANR, and a map $f: X \to X$, we shall define a non-negative integer $N(f)$, called the "Nielsen number" of f. The Nielsen number is a lower bound for the number of fixed points of f. The main result of this chapter is that, if $g: X \to X$ is homotopic to f, then $N(g) = N(f)$. Thus the Nielsen number is a lower bound for the number of fixed points of every map homotopic to f.

A. PATHS

A *path* C in a space X is a map $C: I \to X$. Given a path C in X, define a path $C^{-1}: I \to X$ by $C^{-1}(t) = C(1 - t)$ for all $t \in I$. For paths $C, D: I \to X$ with $C(1) = D(0)$, we can form a new path CD by

$$CD(t) = \begin{cases} C(2t) & \text{if } 0 \leq t \leq \frac{1}{2} \\ D(2t - 1) & \text{if } \frac{1}{2} \leq t \leq 1. \end{cases}$$

Two paths $C, D: I \to X$ are said to be *fixed end-point homotopic* if there is a map $\Psi: I \times I \to X$ such that

$$\begin{aligned} \Psi(s, 0) &= C(0) = D(0) &&\text{for all } s \in I \\ \Psi(s, 1) &= C(1) = D(1) &&\text{for all } s \in I \\ \Psi(0, t) &= C(t) &&\text{for all } t \in I \\ \Psi(1, t) &= D(t) &&\text{for all } t \in I. \end{aligned}$$

The relation "is fixed end-point homotopic to" is an equivalence relation on the set of all paths in X (Ex. 1). Denote the equivalence class containing a path C by $\{C\}$. We note that the classes $\{C^{-1}\}$ and $\{CD\}$ are independent of the choice of elements of $\{C\}$ and $\{D\}$ used to define them (Ex. 2).

We will need one other operation on paths. For C a path in X, and $r,s \in I$, define $C_r^s: I \to X$ by

$$C_r^s(t) = C(r + t(s - r))$$

Thus C_r^s is the restriction of C to the interval $[r, s] \subseteq [0, 1]$, reparametrized so that it is again a path.

Lemma 1. *Let* $C: I \to X$ *be a path, then* $(C_q^r)^{-1} = C_r^q$ *and* $\{C_q^r C_r^s\} = \{C_q^s\}$.

Proof The first statement is evident because

$$(C_q^r)^{-1}(t) = C(q + (1 - t)(r - q)) = C(r + t(q - r)) = C_r^q(t)$$

For the second statement, we define the required fixed end-point homotopy $\Psi: I \times I \to X$ by

$$\Psi(u, t) = \begin{cases} C[u(q + t(s - q)) + (1 - u)(q + 2t(r - q))] \\ \qquad \text{if } 0 \leq t \leq \tfrac{1}{2} \\ C[u(q + t(s - q)) + (1 - u)(r + (2t - 1)(s - r))] \\ \qquad \text{if } \tfrac{1}{2} \leq t \leq 1. \quad \blacksquare \end{cases}$$

B. FIXED POINT CLASSES

Let $f: X \to X$ be a map on a compact ANR; we say that fixed points x_0 and x_1 of f are *f-equivalent* if there is a path $C: I \to X$ such that $C(0) = x_0$, $C(1) = x_1$, and for the path $fC: I \to X$ we have $\{fC\} = \{C\}$. Let $\Phi(f)$ denote the set of all fixed points of f; then it is easy to see that the relation of *f*-equivalence is an equivalence relation on $\Phi(f)$. The equivalence classes are called *fixed point classes* of f.

Theorem 1. *A map* $f: X \to X$ *on a compact* ANR *has a finite number of fixed point classes.*

Proof By Theorem III.A.3 there exists $\delta > 0$ such that, if $W_1 = \{(x, x') \in X \times X \mid d(x, x') < \delta\}$, then there is a map $\gamma_1: W_1 \times I \to X$ such that $\gamma_1(x, x', 0) = x$, $\gamma_1(x, x', 1) = x'$, and $\gamma_1(x, x, t) = x$ for all $t \in I$. By the uniform continuity of f, given $\delta > 0$, there exists $\zeta > 0$, $\zeta < \delta/2$, such that if $x, y \in X$ and $d(x, y) < \zeta$, then $d(f(x), f(y)) < \delta/2$. By Theorem III.A.3 again, there exists $\eta > 0$ such that if $W_0 = \{(x, x') \in X \times X \mid d(x, x') < \eta\}$ then there is a map $\gamma_0: W_0 \times I \to X$ with the properties: $\gamma_0(x, x', 0) = x$, $\gamma_0(x, x', 1) = x'$, $\gamma_0(x, x, t) = x$, and $\text{diam}(\gamma_0((x, x') \times I)) < \zeta$. Now suppose $x,x' \in \Phi(f)$ and $d(x, x') < \eta$; then $C(t) = \gamma_0(x, x', t)$ is a path from x to x' such that $\text{diam}(C(I)) < \zeta < \delta/2$ and hence $\text{diam}(fC(I)) < \delta/2$. Therefore, for each $t \in I$, $d(C(t), fC(t)) < \delta$ and we have a map $H: I \times I \to X$ given by $H(s, t) = \gamma_1(C(s), fC(s), t)$, which shows that x and x' are f-equivalent. We have proved that each fixed point class is open in $\Phi(f)$, and since $\Phi(f)$ is compact (see IEV. x. 2), the theorem follows. ∎

Henceforth, we will denote the set of fixed point classes of a map $f: X \to X$ on a compact ANR by $\Phi'(f) = \{F_1, \ldots, F_n\}$.

C. THE NIELSEN NUMBER

Let $f: X \to X$ be a map on a compact ANR with fixed point classes $F_1, \ldots, F_n$. From the proof of Theorem B.1, for each $j = 1, \ldots, n$, there is an open set U_j in X such that $F_j \subseteq U_j$ and $\text{cl}(U_j) \cap \Phi(f) = F_j$, where "cl" denotes closure. Let i be the index on $\mathscr{C}_A$ defined in the last chapter. Note that $(X, f, U_j) \in \mathscr{C}'_A$. Define the *index* $i(F_j)$ of the fixed point class F_j by $i(F_j) = i(X, f, U_j)$.

Theorem 1. *The definition of $i(F_j)$ is independent of the choice of the open set $U_j \subseteq X$ such that $F_j \subseteq U_j$ and $\text{cl}(U_j) \cap \Phi(f) = F_j$.*

Proof Let U and V be open subsets of X satisfying the hypotheses of the theorem. If $x \in U - (U \cap V)$ then, since x belongs to U, $x \notin F_k$ for $k \neq j$, while x does not belong to V, so $x \notin F_j$. Thus $x \notin \Phi(f)$. By the additivity axiom, $i(X, f, U) = i(X, f, U \cap V)$. The same reasoning implies $i(X, f, V) = i(X, f, U \cap V)$ and completes the proof. ∎

For X a compact ANR and $f: X \to X$ a map, a fixed point class F of f is said to be *essential* if $i(F) \neq 0$ and *inessential* if $i(F) = 0$. The *Nielsen number* $N(f)$ of the map f is defined to be the number of fixed point classes of f that are essential.

The following result is a trivial consequence of the definition but, nevertheless, it will turn out to be important later:

Theorem 2. *A map $f: X \to X$ on a compact ANR has at least $N(f)$ fixed points.*

D. H-RELATED CLASSES

For spaces X and Y, let $\text{Map}(X, Y)$ denote the set of all maps from X to Y. A homotopy $H': X \times I \to Y$, where Y is metric, induces a Map $H: I \to \text{Map}(X, Y)$ (with respect to the uniform metric topology on $\text{Map}(X, Y)$)

by the rule $H(t)(x) = H'(x, t)$. Thus a homotopy may be thought of as a path in Map(X, Y).

If X and Y are ANRs, H is a path in Map(X, Y) and C is a path in X, then we form a new path $\langle H, C \rangle : I \to Y$ by defining $\langle H, C \rangle(t) = H(t)(C(t))$ for all $t \in I$.

Our first result shows that the operation of forming $\langle H, C \rangle$ behaves in a reasonable way with respect to the operations of the inverse and composition of paths defined in Section A.

Lemma 1. *Let H and H' be paths in* Map(X, Y) *such that $H(1) = H'(0)$, and let C and C' be paths in X such that $C(1) = C'(0)$; then*

(1) $\langle H^{-1}, C^{-1} \rangle = \langle H, C \rangle^{-1}$

(2) $\langle HH', CC' \rangle = \langle H, C \rangle \langle H', C' \rangle$.

Proof By definition, for $t \in I$, $\langle H^{-1}, C^{-1} \rangle(t) = H(1 - t)(C(1 - t)) = \langle H, C \rangle^{-1}(t)$. The definitions state that

$$\langle HH', CC' \rangle(t) = HH'(t)(CC'(t))$$
$$= \begin{cases} HH'(t)(C(2t)) & \text{if } 0 \le t \le \tfrac{1}{2} \\ HH'(t)(C'(2t - 1)) & \text{if } \tfrac{1}{2} \le t \le 1 \end{cases}$$
$$= \begin{cases} H(2t)(C(2t)) & \text{if } 0 \le t \le \tfrac{1}{2} \\ H'(2t - 1)(C'(2t - 1)) & \text{if } \tfrac{1}{2} \le t \le 1 \end{cases}$$
$$= \begin{cases} \langle H, C \rangle(2t) & \text{if } 0 \le t \le \tfrac{1}{2} \\ \langle H', C' \rangle (2t - 1) & \text{if } \tfrac{1}{2} \le t \le 1 \end{cases}$$
$$= \langle H, C \rangle \langle H', C' \rangle(t). \quad \blacksquare$$

The next result shows that the operation of forming $\langle H, C \rangle$ also shows good behavior with respect to fixed end-point homotopy. Note that, if C and C' are paths in X (a metric space), then a definition of a fixed end-point homotopy between C and C' equivalent to the one we gave in Section A is that there exist a path γ in Map(I, X) such that $\gamma(0) = C$, $\gamma(1) = C'$, $\gamma(t)(0) = C(0) = C'(0)$, and $\gamma(t)(1) = C(1) = C'(1)$, for all $t \in I$.

Lemma 2. *If H and H' are paths in* Map(X, Y), *where X and Y are compact ANRs, such that $\{H\} = \{H'\}$, and C and C' are paths in X such that $\{C\} = \{C'\}$, then $\{\langle H, C \rangle\} = \{\langle H', C' \rangle\}$.*

Proof By hypothesis, there is a path Ψ in Map(I, Map(X, Y)) with $\Psi(0) = H$, $\Psi(1) = H'$, $\Psi(t)(0) = H(0) = H'(0)$, and $\Psi(t)(1) = H(1) = H'(1)$; and a path γ in Map(I, X) with $\gamma(0) = C$, $\gamma(1) = C'$, $\gamma(t)(0) = C(0) = C'(0)$, and $\gamma(t)(1) = C(1) = C'(1)$; for all $t \in I$. Define a path δ in Map(I, Y) by

$\delta(t) = \langle \Psi'(t), \gamma(t) \rangle$ for $t \in I$. Then δ is a fixed end-point homotopy between $\langle H, C \rangle$ and $\langle H', C' \rangle$. ∎

Let X be a compact ANR, let $f, g: X \to X$ be maps, and let H be a homotopy from f to g which we can describe as a path in Map(X, X) such that $H(0) = f$ and $H(1) = g$. For $x_0 \in \Phi(f)$ and $x_1 \in \Phi(g)$, say that x_0 and x_1 are *H-related* if there exists a path $C: I \to X$ with $C(0) = x_0$, $C(1) = x_1$, such that $\{\langle H, C \rangle\} = \{C\}$. We write "$x_0 H x_1$" to designate the *H*-relation between x_0 and x_1 (see Figure 1).

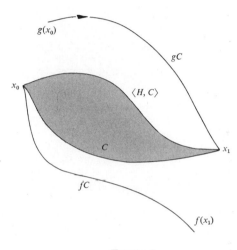

FIGURE 1

Fixed points of homotopic maps are associated to each other by being *H*-related. Since this concept operates between two different sets, it cannot be an equivalence relation. However, the next three results show that the operation of *H*-relation is as close to being an equivalence relation as it could be under the circumstances.

Lemma 3. *Let $f: X \to X$ be a map and H the constant path in* Map(X, X) *such that $H(t) = f$ for all $t \in I$. If $x \in \Phi(f)$, then xHx.*

Proof Let C be the constant path in X at x, then

$$\langle H, C \rangle(t) = H(t)(C(t)) = f(x) = x = C(t)$$

for all $t \in I$, so $\langle H, C \rangle = C$. ∎

Lemma 4. *If H is a path in* Map(X, X) *from f to g, $x_0 \in \Phi(f)$, and $x_1 \in \Phi(g)$, then $x_0 H x_1$ implies that $x_1 H^{-1} x_0$.*

Proof We have a path C from x_0 to x_1 such that $\{\langle H, C \rangle\} = \{C\}$. The path C^{-1} goes from x_1 to x_0 and, by part (1) of Lemma 1, $\{\langle H^{-1}, C^{-1} \rangle\} = \{\langle H, C \rangle^{-1}\} = \{C^{-1}\}$. ∎

Lemma 5. *Suppose H and H' are paths in $\mathrm{Map}(X, X)$ such that $H(0) = f$, $H(1) = H'(0) = g$, and $H'(1) = h$. If $x_0 \in \Phi(f)$, $x_1 \in \Phi(g)$, and $x_2 \in \Phi(h)$ such that $x_0 H x_1$ and $x_1 H' x_2$, then $x_0 H H' x_2$.*

Proof There is a path C from x_0 to x_1 with $\{\langle H, C \rangle\} = \{C\}$ and a path C' from x_1 to x_2 with $\{\langle H', C' \rangle\} = \{C'\}$. Now HH' is a path from f to h and CC' is a path from x_0 to x_2, and we apply part (2) of Lemma 1 to prove that

$$\{\langle HH', CC' \rangle\} = \{\langle H, C \rangle \langle H', C' \rangle\} = \{CC'\}. \quad ∎$$

Lemma 6. *Let H and H' be paths in $\mathrm{Map}(X, X)$ such that $H(0) = H'(0) = f$, $H(1) = H'(1) = g$ and $\{H\} = \{H'\}$. If $x_0 \in \Phi(f)$ and $x_1 \in \Phi(g)$ such that $x_0 H x_1$, then $x_0 H' x_1$.*

Proof By hypothesis, there is a path C from x_0 to x_1 with $\{\langle H, C \rangle\} = \{C\}$. By Lemma 2, $\{H\} = \{H'\}$ implies $\{\langle H, C \rangle\} = \{\langle H', C \rangle\}$. Thus $\{\langle H', C \rangle\} = \{C\}$. ∎

The next result shows that the operation "is H-related to" relates not just individual fixed points of homotopic maps but, actually, entire fixed point classes.

Theorem 7. *Let H be a path in $\mathrm{Map}(X, X)$ from f to g. Let $x_0 \in \Phi(f)$ be contained in a fixed point class F and let $x_1 \in \Phi(g)$ be contained in a fixed point class G of g. If $x_0 H x_1$ then $x_0' H x_1'$ for any $x_0' \in F$ and $x_1' \in G$.*

Proof Let F be the constant path in $\mathrm{Map}(X, X)$ at f, and let G be the constant path in $\mathrm{Map}(X, X)$ at g. Now, to say that x_0 and x_0' are in the same fixed point class F of f means that there is a path C_0 in X from x_0 to x_0' such that $\{C_0\} = \{fC_0\}$. But, for all $t \in I$,

$$\langle F, C_0 \rangle(t) = F(t)(C_0(t)) = fC_0(t),$$

so $fC_0 = \langle F, C_0 \rangle$, and we have $\{C_0\} = \{\langle F, C_0 \rangle\}$, that is, $x_0 F x_0'$. Similarly, $x_1 G x_1'$. Note also that $x_0' F^{-1} x_0$ by Lemma 4 and that $F^{-1} = F$. Thus, by Lemma 5, since $x_0 H x_1$, then $x_0 HG x_1'$. Applying Lemma 5 again, it follows that $x_0' F(HG) x_1'$.

Define a path Ψ' in $\text{Map}(I, X)$ by

$$\Psi'(t)(s) = \begin{cases} F\left(\dfrac{2s}{1-t}\right) & \text{if } 0 \leq s \leq \dfrac{1-t}{2}, \quad t \neq 1 \\[2ex] H\left(\dfrac{4s + 2(t-1)}{3t+1}\right) & \text{if } \dfrac{1-t}{2} \leq s \leq \dfrac{t+3}{4} \\[2ex] G\left(\dfrac{4s - t - 3}{1-t}\right) & \text{if } \dfrac{t+3}{4} \leq s \leq 1, \quad t \neq 1. \end{cases}$$

Then Ψ' shows us that $\{F(HG)\} = \{H\}$ and, by Lemma 6, we have proved that $x_0' H x_1'$. ∎

Let $f,g: X \to X$ be maps on an ANR and let H be a path in $\text{Map}(X, X)$ from f to g. For F a fixed point class of f and G a fixed point class of g, we say that F and G are *H-related*, written FHG, if there exists $x_0 \in F$ and $x_1 \in G$ such that x_0 and x_1 are *H*-related. Theorem 7 tells us that the definition is independent of the choice of x_0 and x_1.

The next four results are analogs, for fixed point classes, of Lemmas 3 through 6.

Lemma 8. *Let* $f: X \to X$ *be a map and let* F *be the constant path in* $\text{Map}(X, X)$ *at* f. *Fixed point classes* $F, F' \in \Phi'(f)$ *are F-related if and only if they are identical.*

Proof Suppose $F = F'$ and let $x \in F$. By Lemma 3, xFx; so, by definition, FFF. On the other hand, if FFF', then xFx' for some $x \in F$ and $x' \in F'$, that is, there is a path C in X from x to x' such that $\{\langle F, C \rangle\} = \{C\}$. But $\langle F, C \rangle = fC$ so $\{fC\} = \{C\}$. Thus x and x' are in the same fixed point class of f and $F \cap F' \neq \varnothing$. Fixed point classes are equivalence classes and therefore $F = F'$. ∎

Lemma 9. *Let* H *be a path in* $\text{Map}(X, X)$ *with* $H(0) = f$ *and* $H(1) = g$. *Let* $F \in \Phi'(f)$, $G \in \Phi'(g)$ *such that* FHG, *then* $GH^{-1}F$.

Proof By definition, there is a point $x \in F$ which is *H*-related to a point $x' \in G$. By Lemma 4, $x' H^{-1} x$; so $GH^{-1}F$. ∎

Similarly, from Lemma 5, we have

Lemma 10. *Let* H *and* H' *be paths in* $\text{Map}(X, X)$ *such that* $H(0) = f$, $H(1) = H'(0) = g$, *and* $H'(1) = h$. *Let* $F \in \Phi'(f)$, $G \in \Phi'(g)$, $H \in \Phi'(h)$ *such that* FHG *and* $GH'H$; *then* $FHH'H$.

An easy consequence of Lemma 6 is

Lemma 11. *Suppose f,g: X → X are maps and H and H' are paths in* Map(X, X) *from f to g such that* {H} = {H'}. *If F ∈ Φ'(f) is H-related to G ∈ Φ'(g), then FH'G also.*

Finally, we come to the principal result of this section:

Theorem 12. *Let H be a path in* Map(X, X) *from f to g. Let **F,F'** ∈ Φ'(f) and **G,G'** ∈ Φ'(g). If **FHG** and **FHG'** then **G = G'**, and if **FHG** and **F'HG** then **F = F'**.*

Proof If **FHG** and **FHG'**, then, by Lemma 9, $GH^{-1}F$; so, by Lemma 10, $GH^{-1}HG'$. Define G to be the constant path in Map(X, X) at g and define a path Ψ in Map(I, Map(X, X)) by

$$
\Psi(t)(s) =
\begin{cases}
G(s) & \text{if } 0 \leq s \leq \dfrac{t}{2} \\[2ex]
H^{-1}(2s - t) & \text{if } \dfrac{t}{2} \leq s \leq \dfrac{1}{2} \\[2ex]
H(2s + t - 1) & \text{if } \dfrac{1}{2} \leq s \leq \dfrac{2 - t}{2} \\[2ex]
G(s) & \text{if } \dfrac{2 - t}{2} \leq s \leq 1.
\end{cases}
$$

Then Ψ shows that $\{H^{-1}H\} = \{G\}$. Now, by Lemma 11, G is G-related to G' and so, by Lemma 8, **G = G'**, which proves the first part of the theorem. For the second part, suppose that **FHG** and **F'HG**; then, by Lemma 9, $GH^{-1}F$ and $GH^{-1}F'$. ∎

Theorem 12 states that there is a one-to-one correspondence induced by H between a subset of Φ'(f) and a subset of Φ'(g). We will prove in the next section that the correspondence carries the essential fixed point classes of f onto the essential fixed point classes of g and, therefore, that homotopic maps have the same Nielsen number.

E. INVARIANCE UNDER HOMOTOPY

Lemma 1. *Let H be a path in* Map(X, X) *and let q,r,s ∈ I. Suppose for F(q) ∈ Φ'(H(q)), F(r) ∈ Φ'(H(r)), and F(s) ∈ Φ'(H(s)) that $F(q)H_q^r F(r)$ and $F(r)H_r^s F(s)$; then $F(q)H_q^s F(s)$.*

Proof By D.10, $F(q)$ is $H^r_q H^s_r$-related to $F(s)$. By A.1, $\{H^r_q H^s_r\} = \{H^q_s\}$; so D.11 gives the desired result. ∎

The more complicated technicalities in the proof of the invariance of the Nielsen number under homotopy are disposed of in the following lemma:

Lemma 2. *Let H be a path in* Map(X, X) *where X is a compact ANR, and let $r \in I$. Denote the fixed point classes of the map $H(r)$ by $F_1(r), \ldots, F_n(r)$. There exist open sets $U_1, \ldots, U_n$ and an $\epsilon > 0$ such that*

(1) $F_j(r) \subseteq U_j$.

(2) $U_j \cap U_k = \varnothing$ *whenever $j \neq k$.*

(3) *If $|r - s| \leq \epsilon$ and $F(s) \in \Phi'(H(s))$, then there exists j such that $F(s) \subseteq U_j$ and $F(s)$ is H^r_s-related to $F_j(r)$.*

(4) *If $|r - s| \leq \epsilon$, then $(X, H(s), U_j) \in \mathscr{C}'_A$ for all $j = 1, \ldots, n$.*

Proof From the proof of Theorem B.1 we can construct open sets $U'_1, \ldots,$ U'_n satisfying (1) and (2). Let $\epsilon' > 0$ be the number guaranteed by III.A.3. Then there exists $\delta > 0$, $\delta < \epsilon'/4$, such that $x, x' \in X$, $d(x, x') < \delta$, and $|r - s| < \delta$ all imply $d(H(r)(x), H(s)(x')) < \epsilon'/4$ (because H is uniformly continuous.) For $x \in F_j(r)$, choose $\epsilon_x > 0$ so that $\epsilon_x \leq \delta$ and $U(x, \epsilon_x) \subseteq U'_j$. Since $\Phi(H(r))$ is compact, there is a finite set of connected open sets $U(x(1), \epsilon_{x(1)}), \ldots, U(x(m), \epsilon_{x(m)})$, with $x(k) \in \Phi(H(r))$, so that

$$\Phi(H(r)) \subseteq \sum_{k=1}^{m} U(x(k), \epsilon_{x(k)}).$$

Let $U_j = \bigcup U(x(k), \epsilon_{x(k)})$, where the union is taken over those k such that $x(k) \in F_j(r)$. Let $x \in F_j(r)$; then $x \in U(x(k), \epsilon_{x(k)})$ for some k. Since $U(x(k), \epsilon_{x(k)})$ is an open and connected subset of the ANR X (which, we recall, is locally pathwise connected), there is a path C from x to $x(k)$ in $U(x(k), \epsilon_{x(k)})$. For $t \in I$, $d(C(t), x) < \epsilon_{x(k)} \leq \delta$, which implies that

$$d(H(r)(C(t)), H(r)(x)) = d(H(r)(C(t)), x) < \frac{\epsilon'}{4},$$

so $d(H(r)(C(t)), C(t)) < \epsilon'$ and thus, by III.A.3 $\{H(r)(C)\} = \{C\}$.

We have shown that x and $x(k)$ are in the same fixed point class of $H(r)$. Hence $x(k) \in F_j(r)$ and $x \in U_j$, so $F_j(r) \subseteq U_j$. On the other hand, $U(x(k), \epsilon_{x(k)}) \subseteq U'_j$ when $x(k) \in F_j(r)$, which implies that $U_j \subseteq U'_j$. Therefore the sets $U_j, j = 1, \ldots, n$, satisfy properties (1) and (2). Let ϵ_1 be the smallest of the numbers $\epsilon_{x(1)}, \ldots, \epsilon_{x(m)}$. Since $\Phi(H(r)) \subseteq \bigcup_{j=1}^{n} U_j$, there exists $\eta > 0$ such that $x \in X - \bigcup_{j=1}^{n} U_j$ implies $d(H(r)(x), x) > \eta$. Again, using uniform continuity, there exists $\epsilon_2 > 0$ with the property that, if $|r - s| < \epsilon_2$, then $d(H(r)(x), H(s)(x)) < \eta$ for all $x \in X$. Thus, if $|r - s| < \epsilon_2$ and $x \in X - \bigcup_{j=1}^{n} U_j$, then $H(s)(x) \neq x$. Equivalently, $\Phi(H(s)) \subseteq \bigcup_{j=1}^{n} U_j$. Let ϵ be the smaller of ϵ_1 and ϵ_2. It remains to prove that the open sets $U_1, \ldots, U_n$ and the number $\epsilon > 0$ satisfy conditions (3) and (4).

Suppose $|r - s| \leq \epsilon$ and $x_s \in F(s) \in \Phi'(H(s))$. Since $\epsilon \leq \epsilon_2$, $x_s \in U_j$ for some $j = 1, \ldots, n$ and hence $x_s \in U(x(k), \epsilon_{x(k)})$ for some $x(k) \in F_j(r)$. Let C be a path in $U(x(k), \epsilon_{x(k)})$ from x_s to $x(k)$. For any $t \in I$, $H_s^r(t) = H(t')$, where $t' = s + t(r - s)$, so

$$|r - t'| = |1 - t| \, |r - s| \leq |r - s| < \epsilon.$$

Also, since $\epsilon \leq \epsilon_1 \leq \delta \leq \epsilon'/2$, we have

$$d(H_s^r(t)C(t), C(t)) = d(H(t')(C(t)), C(t))$$
$$\leq d(H(r)(C(t)), H(t')(C(t))) + d(H(r)(C(t)), C(t))$$
$$< \frac{\epsilon'}{4} + \frac{\epsilon'}{2} < \epsilon'$$

and, by the definition of ϵ', $\{\langle H_s^r, C \rangle\} = \{C\}$, which states that x_s is H_s^r-related to $x(k)$. By definition, then, $F(s)$ is H_s^r-related to $F_j(r)$. If there were a point $x_s' \in F(s)$ such that $x_s' \in U_k$, by the same reasoning, $F(s)$ would be H_s^r-related to $F_k(r)$. Thus, by D.12, it must be that $k = j$, so $F(s) \subseteq U_j$, which completes the proof of condition (3).

Condition (4) is easy. Since $\epsilon \leq \epsilon_2$, if $|r - s| \leq \epsilon$ then we know, by the way we defined ϵ_2, that $H(s)$ has no fixed points on $X - \bigcup_{j=1}^{n} U_j$; so, in particular, it has no fixed points on $\bigcup_{j=1}^{n} \partial U_j$, which implies $(X, H(s), U_j) \in \mathscr{C}_A'$ as required.   ∎

We now come to the main result of this section:

Theorem 3.   *Let H be a path in $\mathrm{Map}(X, X)$ from f to g where X is a compact ANR. Let $F \in \Phi'(f)$. If F is H-related to some $G \in \Phi'(g)$, then $i(F) = i(G)$; and if F is not H-related to any element of $\Phi'(g)$, then $i(F) = 0$.*

Proof   Let $x \in F \in \Phi'(f)$, and let $\mathbf{H}(s)$ be the set of points x' in $\Phi(H(s))$ such that x is H_0^s-related to x'. By D.12, $\mathbf{H}(s)$ is either empty or a single fixed point class of $H(s)$. If $\mathbf{H}(s) = \varnothing$, then, letting $i(\mathbf{H}(s)) = i(X, H(s), \mathbf{H}(s))$, we have $i(\mathbf{H}(s)) = 0$ from the proof of IV.A.1. So, in any case, what we have to prove is that $i(F) = i(\mathbf{H}(1))$ and, that way, take care of both parts of the theorem at once. We claim that, given $r \in I$, there exists $\epsilon > 0$ such that $|r - s| < \epsilon$ implies $i(\mathbf{H}(r)) = i(\mathbf{H}(s))$. If our claim is correct, then, since I is connected, it must be that $i(H(s)) = i(F)$ for all $s \in I$. We will let ϵ be the number obtained from Lemma 2. Suppose $H(s) \neq \varnothing$; then, by Lemma 2, $H(s)$ is H_s^r-related to some $F_j(r) \in \Phi'(H(r))$. Now $H(s)$ is H_0^s-related to F, so, by Lemma 1, $F_j(r)$ is H_0^r-related to F. Thus, by D.12, $F_j(r) = H(r)$ and $H(r) \neq \varnothing$. The contrapositive statement is that, if $H(r) = \varnothing$, then $H(s) = \varnothing$ and $i(H(r)) = i(H(s)) = 0$. This completes the proof of the claim, when $H(r) = \varnothing$. In the case $H(r) \neq \varnothing$, the important point is that, if U is the open set from Lemma 2 containing $H(r)$ and $|r - s| \leq \epsilon$, then

$$U \cap \Phi(H(s)) = H(s). \tag{1}$$

In order to prove (1), first note that if $H(s) \neq \varnothing$ then, by Lemma 2, $H(s) \subseteq U_j$ for some j, and $H(s)$ is H_s^r-related to $F_j(r)$. But we showed above that $F_j(r) = H(r)$, so $U_j = U$ and $H(s) \subseteq U$. Therefore $U \cap \Phi(H(s)) = \varnothing$ must imply that $H(s) = \varnothing$, and in that case (1) is certainly true. We assume that $U \cap \Phi(H(s)) \neq \varnothing$. Take $x_s \in U \cap \Phi(H(s))$; then x_s is in some fixed point class K of $H(s)$. By Lemma 2, $K \subseteq U_j$ for some j. But $x_s \in U \cap U_j$, so, by Lemma 2 again, $U = U_j$, which means that $K \subseteq U$ and therefore K is H_s^r-related to $H(r)$. By definition, F is H_0^s-related to $H(r)$, so, by Lemma 1, F is H_0^s-related to K which, by D.12, implies that $K = H(s)$. Thus, if $x_s \in U \cap \Phi(H(s))$, then we have shown that $x_s \in H(s)$, which means that $U \cap \Phi(H(s)) \subseteq H(s)$. On the other hand we have already seen that $H(s) \subseteq U$, and it follows that $H(s) \subseteq U \cap \Phi(H(s))$, which proves (1). By definition, $i(H(r)) = i(X, H(r), U)$, and by (1) we can take $i(H(s)) = i(X, H(s), U)$ since Lemma 2 states that $(X, H(s), U) \in \mathscr{C}_A'$ when $|r - s| \leq \epsilon$. Finally, H_s^r is a homotopy from $H(s)$ to $H(r)$ and, for $t \in I$, $H_s^r(t) = H(t')$, where $|r - t'| \leq |r - s| \leq \epsilon$. So, by Lemma 2, $(X, H_s^r(t), U) \in \mathscr{C}_A'$. Therefore, by the homotopy axiom of the fixed point index, $i(H(r)) = i(H(s))$. ∎

It is clear from Theorem 3 why the fixed point class F of a map $f : X \to X$ is called "essential," if $i(F) \neq 0$. Any path H in Map(X, X) which starts at f must induce a correspondence which takes F to a fixed point class of $H(1)$. Thus F is essential in the sense that it cannot be eliminated by moving the map f through a homotopy.

Theorem 4. *Let X be a compact* ANR *and let $f, g : X \to X$ be homotopic maps; then $N(f) = N(g)$.*

Proof Let H be a homotopy between f and g. By D.12, H induces a one-to-one correspondence from some of the fixed point classes of f to some of the classes of g where the correspondence is given by H-relation. By Theorem 3, every essential class of f is H-related to a class of g, so the essential classes are contained in the domain of the correspondence. Since the correspondence preserves index according to Theorem 3, the images of the essential classes of f are essential classes of g. Thus there is a one-to-one correspondence from the set of essential fixed point classes of f into the set of essential classes of g, and that means $N(f) \leq N(g)$. On the other hand, H^{-1} induces a one-to-one correspondence of fixed point classes which, by the same argument, carries the essential classes of g into the set of essential classes of f; so $N(g) \leq N(f)$, and the proof is complete. ∎

NOTES

In the course of his work with a very restricted class of polyhedra, Nielsen introduced the number bearing his name in [43]. He used an approach rather different from the present one. A modern treatment along those same lines is given by Jiang [30]. The results of this chapter were proved for all polyhedra by Wecken [51] and extended to ANRs in Browder's dissertation [10]. Theorem E.3 has been generalized by Brooks [5] and by Brown [13].

EXERCISES

1. Prove that the relation "is fixed end-point homotopic to" is an equivalence relation on the set of paths in a space X.
2. For $C, D: I \to X$ paths with $C(1) = D(0)$, prove that the classes $\{C^{-1}\}$ and $\{CD\}$ are independent of the choice of representatives of $\{C\}$ and $\{D\}$ used to define them.
3. Prove that, for $f: X \to X$ a map and $x, x' \in \Phi(f)$, x and x' are f-equivalent if and only if there is a path C from x to x' such that the path $C(fC)^{-1}$ is fixed end-point homotopic to the constant path at x.
4. Prove that, if $f: X \to X$ is a deformation (see Section II.D), then $N(f) = 0$ if $\chi(x) = 0$ and $N(f) = 1$ otherwise.
5. Prove that, for any integer $n > 0$, there exists a deformation of S^{2n} with exactly one fixed point.
6. Prove that if X is a compact ANR such that $\pi_1(X, x_0) = 0$ (see Section I.N) and $f: X \to X$ is any map, then $N(f) = 0$ if $L(f) = 0$ and $N(f) = 1$ otherwise.
7. For any map $f: X \to X$, prove that $L(f) \neq 0$ implies $N(f) \geq 1$.
8. Prove that, if $f: X \to X$ is a map and $h: X \to Y$ is a homeomorphism, then $N(hfh^{-1}) = N(f)$.

Chapter VII

Computation of the Nielsen Number

Given a map $f: X \to X$, what sort of information about X and f do we need in order to compute $N(f)$, the Nielsen number of f? We will show in this chapter that in some cases it is enough to know $L(f)$ and the homomorphism which f induces on the fundamental group of X.

The main tool in these computations is the Jiang subgroup $T(f)$, a subgroup of the fundamental group of X which depends on f. The Jiang subgroup is employed, when $L(f) = 0$, to obtain a useful sufficient condition for $N(f)$ to be zero. It has an important part in the establishment of bounds on $N(f)$ when $L(f) \neq 0$.

This chapter contains several examples of the computation of the Nielsen number, including that of the map on the figure-eight that we introduced in Chapter II.

A. THE JIANG SUBGROUP

Let X be a compact ANR and $f: X \to X$ a map. An element $\alpha \in \pi_1(X, f(x_0))$ is said to be in the *Jiang subgroup* $T(f, x_0)$ of f if there is a loop H in Map(X, X) based at f such that the loop C in X defined by $C(t) = H(t)(x_0)$ is an element of α. It is clear that $T(f, x_0)$ is a subgroup of $\pi_1(X, f(x_0))$.

An equivalent definition of $T(f, x_0)$ is the following: Define $p: \text{Map}(X, X) \to X$ by $p(g) = g(x_0)$; then p induces $p_\pi: \pi_1(\text{Map}(X, X), f) \to \pi_1(X, x_0)$. The Jiang subgroup $T(f, x_0)$ is the image of the homomorphism p_π (Ex. 10).

We will need the following well-known result:

Theorem 1 (The Homotopy Extension Theorem).   *Let X be a compact metric space and A a closed subset of X. Define*

$$T = (X \times 0) \cup (A \times I) \subseteq X \times I.$$

If Y is a compact ANR and $g: T \to Y$ is a map, then there is a map

$$G: X \times I \to Y$$

whose restriction to T is g.

We assume throughout this section that all the spaces we consider are connected compact ANRs.

The Jiang subgroup, like the fundamental group, is independent, up to isomorphism, of the choice of base point.

Lemma 2.   *For x_0 and x_1 any points of X and $f: X \to X$ any map, $T(f, x_0)$ is isomorphic to $T(f, x_1)$.*

Proof   Let P be a path in X from x_0 to x_1, then fP is a path from $f(x_0)$ to $f(x_1)$. We will show that $(fP)_\pi(T(f, x_0)) \subseteq T(f, x_1)$. Let $\alpha \in T(f, x_0)$, then there is a loop H in $\mathrm{Map}(X, X)$ based at f such that the loop $C(t) = H(t)(x_0)$ is in α. Define $T = (X \times 0) \cup (x_1 \times I)$ and a map $g: T \to X$ by

$$g(x, t) = \begin{cases} P^{-1}(t) & \text{if } x = x_1 \\ x & \text{if } t = 0. \end{cases}$$

Extend g to a map $G: X \times I \to X$ by Theorem 1. We have a loop K in $\mathrm{Map}(X, X)$ based at f whose definition is

$$K(t)(x) = \begin{cases} fG(x, 3t) & \text{if } 0 \leq t \leq \tfrac{1}{3} \\ H(3t - 1)(G(x, 1)) & \text{if } \tfrac{1}{3} \leq t \leq \tfrac{2}{3} \\ fG(x, 3 - 3t) & \text{if } \tfrac{2}{3} \leq t \leq 1. \end{cases}$$

Since $K(t)(x_1) = [(fP)^{-1}C(fP)](t)$ we have proved that $(fP)_\pi(\alpha) \in T(f, x_1)$. A similar argument shows that $(fP)_\pi^{-1}(T(f, x_1)) \subseteq T(f, x_0)$ and completes the proof. ∎

Lemma 3.   *Let $f: X \to X$ be a map and let α be an element of $T(f, x_0)$. If C is a loop in X based at $f(x_0)$ such that $\{C\} = \alpha$, then there is a loop H in $\mathrm{Map}(X, X)$ based at f such that $C(t) = H(t)(x_0)$ for all $t \in I$.*

Proof   Since $\alpha \in T(f, x_0)$, there is a loop C' in X based at $f(x_0)$ such that $\{C'\} = \{C\}$ and a loop H' in $\mathrm{Map}(X, X)$ based at f with the property that $H'(x_0)(t) = C'(t)$ for all $t \in I$. Let J be the path in $\mathrm{Map}((I, \partial I), (X, f(x_0)))$

such that $J(0) = C'$ and $J(1) = C$. Consider the closed subset $A = (x_0 \times I) \cup (X \times \partial I)$ of $X \times I$ and define

$$T = ((X \times I) \times 0) \cup (A \times I) \subset X \times I \times I.$$

The map $k: T \to X$, where

$$k(x, t, u) = \begin{cases} H'(t)(x) & \text{if } u = 0 \\ f(x) & \text{if } t \in \partial I \\ J(u)(t) & \text{if } x = x_0, \end{cases}$$

can be extended to a map $K: X \times I \times I \to X$ by Theorem 1. Define the desired loop $H: I \to \text{Map}(X, X)$ by $H(t)(x) = K(x, t, 1)$. ∎

One very important reason for studying the Jiang subgroup is indicated by the following theorem:

Theorem 4. *Let $f: X \to X$ be a map such that $T(f, x_0) = \pi_1(X, x_0)$; then all the fixed point classes of f have the same index.*

Proof If $\Phi(f) = \varnothing$, then the theorem is vacuously true. Otherwise, denote the fixed point classes of f by $F_1, \ldots, F_m$. By Lemma 2, we can assume that $x_0 \in F_1$. Choose some $x_j \in F_j$ for any $j = 2, \ldots, m$. We will prove that there is a loop H in $\text{Map}(X, X)$ based at f such that x_0 and x_j are H-related. Thus, by VI.D.7, F_1 is H-related to F_j and the conclusion follows by VI.E.3. Let P be a path in X from x_0 to x_j, then $P(fP)^{-1}$ is contained in an element $\alpha \in \pi_1(X, x_0) = T(f, x_0)$ and, as a consequence of Lemma 3, there is a loop H' in $\text{Map}(X, X)$ based at f such that $H'(t)(x_0) = (P(fP)^{-1})(t)$ for all $t \in I$. Define $J: I \times I \to X$ by

$$J(t, u) = \begin{cases} P(3(1 - t)u + t) & \text{if } 0 \le u \le \tfrac{1}{3} \\ fP(3(t - 1)u + 2 - t) & \text{if } \tfrac{1}{3} \le u \le \tfrac{2}{3} \\ H'(3(t - 1)(u - 1) + t)(P(t)) & \text{if } \tfrac{2}{3} \le u \le 1. \end{cases}$$

Then $J(t, 0) = P(t)$, $J(t, 1) = \langle H', P \rangle(t)$, $J(1, u) = x_j$, and $J(0, u) = (P(fP)^{-1}(fP)P^{-1})(u)$ for all $t, u \in I$. Let $\bar{x}_0$ be the constant path at x_0; then $\{P(fP)^{-1}(fP)P^{-1}\} = \{\bar{x}_0\}$, and there is a map $K: I \times I \to X$ such that $K(0, u) = K(t, 0) = K(t, 1) = x_0$ and $K(1, u) = (P(fP)^{-1}(fP)P^{-1})(u)$ for all $t, u \in I$. Define $L: I \times I \to X$ by

$$L(t, u) = \begin{cases} K(2t, u) & \text{if } 0 \le t \le \tfrac{1}{2} \\ J(2t - 1, u) & \text{if } \tfrac{1}{2} \le t \le 1. \end{cases}$$

Then $L(0, u) = x_0$, $L(1, u) = x_j$ for all $u \in I$; and $L(t, 0) = (\bar{x}_0 P)(t)$, $L(t, 1) = (\bar{x}_0 \langle H', P \rangle)(t)$ for all $t \in I$. Define $D = \bar{x}_0 P$; then D is a path from x_0 to x_j. For F the constant path in Map(X, X) at f, let $H = FH'$; then $\langle H, D \rangle = \bar{x}_0 \langle H', P \rangle$. The homotopy L proves that $\{D\} = \{\langle H, D \rangle\}$; so, for this loop H, x_0 and x_j are H-related.   ∎

Corollary 5.   *Suppose that $f: X \to X$ is a map such that $T(f, x_0) = \pi_1(X, x_0)$. If $L(f) = 0$, then $N(f) = 0$.*

Proof   If $\Phi(f) = \varnothing$, then certainly $N(f) = 0$. Otherwise, let $F_1, \ldots, F_m$ be the fixed point classes of f, and assume that x_0 belongs to F_1 (Lemma 2). By Theorem 4, $i(F_j) = i(F_1)$ for all $j = 1, \ldots, m$; so, by the additivity and normalization axioms,

$$0 = L(f) = \sum_{j=0}^{m} i(F_j) = m(i(F_1)).$$

Thus $i(F_1) = 0$, and we see that all the fixed point classes of f are inessential. By definition, $N(f) = 0$.   ∎

The next two results will be used to eliminate some technical problems in the material that follows.

Lemma 6.   *If $f, g: X \to X$ are homotopic maps, then $T(f, x_0)$ and $T(g, x_0)$ are isomorphic groups.*

Proof   Let J be a path in Map(X, X) from f to g and let $P(t) = J(t)(x_0)$ for all $t \in I$. Then P is a path from $f(x_0)$ to $g(x_0)$. We will prove that $P_\pi(T(f, x_0)) \subseteq T(g, x_0)$. A similar argument would show that $P_\pi^{-1}(T(g, x_0)) \subseteq T(f, x_0)$, and thus that the groups are isomorphic. Let $\alpha \in T(f, x_0)$ and let H be a loop in Map(X, X) such that, for $C(t) = H(x_0)(t)$, $\{C\} = \alpha$. Consider the loop $K = J^{-1}HJ$ in Map(X, X) based at g. Then $K(t)(x_0) = (P^{-1}CP)(t)$ and, since $\{P^{-1}CP\} = P_\pi\{C\} = P_\pi(\alpha)$, we have proved that $P_\pi(\alpha) \in T(g, x_0)$.   ∎

Lemma 7.   *Given a map $f: X \to X$ and any points $x_0, x_1 \in X$, there is a map $g: X \to X$ homotopic to f such that $f^{-1}(x_0)$ and x_1 are in $g^{-1}(x_0)$.*

Proof   Apply Theorem 1 to the closed set $A = f^{-1}(x_0) \cup x_1$ and to the map $h: (X \times 0) \cup (A \times I) \to X$ defined by

$$h(x, t) = \begin{cases} f(x) & \text{if } t = 0 \\ x_0 & \text{if } x \in f^{-1}(x_0) \\ C(t) & \text{if } x = x_1, \end{cases}$$

where C is a path from $f(x_1)$ to x_0. For $H: X \times I \to X$ an extension of h, define g by $g(x) = H(x, 1)$.   ∎

Lemma 7 implies that, given $f: X \to X$ and $x_0 \in X$, there is a map $g: X \to X$ homotopic to f such that $g(x_0) = x_0$.

Bemmas 2, 6 and 7 permit us to assume that the base point $x_0 \in X$, that we choose, is a fixed point of the map with which we are working. We will drop the base point from the notation for the fundamental group and the Jiang subgroup.

The Jiang subgroup of the identity map on X is denoted by $T(X)$.

Theorem 8. *For any map $f: X \to X$, $T(X) \subseteq T(f)$.*

Proof Let $\alpha \in \pi_1(X)$ be an element of $T(X)$. Then there is a loop H in Map(X, X) based at the identity map such that, for the loop C defined by $C(t) = H(t)(x_0)$, $\{C\} = \alpha$. Define a loop H' in Map(X, X) (based at f) by $H'(t)(x) = H(t)(f(x))$. Then, since $f(x_0) = x_0$, it follows that $H'(t)(x_0) = C(t)$, which proves that $\{C\} = \alpha \in T(f)$. ∎

An ANR, designated as X, is an *H-space* if there is a point $e \in X$ and a map $\mu: X \times X \to X$ such that $\mu(x, e) = \mu(e, x) = x$ for all $x \in X$. An important property of H-spaces from our point of view is:

Theorem 9. *If X is an H-space, then $T(X) = \pi_1(X)$.*

Proof We use e as the base point. Let C be any loop in X based at e and define $H: I \to$ Map(X, X) by $H(t)(x) = \mu(C(t), x)$. Thus $\{C\} \in T(X)$. ∎

A space X is *aspherical* if $\pi_n(X)$ is the trivial group for all $n \geq 2$. Hence, given any map $g: (I^n, \partial I^n) \to (X, x_0)$ into an aspherical space, where $n \geq 2$, there is a homotopy $H: (I^n, \partial I^n) \times I \to (X, x_0)$ such that $H(r, 0) = g(r)$ and $H(r, 1) = x_0$ for all $r \in I^n$. If X is pathwise connected, an equivalent statement is that given any map $m: \partial I^{n+1} \to X$, $n \geq 2$, there is a map $M: I^{n+1} \to X$ whose restriction to ∂I^{n+1} is m.

For a group G and a subgroup H, the *centralizer of H in G, $Z(H, G)$,* is the subgroup of G defined by

$$Z(H, G) = \{g \in G \mid gh = hg \text{ for all } h \in H\}.$$

If $H = G$, we write $Z(G, G) = Z(G)$, and the subgroup is the *center of G.*

In the rest of the section, the spaces with which we will work will all be connected polyhedra. Given a polyhedron X, we fix a triangulation (K, τ) of X. Define (for $m = 0, 1, 2, \ldots$) $X^{u} = \tau |K^m|$, where K^m is the m-skeleton of K, and let

$$Q^m = (X \times \partial I) \cup (X^{m-1} \times I) \subseteq X \times I.$$

The main result concerning the Jiang subgroup of maps on connected aspherical polyhedra is

Theorem 10. *If X is a connected aspherical polyhedron and $f: X \to X$ is a map, then*

$$Z(f_\pi(\pi_1(X)), \pi_1(X)) \subseteq T(f).$$

Proof   Take a triangulation (K, τ) of X and choose $x_0 \in X^0$. By Lemmas 2, 6, and 7 we can assume that $f(x_0) = x_0$. Applying Lemma 7 a finite number of times, there is a map $d: X \to X$ homotopic to the identity map such that $d(X^0) = x_0$. Define $\bar{f} = fd$; then $\bar{f}(X^0) = x_0$. Let α be an element of $Z(f_\pi(\pi_1(X)), \pi_1(X))$ and select a loop C in α. Define $h_1: Q^1 \to X$ by

$$h_1(x, u) = \begin{cases} \bar{f}(x) & \text{if } u = 0 \text{ or } u = 1 \\ C(u) & \text{if } x \in X^0. \end{cases}$$

For a 1-simplex s_j of K, let

$$\sigma_j = \tau(\text{cl} |s_j|) \times 0 \subseteq Q^1,$$

then there is a homeomorphism $\varphi_j: I \to \sigma_j$. Define $C_j = h_1\varphi_j: I \to X$, and observe that C_j is a loop in X based at x_0. Since $\sigma_j \subseteq X \times 0$, then

$$C_j = h_1\varphi_j = \bar{f}\varphi_j = f\,d\varphi_j,$$

but $d\varphi_j$ is a loop in X based at x_0, so $\{C_j\} = f_\pi\{d\varphi_j\} \in f_\pi(\pi_1(X))$. The facts that $\{C\} = \alpha \in Z(f_\pi(\pi_1(X)), \pi_1(X))$ and $\{C_j\} \in f_\pi(\pi_1(X))$ imply, by I.N.1, that there is a map $L_j: I \times I \to X$ such that $L_j(t, 0) = L_j(t, 1) = C_j(t)$ and $L_j(0, u) = L_j(1, u) = C(u)$ for all $t, u \in I$. Define $H_j: \sigma_j \times I \to X$ by $H_j(x, u) = L_j(\varphi_j^{-1}(x), u)$ and observe that, if $(x, u) \in \partial(\sigma_j \times I) \subseteq Q^1$, then $H_j(x, u) = h_1(x, u)$. Write the 1-simplices of K as $s_1, \ldots, s_{r(1)}$; then

$$Q^2 = (X \times \partial I) \cup \bigcup_{j=1}^{r(1)} (\sigma_j \times I). \quad \text{Extend } h_1 \text{ to a map } h_2: Q^2 \to X \text{ by}$$

$$h_2(x \; u) = \begin{cases} \bar{f}(x) & \text{if } u = 0 \text{ or } u = 1 \\ H_j(x, u) & \text{if } x \in \sigma_j \text{ for some } j = 1, \ldots, r(1). \end{cases}$$

Assume that h_2 has been extended to a map $h_p: Q^p \to X, p \geq 2$. Take some p-simplex S_j of K and again define

$$\sigma_j = \tau(\text{cl} |s_j|) \times 0 \subseteq X \times 0.$$

Since $\partial(\sigma_j \times I) \subseteq Q^p$, we have the restriction $h_{p,j}: \partial(\sigma_j \times I) \to X$ of h_p. We assumed that X was aspherical, so $\pi_p(X)$ is trivial. Therefore, since $\sigma_j \times I$ is homeomorphic to I^{p+1}, we can extend $h_{p,j}$ to a map $h_{p+1,j}: \sigma_j \times I \to X$. Write the p-simplices of K as $s_1, \ldots, s_{r(p)}$, and define $h_{p+1}: Q^{p+1} \to X$

by

$$h_{p+1}(x, u) = \begin{cases} \bar{f}(x) & \text{if } u = 0 \text{ or } u = 1 \\ h_{p+1,j}(x, u) & \text{if } x \in \sigma_j \text{ for some } j = 1, \dots, r(p). \end{cases}$$

Then h_{p+1} is an extension of h_p. Since $Q^n = X \times I$ for some n, we have proved the existence of a map $H = h_n: X \times I \to X$ whose restriction to Q^1 is h_1. Thus $H(x, 0) = H(x, 1) = \bar{f}(x)$, and $H(x_0, u) = h_1(x_0, u) = C(u)$ for all $u \in I$. We have established the fact that $\alpha = \{C\}$ is an element of $T(\bar{f})$. From the proof of Lemma 7 we can see that f and $\bar{f}$ are homotopic by a homotopy $J: I \times I \to X$ such that $J(x_0, t) = x_0$ for all $t \in I$. If, in the proof of Lemma 6, we use the homotopy J, then the isomorphism between $T(f)$ and $T(\bar{f})$ is clearly the identity isomorphism, and therefore $T(f) \subseteq Z(f_\pi(\pi_1(X)), \pi_1(X))$. ∎

If $f: X \to X$ is a map such that $f_\pi(\pi_1(X)) \subseteq Z(\pi_1(X))$, then it is immediate from the definition that $Z(f_\pi(\pi_1(X)), \pi_1(X)) = \pi_1(X)$.

Corollary 11. *Let $f: X \to X$ be a map on a connected aspherical polyhedron such that f_π maps $\pi_1(X)$ into $Z(\pi_1(X))$. Then $T(f) = \pi_1(X)$.*

In the case that f is the identity map, f_π is onto, so Theorem 10 implies

Corollary 12. *If X is a connected aspherical polyhedron, then $Z(\pi_1(X)) \subseteq T(X)$.*

B. BOUNDS ON THE NIELSEN NUMBER

Let G be a group and $h: G \to G$ a homomorphism. Two elements α and β of G are *h-equivalent* if there exists $\gamma \in G$ such that $\alpha = \gamma \beta h(\gamma^{-1})$. The *Reidemeister number* $R(h)$ of h is defined to be the cardinality of the set of equivalence classes of G under h-equivalence.

If G is an abelian group and $k: G \to G$ is a homomorphism, then the quotient group $G/k(G)$ — the cokernel of k — is denoted by $\mathrm{Coker}(k)$. Write the group operation of abelian group as addition. Given a homomorphism $h: G \to G$, define a new homomorphism $1 - h: G \to G$ by $(1 - h)(\alpha) = \alpha - h(\alpha)$ for all $\alpha \in G$. Denote the order of a group G by $\mathrm{ord}(G)$.

If $h: G \to G$ is a homomorphism of an abelian group, then its Reidemeister number has a simple interpretation.

Theorem 1. *If G is an abelian group and $h: G \to G$ is a homomorphism, then the h-equivalence classes form a group isomorphic to $\mathrm{Coker}(1 - h)$. Therefore*

$$R(h) = \mathrm{ord}(\mathrm{Coker}(1 - h)).$$

Proof Elements α and β of G are h-equivalent if and only if, for some $\gamma \in G$, $\alpha = \gamma + \beta + h(-\gamma)$ so that $\alpha - \beta = \gamma - h(\gamma) \in (1 - h)(G)$. Therefore the h-equivalence classes are the cosets of $G/((1 - h)(G)) = \mathrm{Coker}$ $(1 - h)$. ∎

Denote the cyclic group of order n by J_n. Let 1 be the generator of J_n.

Theorem 2. *If $h: J_n \to J_n$ is a homomorphism such that $h(1) = q$, then $R(h) = (1 - q, n)$, the greatest common divisor of $1 - q$ and n.*

Proof For $m \in J_n$, let mJ_n denote the subgroup generated by m. Since $h(1) = q$ then $(1 - h)(J_n) = (1 - q)J_n$; so $\mathrm{Coker}\,(1 - h) = J_n/(1 - q)J_n$, which is known to be the cyclic group of order $(1 - q, n)$. By Theorem 1, $R(h) = \mathrm{ord}(\mathrm{Coker}(1 - h)) = (1 - q, n)$. ∎

Theorem 3. *If $h: J \to J$ is a homomorphism such that $h(1) = q$, then $R(h) = |1 - q|$.*

Proof Clearly $(1 - h)(J) = (1 - q)J$, the subgroup of J generated by $1 - q$. But $J/(1 - q)J \cong J_{|1-q|}$, so the result follows by Theorem 1. ∎

We assume throughout the rest of this section that we have X, a compact ANR, and a map $f: X \to X$ such that $L(f) \neq 0$. There is, therefore, at least one essential fixed point class of f (VI. Ex. 7). We choose, once and for all, a fixed point x_0 of f which is in an essential class. When we write $\pi_1(X)$, we will mean the fundamental group of X based at x_0.

Define $R(f)$, the *Reidemeister number* of f, to be the Reidemeister number of the induced homomorphism $f_\pi: \pi_1(X) \to \pi_1(X)$. Let $\pi_1'(X)$ be the set of equivalence classes of $\pi_1(X)$ under f_π-equivalence.

Theorem 4. *There exists a one-to-one function $\varphi: \Phi'(f) \to \pi_1'(X)$. Therefore $N(f) \leq R(f)$.*

Proof For $F \in \Phi'(f)$, choose any point $x \in F$. Let C be a path from x_0 to x; then $C(fC)^{-1}$ is a loop in X based at x_0 and thus it represents an element $\alpha \in \pi_1(X)$. Define $\varphi(F) = [\alpha]$, where $[\alpha]$ is the equivalence class in $\pi_1'(X)$ containing α. We must first prove that φ is well-defined. Let $x' \in F$, let C' be a path from x_0 to x', and define $\beta = \{C'(fC')^{-1}\} \in \pi_1(X)$. Since x and x' are f-equivalent, there is a path D from x to x' such that $\{D\} = \{fD\}$. Consider the loop CDC'^{-1} based at x_0 and let $\{CDC'^{-1}\} = \gamma \in \pi_1(X)$. We have

$$
\begin{aligned}
\alpha &= \{C(fC)^{-1}\} \\
&= \{CDC'^{-1}C'(fC')^{-1}(fC')D^{-1}(fC)^{-1}\} \\
&= \{CDC'^{-1}\}\{C'(fC')^{-1}\}\{(fC')(fD)^{-1}(fC)^{-1}\} \\
&= \gamma\beta f_\pi(\gamma^{-1}).
\end{aligned}
$$

Therefore α and β are f_π-equivalent, which proves that φ is independent of the choice of the fixed point used to represent the class and also of the path from the base point to that point. To see that φ is one-to-one, we suppose that $F,F' \in \Phi'(f)$ such that $\varphi(F) = \varphi(F)'$. Choose $x \in F$, $x' \in F'$. Then we must prove that x and x' are f-equivalent. Since $\varphi(F) = \varphi(F')$, there must be a path C from x_0 to x, a path C' from x_0 to x', and a loop D based at x_0 such that

$$\{C(fC)^{-1}\} = \{D\}\{C'(fC')^{-1}\}\{(fD)^{-1}\}.$$

Let $E = C'^{-1}D^{-1}C$ be a path from x' to x. Then

$$\{E(fE)^{-1}\} = \{C'^{-1}D^{-1}C(fC)^{-1}(fD)(fC')\}$$
$$= \{C'^{-1}D^{-1}DC'(fC')^{-1}(fD)^{-1}(fD)(fC')\},$$

which is the unit element of $\pi_1(X)$. So (by VI. Ex. 3), x and x' are indeed f-equivalent. Finally, we note that the existence of a one-to-one function from $\Phi'(f)$ to $\pi_1'(X)$ means that the number of fixed point classes of f is less than $R(f)$, the cardinality of $\pi_1'(X)$. Thus, in particular, $N(f)$, the number of essential fixed point classes, is less than $R(f)$. ∎

If we apply the equivalence relation of f_π-equivalence to the Jiang subgroup $T(f) \subseteq \pi_1(X)$, then the set of equivalence classes is denoted by $T'(f)$. Let $J(f)$ be the cardinality of $T'(f)$. In other words, $J(f)$ is the number of classes in $\pi_1'(X)$ which contain elements of $T(f)$.

Theorem 5. *If $\alpha \in T(f)$, then there is an essential fixed point class F of f such that $\varphi(F) = [\alpha]$, the element of $\pi_1'(X)$ containing α. It follows that $J(f) \le N(f)$.*

Proof Let A be a loop in X based at x_0 such that $\{A\} = \alpha$. By A.3 there is a loop $H: I \to \mathrm{Map}(X, X)$ based at f such that $H(t)(x_0) = A(t)$ for all $t \in I$. Let F_0 be the essential fixed point class of f containing x_0. The class F_0 is H-related to some fixed point class F of f because, otherwise, we would have $i(F_0) = 0$ by VI.E.3. Theorem VI.D.7 tells us that, for any $x \in F$, there is a path C from x_0 to x such that $\{C\} = \{\langle H, C\rangle\}$. We claim that $\{C(fC)^{-1}\} = \alpha$. Notice that $\{A\} = \{\langle H, \bar{x}_0\rangle\}$ where $\bar{x}_0$ is the constant path at x_0. Let $F: I \to \mathrm{Map}(X, X)$ be the constant path at f. Using VI.D.1 and VI.D.2, we find that

$$\alpha = \{\langle H, \bar{x}_0\rangle\} = \{CC^{-1}\langle H, \bar{x}_0\rangle\}$$
$$= \{C\langle H^{-1}, C^{-1}\rangle\langle H, \bar{x}_0\rangle\} = \{C\langle H^{-1}H, C^{-1}\bar{x}_0\rangle\}$$
$$= \{C\langle F, C^{-1}\rangle\} = \{C(fC)^{-1}\}.$$

Therefore $\varphi(F) = [\alpha]$. Since F and F_0 are H-related and F_0 is essential, we have $i(F) = i(F_0) \neq 0$ by VI.E.3 and consequently that F is essential. Theorem 4 states that φ is one-to-one, and we have shown that every element of $T'(f)$ is in a member of $\pi_1'(X)$ which is the image under φ of an essential fixed point class of f. Thus a subset of the set of essential fixed point classes of f maps in a one-to-one manner onto $T'(f)$, so there can be no more elements in $T'(f)$ than there are essential fixed point classes. In other words, $J(f) \leq N(f)$. ∎

Corollary 6.   *If $T(f) = \pi_1(X)$, then $N(f) = R(f)$.*

Proof   Since $T(f) = \pi_1(X)$ then $T'(f) = \pi_1'(X)$, and therefore $J(f) = R(f)$ by definition. The result follows from Theorems 4 and 5, because they state that $J(f) \leq N(f) \leq R(f)$. ∎

Corollary 7.   *If X is a connected aspherical polyhedron and $\chi(X)$, the Euler characteristic of X, is not zero, then the center of $\pi_1(X)$ is the trivial group.*

Proof   If $f: X \to X$ is the identity map, then $L(f) = \chi(X) \neq 0$. Thus Theorem 5 states that $J(f) \leq N(f)$. By VI. Ex. 4, $\chi(X) \neq 0$ implies that $N(f) = 1$, because the identity map has only one fixed point class. Since X is a connected aspherical polyhedron, $Z(\pi_1(X)) \subseteq T(X) = T(f)$ (by A.12). Now we have seen that $J(f) = 1$, which means that all elements of $T(f)$ are f_π-equivalent and thus, in particular, given any $\alpha, \beta \in Z(\pi_1(X))$, there exists $\gamma \in \pi_1(X)$ such that $\alpha = \gamma \beta f_\pi(\gamma^{-1}) = \gamma \beta \gamma^{-1}$ (since f is the identity map). But $\beta \in Z(\pi_1(X))$ implies that $\alpha = \beta$. ∎

C. EXAMPLES

In the examples that follow we will give certain information without proof. Since the structure of the fundamental group in each case can be found in standard texts, we quote only the results here. We will describe maps only to the extent of telling how their induced homomorphisms on the fundamental groups behave. It is certainly not true that every homomorphism of a fundamental group is the induced homomorphism of an actual map of the space to itself. However, in every example below, it can be proved that such a map really exists. We will also omit the computation of the Lefschetz number of the map when that information is required. The computations depend on additional standard material from homology theory which would serve no purpose in the rest of the book, so we will not take the space to describe it here.

The Circle. Since S^1 is aspherical and $\pi_1(S^1) \simeq J$ which is abelian, then, by A.12, $T(S^1) = \pi_1(S^1)$. If $f: S^1 \to S^1$ is any map, then $T(f) = \pi_1(S^1)$ (See A.8). Now $L(f) = 0$ if and only if f_π is the identity isomorphism and, in that case, $N(f) = 0$ by A.5. Otherwise, identify $\pi_1(S^1) = J$ and suppose that $f_\pi(1) = q \neq 1$; then by B.3 and B.6, $N(f) = |1 - q|$. Thus, no matter what the value of $L(f)$, we find $N(f) = |1 - q|$.

The Lens Spaces. If we identify the complex numbers C with R^2, then $S^3 \subset R^4 = C \times C$ can be thought of as the set of pairs $(z_1, z_2) \in C \times C$ such that $z_1 \bar{z}_1 + z_2 \bar{z}_2 = 1$, where $\bar{z}_j$ denotes the complex conjugate. Given integers $m \geq 2$ and $n \geq 1$ with $(m, n) = 1$, define an equivalence relation on S^3 as follows: For $z = (z_1, z_2)$ and $z' = (z_1', z_2')$ in S^3, call z and z' equivalent if and only if there exists an integer k, $0 \leq k \leq m - 1$, such that

$$(z_1', z_2') = \left(z_1 \exp\left(\frac{1}{m} 2\pi ki\right), z_2 \exp\left(\frac{1}{m} 2\pi kni\right)\right).$$

The equivalence classes with the quotient topology is a polyhedron called the *lens space* $L(m, n)$.

Let $x_0 = (1, 0) \in S^3$. Then $\pi_1(L(m, n), [x_0])$ is isomorphic to J_m ($[x_0]$ denotes the equivalence class of S^3 containing x_0). For each $k = 0, 1, \dots$, $m - 1$, define a loop $C_k: I \to L(m, n)$ at $[x_0]$ by

$$C_k(t) = \left[\exp\left(\frac{1}{m} 2\pi kti\right), 0\right]$$

for all $t \in I$. The elements of $\pi_1(L(m, n), [x_0])$ are $\{C_k\}$, $k = 0, \dots, m - 1$.

Define, for each $k = 0, \dots, m - 1$, $H_k: I \to \mathrm{Map}(L(m, n), L(m, n))$ by

$$H_k(t)[z_1, z_2] = \left[z_1 \exp\left(\frac{1}{m} 2\pi kti\right), z_2 \exp\left(\frac{1}{m} 2\pi knti\right)\right].$$

Since $H_k(0) = H_k(1)$ is the identity map on $L(m, n)$, and $H_k(t)[x_0] = C_k(t)$ for all $t \in I$, we have proved that $T(L(m, n)) = \pi_1(L(m, n))$.

Let $f: L(m, n) \to L(m, n)$ be a map such that $f_\pi\{C_1\} = \{C_k\}$. If $L(f) = 0$ then $N(f) = 0$ by A.8 and A.5. If k^2 is not congruent to one modulo m, then $L(f) \neq 0$ and by A.8, B.2, and B.6 $N(f) = (1 - k, m)$.

The Klein Bottle. Define the following equivalence relation "$\sim$" on $I \times I$: If (t, u) and (t', u') are in the interior of $I \times I$, then $(t, u) \sim (t', u')$ if and only if $(t, u) = (t', u')$. For all $t, t' \in \partial I$ and $u, u' \in I$, $(t, u) \sim (t', u')$ if and only if $u = u'$. For all $t, t' \in I$ and $u, u' \in \partial I$, $(t, u) \sim (t', u')$ if and only if either $(t, u) = (t', u')$ or $t + t' = u + u' = 1$. The quotient space $B = (I \times I)/\sim$ is called the *Klein bottle*.

The fundamental group $\pi_1(B)$ is isomorphic to a group with generators α and β satisfying the single relation $\alpha\beta\alpha = \beta$. Furthermore, B is a connected aspherical polyhedron. We will consider a map $f: B \to B$ such that $f_\pi(\alpha) = 1$ and $f_\pi(\beta) = \beta^{2n}$ for some integer n. It can be shown that $L(f) = 1 - 2n \neq 0$. An easy calculation establishes the fact that $\beta^{2n} \in Z(\pi_1(B))$; so, by A.11, $T(f) = \pi_1(B)$ for this particular map. Thus, by B.6, it remains to compute $R(f)$.

Recall that in order to compute $R(f)$ we must find, given $\mu, \nu \in \pi_1(B)$, necessary and sufficient conditions for the existence of $\gamma \in \pi_1(B)$ such that $\mu = \gamma\nu f_\pi(\gamma^{-1})$. Since $f_\pi(\pi_1(B))$ is the subgroup of $\pi_1(B)$ generated by β^{2n}, then $f_\pi(\gamma^{-1}) = \beta^{2nk}$ for some integer k. Hence $\mu = \gamma\nu\beta^{2nk}$. Let $\omega \in \pi_1(B)$ be any element; then we can write

$$\omega = \alpha^{p(1)}\beta^{p(2)} \cdots \alpha^{p(2r-1)}\beta^{p(2r)}$$

for some $p(j) \in J$ where $r \geq 1$. Define $|\omega| = \sum_{q=1}^{r} p(2q)$. Now although the representation of ω is not unique, the integer $|\omega|$ is independent of the representation because the relation defining $\pi_1(B)$ involves no power of β other than ± 1. Note that $|\omega^{-1}| = -|\omega|$ and that $f_\pi(\omega) = \beta^{2n|\omega|}$. Applying f_π to both sides of the equation $\mu = \gamma\nu\beta^{2nk}$ gives

$$\beta^{2n|\mu|} = \beta^{-2nk}\beta^{2n|\nu|}\beta^{2n(2nk)},$$

or $\beta^{|\mu|-|\nu|} = \beta^{k(2n-1)}$. We have proved that $\mu = \gamma\nu f_\pi(\gamma^{-1})$ for some $\gamma \in \pi_1(B)$ if and only if $|\mu| \equiv |\nu| \pmod{2n - 1}$ and therefore $R(f) = |2n - 1|$. We conclude that $N(f) = |2n - 1|$.

Some Nonorientable Surfaces. Let X_1 and X_2 be spaces with the property that, for any $x_1 \in X_1$ and $x_2 \in X_2$, there are neighborhoods U_1 of x_1 and U_2 of x_2 whose closures are homeomorphic to $I \times I$. For $j = 1, 2$ let $X'_j = X_j - U_j$. Then certainly there is a homeomorphism $h: \partial U_1 \to \partial U_2$. There is an equivalence relation on $X'_1 \cup X'_2$ where the equivalence classes consist of single elements on $(X'_1 - \partial U_1) \cup (X'_2 - \partial U_2)$ and of sets of the form $\{x, h(x)\}$ for each $x \in \partial U_1$. The resulting quotient space is denoted by $X_1 \# X_2$ (the connected sum).

For $g \geq 2$, take $g + 1$ copies $RP_1^2, \ldots, RP_{g+1}^2$ of the real projective space RP^2 and form the space

$$M_g = RP_1^2 \# RP_2^2 \# \cdots \# RP_{g+1}^2.$$

This is a well known topological space, the *nonorientable 2-manifold of genus* $g \geq 2$. It is a connected aspherical polyhedron.

The fundamental group of M_g can be described as follows: If g is even, let $m = g/2$, then $\pi_1(M_g)$ has generators $\alpha_1, \ldots, \alpha_m, \beta_1, \ldots, \beta_m, \epsilon$ satisfying a single relation

$$[\alpha_1 \beta_1] \cdots [\alpha_m \beta_m] \epsilon^2 = 1,$$

where $[\alpha_j \beta_j] = \alpha_j \beta_j \alpha_j^{-1} \beta_j^{-1}$. If g is odd, let $m = (g-1)/2$. Then $\pi_1(M_g)$ is generated by $\alpha_1, \ldots, \alpha_{m+1}, \beta_1, \ldots, \beta_m, \epsilon$. The relation in this case is

$$[\alpha_1 \beta_1] \cdots [\alpha_m \beta_m] \alpha_{m+1} \epsilon \alpha_{m+1}^{-1} \epsilon = 1.$$

For any $g \geq 2$, let $f: M_g \to M_g$ be a map so that $f_\pi(\alpha_1) = \alpha_1^n$ where $n \neq 1, f_\pi(\alpha_j) = 1$ for $j \neq 1, f_\pi(\beta_k) = 1$ for all k, and $f_\pi(\epsilon) = 1$. We ask the reader to accept the fact that $n \neq 1$ implies $L(f) \neq 0$.

Let $\{\alpha_1^n\} = \{\alpha_1^{kn} \mid k \in J\}$; then $f_\pi(\pi_1(M_g)) = \{\alpha_1^n\}$ and, by A.10, $T(f)$ contains the centralizer of $\{\alpha_1^n\}$ in $\pi_1(M_g)$. Since powers of α_1 commute, the subgroup $\{\alpha_1\}$ of $\pi_1(M_g)$ generated by α_1 is contained in $T(f)$, so the number of elements of $T'(f)$ which contain powers of α_1 is a lower bound for $J(f)$.

In order to determine that number, consider α_1^p, α_1^q, and ask when there exists $\gamma \in \pi_1(M_g)$ such that $\alpha_1^p = \gamma \alpha_1^q f_\pi(\gamma^{-1})$. Since $f_\pi(\pi_1(M_g)) = \{\alpha_1^n\}$, then $f_\pi(\gamma^{-1}) = \alpha_1^{nk}$ for some $k \in J$. Solving for γ gives us $\gamma = \alpha_1^{p-q-nk}$ and therefore $\alpha_1^{nk} = f_\pi(\gamma^{-1}) = \alpha_1^{(p-q+nk)n}$ or $p = q + k(n-1)$. Thus the required γ exists if and only if $p \equiv q \pmod{n-1}$. We have established that the elements of $\{\alpha_1\}$ appear in $|n-1|$ classes of $T'(f)$. We will keep in mind, then, that $|n-1| \leq J(f)$.

We next claim that every class of $\pi_1'(M_g)$ contains an element of the form α_1^k for some $k \in J$. For $\omega \in \pi_1(M_g)$, define $|\omega|$ to be the sum of the powers of α_1 in a representation of ω, and observe that $f_\pi(\omega^{-1}) = \alpha_1^{-|\omega|n}$ (compare with the previous example). Thus $\omega = \omega \alpha_1^{|\omega|n} f_\pi(\omega^{-1})$, so taking $\gamma = \omega$ proves that ω and $\alpha_1^{|\omega|n}$ are f_π-equivalent. As a consequence of the already established fact that the elements of $\{\alpha_1\}$ appear in precisely $|n-1|$ elements of $\pi_1'(M_g)$, the definition of $R(f)$ tells us that $R(f) = |n-1|$. By B.4 and B.5 we have that

$$|n-1| \leq J(f) \leq N(f) \leq R(f) = |n-1|,$$

so $N(f) = |n-1|$.

D. THE NUMBER OF kTH ROOTS

Recall from Section III.F that, if G is a topological group, $a \in G$, $k \geq 2$ is an integer, and $x \in G$ satisfies $x^k = a$, then x is called a kth *root of a*. We proved that, if G is a connected compact ANR, then a has a kth root for all $k \geq 2$. In this section we ask for information on the question: For how many $x \in G$ is it true that $x^k = a$?

If G is a topological group and we denote its unit by "1", then given two loops C and D in G based at 1, there is a natural way of defining a "product"

$C * D$ of the loops: $(C * D)(t) = C(t)D(t)$ for all $t \in I$. Thus the loops are multiplied pointwise by the group operation of G to produce a new loop $C * D$. This is not the same loop as the product CD that was defined before, but the important fact is that $\{CD\} = \{C * D\}$, so we can use either product in defining $\pi_1(G)$. This has two consequences that we shall use: The first is that $\pi_1(G)$ is abelian, so that we will write the group operation in $\pi_1(G)$ as addition. The other is that if we define $p_k \colon G \to G$ as before by $p_k(x) = x^k$, then, for any $\alpha \in \pi_1(G)$, $(p_k)_\pi(\alpha) = k\alpha$.

We defined a map $p_{k+1}^a \colon G \to G$ by $p_{k+1}^a(x) = x^{k+1}a^{-1}$ and saw in the proof of III.F.1 that the fixed points of p_{k+1}^a are precisely the kth roots of a. Thus if we could compute the Nielsen number of p_{k+1}^a then we would have a lower bound for the number of kth roots of a. We showed that p_{k+1}^a is homotopic to p_{k+1}, so, by VI.E.4, what we must investigate is $N(p_{k+1})$.

Since G is a topological group, we have $T(G) = \pi_1(G)$ by A.9; and since $L(p_{k+1}) \neq 0$ (from Section III.F) then $N(p_{k+1}) = R(p_{k+1})$ by B.6, where $R(p_{k+1}) = \operatorname{ord}(\operatorname{Coker}[1 - (p_{k+1})_\pi])$ by B.1. Now, for $\alpha \in \pi_1(G)$,

$$[1 - (p_{k+1})_\pi](\alpha) = -k\alpha.$$

Therefore $N(p_{k+1}) = \operatorname{ord}(\operatorname{Coker}(p_k)_\pi)$.

Let π be a finitely generated abelian group. Then the Fundamental Theorem of Abelian Groups states that we can write $\pi = F(\pi) \oplus T(\pi)$, where $F(\pi)$ is a direct sum of infinite cyclic groups and $T(\pi)$ is a direct sum of finite cyclic groups. Denote by $\rho(\pi)$ the number of infinite cyclic summands in $F(\pi)$. The number $\rho(\pi)$ is called the *torsion-free rank* of π.

Since $(p_k)_\pi(\alpha) = k\alpha$ for all $\alpha \in \pi = \pi_1(G)$, then $(p_k)_\pi$ maps $F(\pi)$ to itself. Let $(p_k)_\pi^F$ be the restriction of $(p_k)_\pi$ to $F(\pi)$. Write

$$F(\pi) = J^{(1)} \oplus \cdots \oplus J^{(\rho(\pi))}$$

where $J^{(j)} \cong J$ for $i = 1, \ldots, \rho(\pi)$. Now $(p_k)_\pi(J^{(j)}) = kJ^{(j)}$, the subgroup generated by k, so

$$\operatorname{Coker}((p_k)_\pi^F) = \frac{J^{(1)}}{kJ^{(1)}} \oplus \cdots \oplus \frac{J^{(\rho(\pi))}}{kJ^{(\rho(\pi))}}$$
$$= J_k^{(1)} \oplus \cdots \oplus J_k^{(\rho(\pi))},$$

where $J_k^{(j)} \cong J_k$. Consequently,

$$\operatorname{ord}[\operatorname{Coker}((p_k)_\pi^F)] = k^{\rho(\pi)}.$$

Now

$$k^{\rho(\pi)} = \operatorname{ord}[\operatorname{Coker}((p_k)_\pi^F)] \leq \operatorname{ord}[\operatorname{Coker}((p_k)_\pi)] = N(p_{k+1}).$$

Therefore, although we have not computed $N(p_{k+1})$, we do have a lower bound for it, and a lower bound for the Nielsen number is itself a lower bound for the number of fixed points. We have proved the following theorem:

Theorem 1.   *Let G be a topological group which is a connected compact* ANR, *let* $k \geq 2$ *be an integer, and let* $a \in G$ *be any element. Then a has at least* k^ρ *kth roots, where* ρ *denotes the torsion-free rank of* $\pi_1(G)$.

E. A FINAL LOOK AT THE FIGURE-EIGHT

In Section II.B we defined a map e on the figure-eight such that $L(e) = 0$. We claimed that e is a counterexample to the converse of the Lefschetz Fixed Point Theorem, because every map homotopic to e has at least two fixed points. By VI.E.4 and VI.C.2 it is sufficient to prove that $N(e) = 2$.

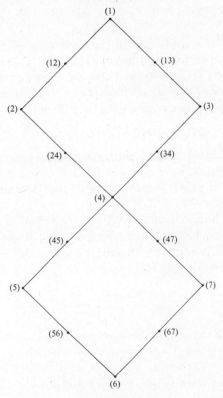

FIGURE 1

Recall the labelling of some points of X — the figure-eight — as given in Section II.B (Figure 1). Recall also the definition of the map e on these points (e is then extended linearly over segments).

x	1	2	3	4	5	6	7	12	13	24	34	45	56	67	47
$e(x)$	1	3	2	4	6	4	6	3	2	3	2	5	7	5	7

The fixed points of e are (1) and (4). We proved in Section IV.E that $i(X, e, U_1) = 1$ and $i(X, e, U_2) = -1$, where U_1 and U_2 are disjoint neighborhoods of (1) and (4) respectively. In order to prove that $N(e) = 2$, the definition tells us that we must show that (1) and (4) are not e-equivalent since, in that case, there are two fixed point classes of e and both are essential.

Let $A \subset X$ be the subset consisting of all of X "from (4) on up" in Figure 1, that is,

$$A = [(1), (2)] \cup [(2), (4)] \cup [(1), (3)] \cup [(3), (4)]$$

in the notation of Section IV.E. Define a retraction r of X onto A by sending all of $X - A$ to (4). Observe that e_A, the restriction of e to A, is a map from A to A.

Suppose that (1) and (4) were in the same fixed point class of e. Then there is a path C in X from (1) to (4) such that $\{C\} = \{eC\}$. If $C(t) \in A$ then $eC(t) \in A$, so $reC(t) = eC(t)$ and also $erC(t) = eC(t)$. If $C(t) \notin A$, then $reC(t) = (4)$ because $e(X - A) = (X - A) \cup (4)$ while $erC(t) = e(4) = (4)$. Thus $reC = erC$. Of course rC is a path in A from (1) to (4) and we see that

$$\{rC\} = \{reC\} = \{erC\} = \{e_A rC\}.$$

Therefore, if (1) and (4) were e-equivalent, then they would also be e_A-equivalent and e_A would have only one fixed point class. This would mean $N(e_A) \leq 1$. We will prove that $N(e_A) = 2$; so (1) and (4) cannot be e-equivalent, and hence $N(e) = 2$.

Note that A is homeomorphic to S^1, so $\pi_1(A, (4)) \cong J$. It is a standard result that $\pi_1(S^1)$ can be generated by an element containing a map from I to S^1 which is a homeomorphism except on ∂I. Define a map $D: I \to A$ such that $D(0) = D(1) = (4)$, $D(\frac{1}{4}) = (2)$, $D(\frac{1}{2}) = (1)$, $D(\frac{3}{4}) = (3)$, and D is linear on each of the segments $\left[\frac{j}{4}, \frac{j+1}{4}\right]$, $j = 0, 1, 2, 3$; then $\{D\}$ generates $\pi_1(A, (4))$.

It is easy to see that $e_A D$ is homotopic (as a loop based at (4)) to the loop D^{-1}. So, writing the group operation of $\pi_1(A, (4))$ as addition, we have $(e_A)\pi\{D\} = -\{D\}$. Therefore, identifying $\pi_1(A, (4)) = J$ so that $\{D\}$ corresponds to 1, we have $(e_A)\pi(1) = -1$ and, by the Circle example (S^1) of Section C, $N(e_A) = |1 - (-1)| = 2$.

NOTES

Jiang defined his subgroup and described many of its properties in [30]. Theorem A.10 is the work of Barnier [1], generalizing earlier results of Gottlieb (e.g., Corollary A.12) [24]. Reidemeister introduced his "number" in [46]. The bound $J(f)$ was discovered by Brooks and its properties were examined by Brooks and Brown in [6]. Jiang [30] was able to prove B.6 earlier without using $J(f)$. Corollary B.7 is a result of Gottlieb [24]. Theorem D.1 is from Brown's paper [11] where a similar result for certain H-spaces can also be found. Much more precise information on the number of kth roots in the case of a Lie group were obtained by Hopf [27]. In connection with the Figure-Eight example in Section E, Daniel McCord has constructed examples of manifolds in all dimensions greater than one, which admit homeomorphisms h such that $L(h) = 0$ but $N(h) = 2$.

EXERCISES

1. Prove that Theorem D.1 gives the correct number of kth roots when G is the group $T^n = S^1 \times S^1 \times \cdots \times S^1$ (n factors).
2. Real projective $(2n + 1)$-space RP^{2n+1} can be described as follows: Let $C^{n+1} = C \times \cdots \times C$ ($n + 1$ factors) be given the topology of R^{2n+2}; then S^{2n+1} is all $(z_0, z_1, \ldots, z_n) \in C^{n+1}$ such that $\sum_{j=0}^{n} z_j \bar{z}_j = 1$. Define $(z_0, \ldots, z_n) \sim (z_0', \ldots, z_n')$ if and only if, for all $j = 0, \ldots, n$ and a fixed k equal either to 0 or to 1, $z' = z_j \exp(k\pi i)$, then $RP^{2n+1} = S^{2n+1}/\sim$. Let $x_0 = [(1, 0, \ldots, 0)] \in RP^{2n+1}$; then $\pi_1(RP^{2n+1}, x_0) \cong J_2$. Define $C_k: I \to RP^{2n+1}$ for $k = 0, 1$ by $C_k(t) = [(\exp(tk\pi i), 0, \ldots, 0)]$ for all $t \in I$. Then $\pi_1(RP^{2n+1}, x_0)$ consists of $\{C_0\}$ and $\{C_1\}$. Prove that $T(RP^{2n+1}) = \pi_1(RP^{2n+1})$.
3. For $f: RP^{2n+1} \to RP^{2n+1}$ a map, what does the behavior of f_π tell us about the value of $N(f)$?
4. If the unitary transformations of C^n (considered as a vector space over C) are given the uniform metric topology, then they form a topological group denoted by U_n, which is a connected polyhedron. It is known that $\pi_1(U_n) \cong J$. If $f: U_n \to U_n$ is a map such that $f_\pi(1) = q \neq 1$ and $L(f) \neq 0$, what is $N(f)$?
5. If $f: U_n \to U_n$ is a map such that f_π is the identity isomorphism, what is $L(f)$? What, therefore is $\chi(U_n)$?

6. Let S_p^2 be the 2-sphere with p handles (see II. Ex. 9). For $p \geq 1$, S_p^2 is a connected aspherical polyhedron, and $\pi_1(S_p^2)$ has generators $\alpha_1, \ldots,$ $\alpha_p, \beta_1, \ldots, \beta_p$ satisfying a single relation $[\alpha_1\beta_1] \cdots [\alpha_p\beta_p] = 1$. Let $f: S_p^2 \to S_p^2$ be a map such that $f_\pi(\alpha_1) = \alpha_1^n$, $f_\pi(\alpha_j) = 1$ for $j > 1$, and $f_\pi(\beta_j) = 1$ for all j. If $L(f) \neq 0$, what is $N(f)$?

7. Let X denote the "figure-eight" of Section E. The figure-eight is a connected aspherical polyhedron, and $\pi_1(X)$ is the free (nonabelian) group on generators α and β. Let $f: X \to X$ be a map such that $f_\pi(\alpha) = \alpha^n$, $n \neq 1$, and $f_\pi(\beta) = \alpha^m$. Assuming that $L(f) \neq 0$, compute $N(f)$.

8. Prove that if X is a compact ANR such that $T(X) = \pi_1(X)$ and $f: X \to X$ is any map, then $L(f)$ is a multiple of $N(f)$.

9. Prove that if X and Y are compact ANRs such that $T(X) = \pi_1(X)$ and $T(Y) = \pi_1(Y)$, then $T(X \times Y) = \pi_1(X \times Y)$.

10. Prove that, if $f: X \to X$ is a map and $x_0 \in \Phi(f)$, then $T(f)$ is the image of the homomorphism $p_\pi: \pi_1(\text{Map}(X, X), f) \to \pi_1(X, x_0)$ that is induced by the map $p: \text{Map}(X, X) \to X$ that is defined by $p(g) = g(x_0)$ for all $g \in \text{Map}(X, X)$.

Chapter VIII

The Converse of the Lefschetz Theorem

The previous chapter ended on a rather negative note, that is, with the completion of our study of an example which shows that the converse of the Lefschetz Fixed Point Theorem is false for polyhedra in general. Our purpose in this chapter is to prove that the converse is true for maps on polyhedra of a reasonably general type.

The converse of the Lefschetz Theorem is a consequence of a stronger result: Given a map f on a polyhedron X, then, if X has certain properties, there is a map g homotopic to f such that g has precisely $N(f)$ fixed points. The proof is accomplished by means of a set of homotopies, each of which reduces the number of fixed points of the original map f. First, f is moved through a homotopy so as to obtain a map with only a finite number of fixed points, each located in a "nice" portion of the polyhedron. Next, we present a technique which eliminates certain fixed points, those of "index zero," moving the map by a homotopy which leaves the other fixed points alone. Finally, we show how, by means of homotopy, it is possible to replace two fixed points in the same class by a single fixed point without affecting the remaining fixed points. A finite composition of the three types of homotopies moves the given map f to the desired map g.

The last two sections of the chapter are concerned with deformations and with polyhedra that have the fixed point property.

A. FINITE FIXED-POINT SETS

We wish to deform a map on a polyhedron to one with only a finite number of fixed points. We first need a technical fact concerning the barycentric subdivision.

Let K be a simplicial complex and let $|K^p|$ be the geometric realization of its p-skeleton. For K_1, the barycentric subdivision of K, we have the usual homeomorphism $\tau_1: |K_1| \to |K|$. Call a p-simplex $s \in K_1$ p-*skeletal* if $\tau_1 |s| \subset |K^p|$.

Lemma 1. *Let K be a simplicial complex and let $s^1, s^2 (s^1 \neq s^2)$ be p-skeletal simplices of K_1. Then there is no simplex of K_1 which contains both s^1 and s^2.*

Proof   First let $t = \{v(s_0), \ldots, v(s_q)\} \in K_1$ (thus $s_i \in K$, $i = 0, \ldots, q$). We order t so that $s_i \subset s_{i+1}$ for $i = 0, \ldots, q - 1$. Now $\tau_1 |v(s_i)| \in |K^p|$ is equivalent, by the definition of τ_1, to the condition $s_i \in K^p$. Since for $j < i$ we have $s_j \subset s_i$, then $s_j \in K^p$ also, which means that $\tau_1 |v(s_j)| \in |K^p|$. We conclude, therefore, that either $\mathrm{cl}(\tau_1 |t|) \cap |K^p|$ is empty or $\mathrm{cl}(\tau_1 |t|) \cap |K^p| = \mathrm{cl}(\tau_1 |t'|)$ for some $t' \subseteq t$ where $t' \in K_1^m$, $m \leq p$. Suppose there exists $t \in K_1$ which contains both s^1 and s^2, then $|s^1| \cup |s^2| \subset \mathrm{cl}(\tau_1 |t'|)$ for some $t' \in K_1^m$. But s^1 and s^2 are both p-simplices and, therefore, it must be that $m = p$ and $t' = s^1 = s^2$, which establishes a contradiction.   ∎

We will generalize the notion of barycentric subdivision to that of *barycentric subdivision modulo a subcomplex*. Let K be a simplicial complex and L a subcomplex. We obtain a new complex K_L, the barycentric subdivision of K modulo L. Define the vertices of K_L to be the vertices of L together with elements $v(s)$, one for each simplex $s \in K - L$. For $p > 0$, define the p-simplices to be all $(p + 1)$-tuples of the form $\{v_0, \ldots, v_q, v(s_{q+1}), \ldots, v(s_p)\}$, where $\{v_0, \ldots, v_q\}$ is a simplex of L contained in the simplex $s_{q+1} \in K - L$ and where $s_i \subset s_{i+1}$ for $i = q + 1, \ldots, p - 1$. The definition is intended to include the degenerate cases $q + 1 = 0$ and $q = p$. Of course, when $L = \varnothing$ then K_L is just K_1, the ordinary barycentric subdivision.

If a complex K' is obtained from a complex K by a succession of barycentric subdivisions modulo subcomplexes, we say that K' is a *refinement* of K.

There is an obvious way to define a homeomorphism $\tau_L: |K_L| \to |K|$. For v a vertex of L, and hence of K_L, let $\tau_L |v| = |v|$, and for $v(s)$ a vertex of

$$K_L \text{ where } s = \{v_0, \ldots, v_p\} \in K - L \text{ define } \tau_L |v(s)| = \sum_{i=0}^{p} \frac{1}{p + 1} v_i; \text{ then}$$

extend τ_L linearly. Therefore, if K' is a refinement of K, there is a homeomorphism $\tau: |K'| \to |K|$, where τ is a composition of homeomorphisms of the form of τ_L above. Since we think of $\tau |K'|$ as just $|K|$ divided up in a different way, we will adopt the convention throughout this chapter of identifying $|K'|$ with $|K|$ and deleting the triangulating homeomorphism τ.

Let K be a simplicial complex. A simplex $s \in K$ is said to be *maximal* if there is no simplex of K which contains s.

The principal technique used in the proof of the main result of this section will be called the *Hopf-construction*. We next describe this construction and examine some of its properties.

Let K be a simplicial complex and K' a refinement of K. Let $|\psi|: |K'| \to |K|$ be a simplicial map and suppose that t is a nonmaximal p-simplex of K' such that $|t| \subseteq |\psi| \, |t|$. Since ψ is simplicial, $\psi(t) = s$ for some q-simplex s of K where $q \leq p$. But $|t| \subseteq |\psi| \, |t| = |s|$, and t is a p-simplex, so it must be that $q \geq p$. Therefore s is in fact a p-simplex of K. Let $t^* \in K'$ be a maximal simplex containing t, then since t is assumed nonmaximal, t^* is an m-simplex where $m > p$. Since t^* is maximal, $|t^*|$ is open in $|K'|$, and because K' is a refinement of K, $|t^*| \subseteq |s^*|$ for a maximal m-simplex s^* of K. Note that $|t| \subset \mathrm{cl} \, |t^*|$; so $|t| \subset \mathrm{cl} \, |s^*|$ and, since $|t| \subseteq |s|$, then $|t| \subseteq |s \cap s^*|$. Now the facts that t is a p-simplex of K' and that s is a p-simplex of K imply that $s \cap s^*$ is a p-simplex of K, so we conclude that $s \subseteq s^*$.

Let L be the subcomplex of K', the refinement of K, consisting of all simplices which do not contain t, and consider the simplicial complex K'_L. Define $\psi': K'_L \to K$ on the vertices as follows: For v a vertex of L, define $\psi'(v) = \psi(v)$. If $t \subset t_j$ ($t \neq t_j$), let $\psi'(v(t_j))$ be any element of s. Finally, let $\psi'(v(t))$ be any element of $s^* - s$ (note that $s^* \neq s$ because s^* is an m-simplex, s is a p-simplex, and $m > p$). The reader may check that ψ' extends in the usual way to a simplicial function $\psi': K'_L \to K$, and thus we have a simplicial map $|\psi'|: |K'_L| \to |K|$. The construction of ψ' from ψ and t is what we refer to as the *Hopf-construction*.

We claim that $|\psi'|\,(x) \neq x$ for all $x \in |t|$. We can write $|t| = \bigcup_{i=1}^{r} |t^i|$, where $t^i \in K'_L$ and $v(t) \in t^i$ for $i = 1, \ldots, r$. Since $\psi'(v(t)) \notin s$, then $\psi'(t^i) = s^i \neq s$, where s^i is a k-simplex of K, $k \leq p$. On the other hand, $|t^i| \subseteq |t| \subseteq |s|$ and, by definition, $|s^i| \cap |s| = \varnothing$; so $|t^i| \cap \psi' \, |t^i| = \varnothing$, which establishes the claim.

Next note that ψ' is identical with ψ on L by definition. If $t \subset t'$, $t \neq t'$, then t' is a q-simplex of K'_L, $q > p$. Thus, if $x \in |K'^p_L|$ (the geometric realization of the p-skeleton of K'_L) and $|\psi|\,(x) \neq x$, then we still have $|\psi'|\,(x) \neq x$.

One last property of the Hopf-construction that we will need is that $|\psi'|$ is, in some sense, "close" to $|\psi|$. Let $x \in |K'|$; then if $x \in |L|$ we have $|\psi|\,(x) = |\psi'|\,(x)$. If $x \in |t_j|$ where $t \subset t_j$, $t \neq t_j$, then $|\psi|\,(x) \in |s'|$, where $s \subseteq s'$ because $\psi(t) = s$ and ψ is simplicial. On the other hand, since $\psi'(v(t_j)) \in s$, then $|\psi'|\,(x) \in |s''|$ where $s'' \in K$ and $s'' \cap s \neq \varnothing$. The remaining case is where $x \in |t|$ and hence $|\psi|\,(x) \in |s|$, while $|\psi'|\,(x) \in \mathrm{cl} \, |s^*|$ (recall that $\mathrm{cl} \, |s^*|$ contains $|s|$). Thus $|\psi|\,(x)$ and $|\psi'|\,(x)$ may be in the geometric realizations of different simplices (say s^1 and s^2 respectively) of K, but it will be true that either $s^1 \cap s^2 \neq \varnothing$ or $s^1 \cup s^2 \subset s^3$ for some $s^3 \in K$.

A polyhedron X is *n-dimensional* if, for any triangulation (K, τ) of X, K is an n-dimensional simplicial complex, i.e., K contains an n-simplex but no m-simplex for $m > n$.

Theorem 2. *Let X be a connected n-dimensional polyhedron, $n \geq 1$, and $f: X \to X$ a map. Given $\epsilon > 0$, there exists a map $f': X \to X$ such that*

(1) *f' has only a finite number of fixed points*

(2) *there is a triangulation (K', τ') of X such that each fixed point of f' lies in a set $\tau' |x|$ for some maximal simplex $s \in K'$*

(3) *$d(f, f') < \epsilon$.*

Proof Let $T = (K, \tau)$ be a triangulation of X of mesh less than $\epsilon/4n$. By I.I.1 there is a simplicial approximation $\psi: (X, T_r) \to (X, T)$ to f. If v_0 is a vertex of K_r such that $|\psi| |v_0| = |v_0|$ then, since no vertex is maximal, we can apply the Hopf-construction to obtain a refinement K' of K_r (and hence of K) and a simplicial function $\psi': K' \to K$. So we see from the definition of ψ' above that, if v is vertex of K' and $|\psi'| |v| = |v|$, then v must correspond to a vertex of K_r (other than v_0). Repeat the Hopf-construction for each vertex v of K_r such that $|\psi| |v| = |v|$, refining the previously obtained K' each time. We have, then, a refinement K' of K and a simplicial function $\psi': K' \to K$ such that, if v is a vertex of K', then $|\psi'| |v| \neq |v|$. Next, if $t \in K'$ is a non-maximal 1-simplex such that $|t| \subseteq |\psi'| |t|$, we apply the Hopf-construction to ψ' and t. Repeat the Hopf-construction first for all nonmaximal *1*-simplices t such that $|t| \subseteq |\psi'| |t|$, then for all nonmaximal 2-simplices with the same property, and so on. Recall that the application of the Hopf-construction to a p-simplex fails to add solutions of the equation $|\psi| (x) = x$ to the geometric realization of any simplex of dimension less than or equal to p in the refinement. Thus, by working up through the simplices dimension-by-dimension, we are protected from picking up solutions to $|\psi'| (x) = x$, except perhaps on the geometric realizations of simplices of higher dimension. Thus, after a finite number of applications of the Hopf-construction, we have a refinement K' of K and a simplicial function $\psi': K' \to K$ such that, if $x \in |K'|$ and x is in the geometric realization of a nonmaximal simplex, then we have $|\psi'| (x) \neq x$. Let $t \in K'$ be a maximal simplex, and suppose $x, x' \in |t|$ such that $|\psi'| (x) = x$ and $|\psi'| (x') = x'$. Note that $|\psi'|$ is linear on $\mathrm{cl} |t|$, so if r is a real number such that $r(x) + (1 - r)x' \in \mathrm{cl} |t|$, then

$$|\psi'| (rx + (1 - r)x') = rx + (1 - r)x'.$$

But there is a real number r such that $y = rx + (1 - r)x' \in \partial |t|$ and $\partial |t| = \text{cl} |t| - |t|$ is the union of the geometric realizations of non-maximal simplices. Since we cannot have $|\psi'| (y) = y$ for such a point y, we conclude that $|t|$ contains at most one point x such that $|\psi'| (x) = x$. Triangulate X by identifying it with $|K|$, and let $f' = |\psi'|$; then condition (2) clearly holds and, since K' has only a finite number of simplices and we proved that each contains in its geometric realization at most one solution to $f'(x) = x$, condition (1) is true as well.

It remains to verify (3). Note that the condition $|t| \subseteq |\psi'| |t|$, which is required in order to use the Hopf-construction, automatically makes t p-skeletal; and recall that the Hopf-construction only moves points in $|t_j|$, where $t \subseteq t_j$. Thus, by Lemma 1, as we employ the Hopf-construction dimension by dimension, each point is moved at most once for each dimension. Since n-simplices are all maximal (X is n-dimensional), each point moves at most n times as we modify ψ to ψ' by means of the Hopf-construction. The "closeness" property of the Hopf-construction tells us each $x \in X$ moves a distance no more than $2(\text{mesh}(T)) < \epsilon/2n$ each time that it moves, so $d(\psi(x), f'(x)) < n(\epsilon/2n) = \epsilon/2$, and $d(\psi, f') < \epsilon/2$. Furthermore, ψ is a simplicial approximation to f with respect to the triangulation T, which implies $d(f, \psi) < \epsilon/2$ and therefore $d(f, f') < \epsilon$. ∎

B. POINTS OF INDEX ZERO

Let $|K|$ be a connected geometric complex (the geometric realization of a simplicial complex), s a maximal p-simplex, $f: |K| \to |K|$ a map, and x an *isolated* fixed point of f in $|s|$; i.e., there exists an open set $U \subseteq |s|$ containing x such that $\text{cl}(U) \cap \Phi(f) = x$. Our first job will be to obtain a simple interpretation of $i(|K|, f, U)$ in this special case.

We again abbreviate the rational singular pth cohomology group of a pair (X, A) by writing $H^p(X, A)$.

Recall the definition of $i(|K|, f, U)$ that we used in Chapter IV. We have an open set $W \subseteq R^n$ (where $|K|$ is imbedded in R^n) and a retraction $r: W \to |K|$. We consider the composition (since $\Phi(f) \cap \text{cl}(U) = x$)

$$H^n(R^n, R^n - 0) \xrightarrow{\;\;d^*\;\;} H^n(V, V - x) \xrightarrow[\cong]{\;\;j^{*-1}\;\;}$$

$$H^n(S^n, S^n - x) \xrightarrow{\;\;k^*\;\;} H^n(S^n),$$

where $V = r^{-1}(U)$ and $d(y) = y - fr(y)$ for $y \in V$. Then for carefully chosen generators μ_n and ν_n we defined

$$k^* j^{*-1} d^*(\mu_n) = i(|K|, f, U) \cdot \nu_n.$$

Since $S^n - x$ is contractible, k^* is an isomorphism by exactness, so if we let $a_n = j^*k^{*-1}(\nu_n)$ then

$$d^*(\mu_n) = i(|K|, f, U) \cdot a_n.$$

Let $B^n = \{y \in R^n \mid d(x, y) \leq \epsilon\}$, where $\epsilon > 0$ is chosen small enough so that $B^n \subseteq V$ and, for $B^p = B^n \cap |s|$, $f(B^p) \subset |s|$. Let $q: (B^n, B^n - x) \to (V, V - x)$ be inclusion, then q^* is an isomorphism by excision. Let $a'_n = q^*(a_n)$; then

$$(d|B^n)^*(\mu_n) = (dq)^*(\mu_n) = i(|K|, f, U) \cdot a'_n$$

where $d|B^n$ denotes the restriction of d to B^n.

We have the commutative diagram

$$
\begin{array}{ccc}
& (d|B^n)^* & \\
H^n(R^n, R^n - 0) & \longrightarrow & H^n(B^n, B^n - x) \\
\uparrow & & \uparrow \\
\delta \,| & & |\, \delta \\
| & & | \\
H^{n-1}(R^n - 0) & \longrightarrow & H^{n-1}(B^n - x). \\
& (d|B^n - x)^* &
\end{array}
$$

Since R^n and B^n are contractible, both δ's are isomorphisms by exactness. Let $\bar{\mu}_n = \delta^{-1}(\mu_n)$, $\bar{a}'_n = \delta^{-1}(a'_n)$. Then, from the diagram,

$$(d|B^n - x)^*(\bar{\mu}_n) = i(|K|, f, U) \cdot \bar{a}'_n.$$

We have shown that it is unnecessary to examine what d does to all of V in order to define $i(|K|, f, U)$; one need only look at d on $B^n - x$. In fact, we can restrict d to an even smaller set. Let $j: \partial B^n \to B^n - x$ be inclusion, then j^* is an isomorphism. Let $\alpha_n = j^*(\bar{a}'_n)$ and we have

$$(d \mid \partial B^n)^*(\bar{\mu}_n) = i(|K|, f, U) \cdot \alpha_n.$$

Consider R^p as the subset of R^n consisting of the ordered n-tuples of reals $(x_1, \ldots, x_n)$ such that $x_i = 0$ for $i > p$. Let $h_t: R^n \to R^n$ be a continuous family of homeomorphisms such that h_0 is the identity map and h_1 is the composition of a translation taking x to $0 \in R^n$ and a rotation such that the p-plane in R^n determined by $|s|$ goes onto R^p. Note that h_1 is an isometry, that is, for $y_1, y_2 \in R^n$, $d(y_1, y_2) = d(h_1(y_1), h_1(y_2))$.

Define $d_t: \partial B^n \to R^n - 0$ by $d_t(y) = h_t(y) - h_t fr(y)$ and note that because $y \neq fr(y)$ for $y \in \partial B^n$ and h_t is a homeomorphism, then d_t is well defined. Since $d_0 = (d|\partial B^n)$ and d_1 are homotopic, we now have

$$d_1^*(\bar{\mu}_n) = i(|K|, f, U) \cdot \alpha_n.$$

We observe that if $y \in \partial B^p = \partial B^n \cap |s|$ (where ϵ is chosen small enough so that ∂B^p is homeomorphic to S^{p-1}) then $fr(y) = f(y) \in |s|$, so $h_1(y)$ and $h_1 fr(y)$ are in R^p, and therefore $d_1(y) \in R^p$.

Let X be a space. The *suspension* of X, ΣX, is defined to be the quotient space of $X \times I$ under the equivalence relation: $(y, 0) \sim (y', 0)$ and $(y, 1) \sim (y', 1)$ for all $y, y' \in X$, while otherwise $(y, t) \sim (y', t')$ if and only if $(y, t) = (y', t')$. For example, S^p is homeomorphic to ΣS^{p-1}. We identify X with $X \times \frac{1}{2} \subset \Sigma X$. Suppose $g: \Sigma X \to \Sigma Y$ is a map such that $g(X \times \frac{1}{2}) \subseteq Y \times \frac{1}{2}$. By the Mayer-Vietoris Theorem there is an isomorphism Δ: $H^{p-1}(X) \to H^p(\Sigma X)$ for $p \geq 2$ such that the diagram

$$
\begin{array}{ccc}
H^p(\Sigma Y) & \xrightarrow{\quad g^* \quad} & H^p(\Sigma X) \\
\Big\uparrow {\scriptstyle \Delta} & & \Big\uparrow {\scriptstyle \Delta} \\
H^{p-1}(Y) & \xrightarrow[\; (g|X)^* \;]{} & H^{p-1}(X)
\end{array}
$$

commutes.

Let $r_n: R^n - 0 \to S^{n-1}$ be defined by $r_n(y) = \left(\dfrac{1}{|y|}\right)y$; then r_n^* is an isomorphism. Consider the diagram

$$
\begin{array}{ccccc}
H^{n-1}(S^{n-1}) & \xrightarrow{\; r_n^* \;} & H^{n-1}(R^n - 0) & \xrightarrow{\; d_1^* \;} & H^{n-1}(\partial B^n) \\
\Big\uparrow {\scriptstyle \Delta^{n-p}} {\scriptstyle\cong} & & & & {\scriptstyle\cong} \Big\uparrow {\scriptstyle \Delta^{n-p}} \\
H^{p-1}(S^{p-1}) & \xrightarrow[\; r_p^* \;]{} & H^{p-1}(R^p - 0) & \xrightarrow[\; (d_1|\partial B^p)^* \;]{} & H^{p-1}(\partial B^p),
\end{array}
$$

where Δ^{n-p} is the composition

$$
H^{p-1}(S^{p-1}) \xrightarrow{\; \Delta \;} H^p(S^p) \xrightarrow{\; \Delta \;} \cdots \xrightarrow{\; \Delta \;} H^{n-1}(S^{n-1}),
$$

and we identify ∂B^{n-1} with S^{n-1}. Since the diagram commutes, if we let $\bar{\mu}_p = r_p^*(\Delta^{n-p})^{-1}r_n^{*-1}(\bar{\mu}_n)$ and $\alpha_p = (\Delta^{n-p})^{-1}(\alpha_n)$, then we have the description of $i(|K|, f, U)$ that we have been seeking: for $d_1: \partial B^p \to R^p - 0$ defined by $d_1(y) = h_1(y) - h_1 f(y)$ and $\bar{\mu}_p \in H^{p-1}(R^p - 0)$, $\alpha_p \in H^{p-1}(\partial B^p)$ appropriately chosen generators,

$$
d_1^*(\bar{\mu}_p) = (|K|, f, U) \cdot \alpha_p.
$$

The additivity axiom tells us that for $x \in |s|$ an isolated fixed point of $f: |K| \to |K|$ in a maximal simplex, $i(|K|, f, U)$ is independent of the choice of the open set U containing x such that $\mathrm{cl}(U) \cap \Phi(f) = x$. It is therefore convenient to define $i(|K|, f, x)$, *the index of f at x*, by $i(|K|, f, x) = i(|K|, f, U)$ for any such set U.

Denote the rational singular cohomology of a space X by $H^*(X; Q)$ and the integral singular cohomology by $H^*(X; J)$. Given a map $g: X \to Y$, we have induced morphisms $g_Q^*: H^*(Y; Q) \to H^*(X; Q)$ and $g_J^*: H^*(Y; J) \to H^*(X; J)$. By the Universal Coefficient Theorem, there is an isomorphism

$$\kappa: H^*(X; J) \otimes Q \to H^*(X; Q)$$

(i.e., $H^m(X; J) \otimes Q \cong H^m(X; Q)$ for all $m \in J$) such that the diagram

$$
\begin{array}{ccc}
H^*(Y; J) \otimes Q & \xrightarrow{\;\; g_J^* \otimes 1 \;\;} & H^*(X; J) \otimes Q \\
\downarrow{\scriptstyle \kappa} & & \downarrow{\scriptstyle \kappa} \\
H^*(Y; Q) & \xrightarrow[\;\; g_Q^* \;\;]{} & H^*(X; Q)
\end{array}
$$

commutes. In particular, for the map $d_1: \partial B^p \to R^p - 0$, we know that

$$(d_1)_Q^* = \kappa((d_1)_J^* \otimes 1)\kappa^{-1}: H^{p-1}(R^p - 0; Q) \to H^{p-1}(\partial B^p; Q).$$

Let $m_p \otimes 1 = \kappa^{-1}(\bar{u}_p)$ and $a_p \otimes 1 = \kappa^{-1}(\alpha_p)$, then we have $(d_1)_J^*(m_p) = i(|K|, f, x) \cdot a_p$. Since the image of $(d_1)_J^*$ is in $H^{p-1}(\partial B^p; J) \cong J$, we have proved

Theorem 1.   *Let $|K|$ be a connected geometric complex, $f: |K| \to |K|$ a map, and x an isolated fixed point of f in the geometric realization of a maximal simplex of K. Then $i(|K|, f, x)$ is an integer.*

We could, in fact, prove that $i(X, f, U) \in J$ for any $(X, f, U) \in \mathscr{C}_P'$ (See IV. Ex. 7).

We will require the following classical result:

Theorem 2 (Hopf Homotopy Theorem).   *If $g, g': S^m \to S^m$ are maps such that $g^* = g'^*: H^m(S^m; J) \to H^m(S^m; J)$, then g is homotopic to g'.*

We need one more preliminary result. It is an easy consequence of VII.B.1.

Lemma 3.   *Let X be an ANR and let $c: B^n \to X$ be a constant map. If $\gamma: \partial B^n \to X$ is a map homotopic to $c \mid \partial B^n$, then there exists a map $\Gamma: B^n \to X$ homotopic to c such that $\Gamma \mid \partial B^n = \gamma$.*

Now for the main result of this section:

Theorem 4. *Let $|K|$ be a connected geometric complex, s a maximal p-simplex of K, $f: |K| \to |K|$ a map, $x \in |s|$ an isolated fixed point of f, and $U \subseteq |s|$ a neighborhood of x such that $\Phi(f) \cap \mathrm{cl}(U) = x$. If $i(|K|, f, x) = 0$ then, given $\epsilon > 0$, there exists a map $f': |K| \to |K|$ with the properties*

(1) $f(y) = f'(y)$ for all $y \in |K| - U$

(2) $d(f, f') < \epsilon$

(3) $\Phi(f') \cap \mathrm{cl}(U) = \varnothing$.

Proof Let $B^p = \{y \in |K| \mid d(x, y) \leq \delta\}$, where $\delta > 0$ is chosen small enough so that $B^p \subset U$ and $f(B^p) \subset |s|$. Furthermore, for $y \in \partial B^p$, we require that $|h_1 f(y)| < \dfrac{\epsilon}{2}$ and $|d_1(y)| < \eta$, where $\eta < \dfrac{\epsilon}{4}$ is so small that $D_{2\eta}^p = \{a \in R^p \mid |a| \leq 2\eta\} \subset h_1 |s|$. Observe that $d_1(\partial B^p) \subset D_\eta^p - 0$. We also require $\delta < \eta$. The existence of such a δ is an easy consequence of the continuity of f and h_1 and the facts that $f(x) = x$ and $h_1(x) = 0$. Let $q: D_\eta^p - 0 \to \partial D_\eta^p$ be defined by $q(a) = \left(\dfrac{\eta}{|a|}\right)a$. Let $d' = qd_1: \partial B^p \to \partial D_\eta^p$. Then, since $i(|K|, f, x) = 0$ and $(d_1)_f^*(m_p) = i(|K|, f, x) \cdot a_p$, we conclude that $(d_1)_f^*$ is the zero homomorphism, so $(d')_f^*$ is also the zero homomorphism. Now ∂B^p and ∂D_η^p are both homeomorphic to S^{p-1}, and thus we can apply Theorem 2 to conclude that d' is homotopic to a constant map $c: \partial B^p \to \partial D_\eta^p$. Clearly, q is homotopic in $D_\eta^p - 0$ to the identity map of ∂D_η^p, so d_1 is homotopic in $D_\eta^p - 0$ to d'. Therefore d_1 is homotopic in $D_\eta^p - 0$ to c. Extend c to the constant map $c: B^p \to \partial D_\eta^p \subset D_\eta^p - 0$. By Lemma 3 we can extend d_1 to $\tilde{d}: B^p \to D_\eta^p - 0$. Define $f': |K| \to |K|$ by

$$f'(y) = \begin{cases} f(y) & \text{if } y \in |K| - B^p \\ h_1^{-1}\tilde{d}((y) + h_1(y)) & \text{if } y \in B^p. \end{cases}$$

The function f' is well defined because, for $y \in B^p$, $|\tilde{d}(y)| \leq \eta$ and $|h_1(y)| \leq \delta < \eta$ (h_1 is an isometry), so $\tilde{d}(y) + h_1(y) \in D_{2\eta}^p \subset h_1 |s|$. If $y \in \partial B^p$, then $\tilde{d}(y) = d_1(y) = h_1(y) - h_1 f(y)$, so $f'(y) = f(y)$ and f' is continuous. Again making use of the fact that h_1 is an isometry, we take $y \in B^p$ and compute that

$$d(f(y), f'(y)) = |h_1 f(y) - h_1 f'(y)|$$

$$\leq |h_1 f(y)| + |\tilde{d}(y)| + |h_1(y)|$$

$$< \frac{\epsilon}{2} + \eta + \delta < \epsilon,$$

so $d(f, f') < \epsilon$. Finally, suppose that $f'(y) = y$ for some $y \in B^p$; then $\tilde{d}(y) + h_1(y) = h_1(y)$ or $\tilde{d}(y) = 0$. But $\tilde{d}(B^p) \subset D_\eta^p - 0$, so it must be that $f'(y) \neq y$ for all $y \in B^p \subset U$. ∎

C. POINTS IN THE SAME CLASS

Let $|K|$ be a connected geometric complex. This section is devoted to the development of machinery for deforming a map $f: |K| \to |K|$ through a homotopy to reduce the number of fixed points when, in contrast to Section B, it may be that none of the fixed points is of index zero. We will be concerned with two techniques. The first replaces a number of fixed points in a single maximal simplex with just one fixed point; the second moves a fixed point from one maximal simplex to an adjacent one (thus after a number of such moves, the first technique can be used to reduce the number of fixed points). Our approach will be to work out the methods first in the case where f is close to the identity map and then to show how to modify a more general situation in order to reduce the problem to the special case.

For $x \in |K|$, let $\sigma(x)$ denote the unique simplex of K such that $x \in |\sigma(x)|$.

We will use the following notation: For A a subset of $|K|$ and $\epsilon > 0$, define $U(A, \epsilon) = \{x \in |K| \mid d(x, A) < \epsilon\}$ and let $\bar{U}(A, \epsilon)$ be the closure of $U(A, \epsilon)$. For $x_1, x_2 \in R^n$, denote the line segment from x_1 to x_2 by $[x_1, x_2]$, that is, $[x_1, x_2] = \{(1 - t)x_1 + tx_2 \mid t \in I\}$. For $x_1, x_2, \ldots, x_r \in R^n$, let

$$[x_1, x_2, \ldots, x_r] = [x_1, x_2] \cup [x_2, x_3] \cup \cdots \cup [x_{r-1}, x_r].$$

Corresponding to each $x \in |K|$, there is a set $V(x)$ which is defined to be the union of all $|t|$ such that $t \in K$ and $t \cap \sigma(x) \neq \emptyset$. We know that $V(X)$ is open in $|K|$ because the set of all $t \in K$ such that $t \cap \sigma(x) = \emptyset$ is a subcomplex of K. For $A \subseteq |K|$, say that a map $f: |K| \to |K|$ is a *proximity map on* A if $f(x) \in V(x)$ for all $x \in A$.

A convenient tool for much of what follows is:

Lemma 1. *Define*

$$\mathcal{N} = \{(x, y) \in |K| \times |K| \mid \sigma(x) \cap \sigma(y) \neq \emptyset\}.$$

There exists a map $\alpha: \mathcal{N} \times I \to |K|$ *such that*

(1) $\alpha(x, y, 0) = x$ $\alpha(x, y, 1) = y$

(2) $\alpha(x, x, t) = x$ *for all* $t \in I$

(3) $\alpha(x, y, t) \neq x$ *if* $x \neq y$ *and* $t \neq 0$.

Proof If K has vertices $v_1, \ldots, v_n$, then for $x \in |K|$ we can write $x = \sum_{j=1}^{n} \lambda_j v_j$. For $(x, y) \in \mathcal{N}$ where $x = \sum_{j=1}^{n} \lambda_j v_j$ and $y = \sum_{j=1}^{n} \lambda'_j v_j$ we define

$$\beta(x, y) = \sum_{j=1}^{n} (\lambda_j \lambda'_j)^{\frac{1}{2}}.$$

Let $v_j \in \sigma(x) \cap \sigma(y) \neq \varnothing$, then $\lambda_j \neq 0$ and $\lambda'_j \neq 0$, so $\beta(x, y) \neq 0$. Furthermore $(\lambda_j - \lambda'_j)^2 \geq 0$ implies that $4\lambda_j \lambda'_j \leq (\lambda_j + \lambda'_j)^2$, so

$$\beta(x, y) = \sum_{j=1}^{n} (\lambda_j \lambda'_j)^{\frac{1}{2}} \leq \frac{1}{2} \sum_{j=1}^{n} \lambda_j + \frac{1}{2} \sum_{j=1}^{n} \lambda'_j = 1.$$

Define $\lambda''_j = (\lambda_j \lambda'_j)^{\frac{1}{2}} / \beta(x, y)$ for $j = 1, \quad . , n$; then $\lambda''_j \geq 0$ and $\sum_{j=1}^{n} \lambda''_j = 1$.

Let $z = \sum_{j=1}^{n} \lambda''_j v_j$ and observe that $\sigma(z) = \sigma(x) \cap \sigma(y)$, which implies that $[x, z, y] \in |K|$. Let $\ell(x, z, y) = d(x, z) + d(z, y)$, and define $\alpha(x, y, t)$ to be the point on $[x, z, y]$ such that $d(x, \alpha(x, y, t)) = t\ell(x, z, y)$ if $t\ell(x, z, y) \leq d(x, z)$, and such that $d(x, z) + d(z, \alpha(x, y, t)) = t\ell(x, z, y)$ if $t\ell(x, z, y) \geq d(x, z)$. It is obvious that α satisfies properties (1) and (2). To verify (3), note that it is impossible for $\alpha(x, y, t)$ to be the point x if $0 < t\ell(x, z, y) \leq d(x, z)$. We will prove that $x \notin [z, y]$ when $x \neq y$, and this will eliminate the possibility that $\alpha(x, y, t) = x$ when $t\ell(x, z, y) > d(x, z)$. If $t\ell(x, z, y) > d(x, z)$ then $\alpha(x, y, t) \in |\sigma(y)|$; so if $\sigma(y) \neq \sigma(x)$ we are through. On the other hand, if $\sigma(x) = \sigma(y)$ and $x \in [z, y]$, then we can write $x = ty + (1 - t)z$ for some $t \in I$. Hence

$$\lambda_j = t\lambda'_j + (1 - t) \frac{(\lambda_j \lambda'_j)^{\frac{1}{2}}}{\beta(x, y)}$$

for all $j = 1, \ldots, n$. When $\lambda_j > 0$, we use the fact that $\beta(x, y) \leq 1$ to write

$$1 = \frac{t\lambda'_j}{\lambda_j} + \frac{(1 - t)}{\beta(x, y)} \left(\frac{\lambda'_j}{\lambda_j} \right)^{\frac{1}{2}}$$

$$\geq \frac{t\lambda'_j}{\lambda_j} + (1 - t) \left(\frac{\lambda'_j}{\lambda_j} \right)^{\frac{1}{2}}.$$

If $\lambda'_j / \lambda_j > 1$ then we would have

$$\frac{t\lambda'_j}{\lambda_j} + (1 - t) \left(\frac{\lambda'_j}{\lambda_j} \right)^{\frac{1}{2}} > 1$$

in contradiction to the last inequality. Therefore $\lambda'_j \leq \lambda_j$ for all $j = 1, \ldots, n$.

But, since $\sum_{j=1}^{n} \lambda'_j = \sum_{j=1}^{n} \lambda_j = 1$, it must be that $\lambda_j = \lambda'_j$ for all j, and hence $x = y$. ∎

Suppose that $f, g: |K| \to |K|$ are maps and that $A \subseteq |K|$ such that $f(x) = g(x)$ for all $x \notin A$. If there is a map $H: |K| \times I \to |K|$ with the properties $H(x, 0) = f(x)$, $H(x, 1) = g(x)$ for all $x \in |K|$ and $H(x, t) = f(x) = g(x)$ for all $x \notin A$, $t \in I$, then we say that f and g are *homotopic on A*. In other words, f and g are homotopic in such a way that the only place the homotopy does anything is on A.

Lemma 2. *Given a point $x \in |K|$ contained in a maximal simplex of $|K|$, a map $f: |K| \to |K|$, and a real number $\eta > 0$ such that $U(x, \eta) \subseteq |\sigma(x)|$, $\Phi(f) \cap \partial U(x, \eta) = \varnothing$, and f a proximity map on $\overline{U}(x, \eta)$, there exists a map $f': |K| \to |K|$ such that*

(1) *f' is homotopic to f on $U(x, \eta)$*

(2) *$\Phi(f') \cap \overline{U}(x, \eta) = x$*

(3) *f' is a proximity map on $\overline{U}(x, \eta)$.*

Proof The hypothesis $\Phi(f) \cap \partial U(x, \eta) = \varnothing$, together with V.A.1 gives us a real number ϵ, $0 < \epsilon < \eta$, with the property $\Phi(f) \cap [\overline{U}(x, \eta) - U(x, \epsilon)] = \varnothing$. Since f is a proximity map on $\overline{U}(x, \eta)$, given $y \in \overline{U}(x, \eta)$ we know that $(y, f(y)) \in \mathcal{N}$. Thus we can define a map

$$G: \overline{U}(x, \eta) \times I \to |K| \qquad \text{by} \qquad G(y, t) = \alpha(y, f(y), t).$$

Since G is uniformly continuous there exists $\delta > 0$ such that $d(y, y') + |t - t'| \leq \delta$ implies $d(G(y, t), G(y', t')) < \eta - \epsilon$. So, in particular, if $t \leq \delta$ then $d(y, G(y, t)) < \eta - \epsilon$. Define $D: [0, \eta] \to I$ by

$$D(t) = \begin{cases} \left(\dfrac{\delta}{\epsilon}\right) t & \text{if } 0 \leq t \leq \epsilon \\[2ex] \dfrac{(1 - \delta)t + \delta\eta - \epsilon}{\eta - \epsilon} & \text{if } \epsilon \leq t \leq \eta. \end{cases}$$

Then, if $y \in \overline{U}(x, \epsilon)$, we have that $G(y, D(d(x, y)) \in \overline{U}(x, \eta) \subset |\sigma(x)|$. Define $f_1: |K| \to |K|$ by

$$f_1(y) = \begin{cases} f(y) & \text{if } y \notin U(x, \eta) \\[1.5ex] G(y, D(d(y, x))) & \text{if } y \in \overline{U}(x, \eta). \end{cases}$$

Since

$$G(y, t) = \alpha(y, f(y), t) \in |\sigma(y)| \cup |\sigma(f(y))| \cup |\sigma(y) \cap \sigma(f(y))|,$$

we know that f_1 is a proximity map on $\overline{U}(x, \eta)$. If we let $H: |K| \times I \to |K|$ be given by

$$H(y, t) = \begin{cases} f(y) & \text{if } y \notin U(x, \eta) \\ G(y, tD(d(x, y)) + 1 - t) & \text{if } y \in \overline{U}(x, \eta) \end{cases}$$

for $t \in I$, then we see that f_1 is homotopic to f on $U(x, \eta)$. We remark that f_1 has no fixed points on $\overline{U}(x, \eta) - U(x, \epsilon)$ since, for a point y in that set, $f_1(y) = \alpha(y, f(y), D(d(x, y)))$ and $d(x, y) > \epsilon$, which implies that $D(d(x, y)) \geq \delta > 0$; so the remark is a consequence of conclusion (3) of Lemma 1 and the definition of ϵ. Given a point $y \in \overline{U}(x, \epsilon)$ other than x, we let $\Lambda(y)$ be the ray from x through y. Let $\rho(y) = \Lambda(y) \cap \partial U(x, \epsilon)$. There exists a unique t_y, $0 < t_y \leq 1$, such that

$$y = t_y\rho(y) + (1 - t_y)x.$$

The map $f': |K| \to |K|$, promised in the conclusion of this Lemma, is defined by

$$f'(y) = \begin{cases} f_1(y) & \text{if } y \notin U(x, \epsilon) \\ t_y f_1(\rho(y)) + (1 - t_y)x & \text{if } y \in U(x, \epsilon) - x \\ x & \text{if } y = x. \end{cases}$$

The continuity of f' at x is clear when we notice that $f_1(\partial U(x, \epsilon))$ is bounded in R^n. If $y \in U(x, \epsilon)$ then $f_1(y) \cup f'(y) \in |\sigma(x)|$, so it is easy to construct a function which proves that f' is homotopic to f_1 on $U(x, \epsilon) \subseteq U(x, \eta)$ and therefore homotopic to f on $U(x, \eta)$. Clearly f' is a proximity map on $U(x, \epsilon)$ and, since f' agrees with f_1 on $\overline{U}(x, \eta) - U(x, \epsilon) = \mathscr{A}$ and f_1 is a proximity map on $\mathscr{A}$, then (2) is satisfied. To verify (3), suppose that $y \in U(x, \epsilon) - x$ and that $f'(y) = y$, then

$$t_y\rho(y) + (1 - t_y)x = y = t_y f_1(\rho(y)) + (1 - t_y)x$$

or $f_1(\rho(y)) = \rho(y)$. But we have already established the fact that f_1 has no fixed points on $\mathscr{A}$. Since $\rho(y) \in \mathscr{A}$, f' cannot have fixed points on $U(x, \epsilon)$ other than x and, because f' agrees with f_1 on $\mathscr{A}$, we see that f' has no other fixed points on the larger set $\overline{U}(x, \eta)$. ∎

Let S be a polyhedron homeomorphic to I located in a maximal p-simplex of $|K| \subset R^n$. Let $f_1: |K| \to |K|$ be a map with an isolated fixed point $x \in S$, where x is not an end point of S, and suppose there is a neighborhood U of x whose closure is in the maximal simplex, that $\mathrm{cl}(U)$ is homeomorphic to B^p, and $f_1(\mathrm{cl}(U)) \subseteq S$. Let $S - x$ consist of components C_1 and C_2. If $f_1(C_1) \subseteq C_2$ and $f_1(C_2) \subseteq C_1$ then, as in Section IV.E, the restriction of f to $\mathrm{cl}(U)$ is homotopic to a map taking $\mathrm{cl}(U)$ to x, by a homotopy without fixed points on ∂U. By the homotopy axiom and IV.B.2 we have that $i(|K|, f_1, x) = 1$.

Now let $f_2 \colon |K| \to |K|$ have the same properties as f_1, except that, on $\mathrm{cl}(U) \cap (S - x)$, f_2 is homotopic to the identity map. We may think of $\mathrm{cl}(U) \cap S$ as lying on $R^1 \subseteq R^n$ with x at the origin. For $j = 1, 2$, $d_j \colon |K| \to R^n$ is defined by $d_j = y - f_j(y)$. Define, as in section I.M, $\eta \colon R^n \to R^n$ by $\eta(x_1, x_2, \ldots, x_n) = (-x_1, x_2, \ldots, x_n)$; then for $\bar{\mu}_p \in H^{p-1}(R^p - 0)$ recall that $\eta^*(\bar{\mu}_p) = -\bar{\mu}_p$. Now d_2 is homotopic in $\mathrm{cl}(U) \cap (S - X)$ to ηd_1. By Section B, for appropriately chosen generators $\bar{\mu}_p \in H^{p-1}(R^p - 0)$, $\alpha_p \in H^{p-1}(\partial U)$ we have

$$i(|K|, f_2, x)\alpha_p = d_2^*(\bar{\mu}_p)$$
$$= d_1^* \eta^*(\bar{\mu}_p) = -i(|K|, f_1, x) \cdot \alpha_p.$$

By the previous computation, $i(|K|, f_2, x) = -1$.

The computation above plays an important role in the next result:

Lemma 3. *Let $s_1, s_2 \in K$ be simplices of dimension greater than one such that $s_1 \cap s_2$ has dimension greater than zero. Let $a \in |s_1|$, $b \in |s_1 \cap s_2|$, and let $f \colon |K| \to |K|$ be a map such that*

(1) *a is an isolated fixed point of f: $i(|K|, f, a) \neq 0$, and $\Phi(f) \cap [a, b] = a$,*

(2) *f is a proximity map on $[a, b]$.*

There exists $\epsilon > 0$ and a map $f' \colon |K| \to |K|$ with the properties:

(3) *f' is homotopic to f on $U([a, b], \epsilon)$.*

(4) *$\Phi(f') \cap \overline{U}([a, b], \epsilon) = c$ for some $c \in U(b, \epsilon) \cap |s_2|$.*

(5) *f' is a proximity map on $\overline{U}([a, b], \epsilon)$.*

Proof For a simplex $s \in K$, define $\mathrm{St}(s)$ to be all simplices in K which contain s. Observing that $K - \mathrm{St}(s)$ is a subcomplex of K, it follows that $|\mathrm{St}(s)| = \bigcup_{s \subseteq t} |t|$ is open in $|K|$. The first thing we will need are some ϵ's. Since $|\mathrm{St}(\sigma(b))|$ is a neighborhood of b, there exists our first ϵ, $\epsilon_1 > 0$, with the property that $\overline{U}(b, \epsilon_1) \subseteq |\mathrm{St}(\sigma(b))|$. Using the hypothesis $f(b) \neq b$ and the continuity of f, we can find $\epsilon_2 > 0$ such that $U(b, \epsilon_2) \cap f(U(b, \epsilon_2)) = \varnothing$. Since a is an isolated fixed point of f, there is a neighborhood U_1 of a on which the only fixed point of f is a. Let $a' \in [a, b] \cap U_1$, $a' \neq a$, then there are no fixed points of f on $[a', b]$, and therefore there is a neighborhood U_2 of $[a', b]$ on which f is fixed point free. Choose $\epsilon_3 > 0$ so that $\overline{U}([a, b], \epsilon_3) \subseteq U_1 \cup U_2$; then we know that $\Phi(f) \cap \overline{U}([a, b], \epsilon_3) = a$. If $s \in K$ and $s \cap \sigma(b) \neq \varnothing$, then $s \cap t \neq \varnothing$ for all $t \in \mathrm{St}(\sigma(b))$. Therefore $x \in |\mathrm{St}(\sigma(b))|$ implies $V(b) \subseteq V(x)$. Since f is a proximity map on $[a, b]$, $f(b)$ is in the open set $V(b)$, so there exists $\epsilon'_4 > 0$ such that $U(b, \epsilon'_4) \subseteq |\text{St}(\sigma(b))|$ and $f(U(b, \epsilon'_4)) \subseteq V(b)$. By the previous remark, f is a proximity map on $U(b, \epsilon'_4)$. Choose $b' \in [a, b] \cap U(b, \epsilon'_4)$, $b' \neq b$; then for $x \in [a, b'], f(x) \in V(x) = V(a)$ by hypothesis (2) above. Choose ϵ''_4 so that $U([a, b'], \epsilon''_4) \subseteq |s_1|$ and $f(U([a, b'], \epsilon''_4)) \subseteq V(a)$. Then, of course, f is a proximity map on $U([a, b], \epsilon''_4)$. Take $\epsilon_4 > 0$ small enough so that $\overline{U}([a, b], \epsilon_4) \subseteq U([a, b'], \epsilon''_4) \cup U(b, \epsilon'_4)$. Let $\epsilon > 0$ be the smallest of all the ϵ's; it has the following properties:

1. $\overline{U}(b, \epsilon) \subseteq |\text{St}(\sigma(b))|$.

2. If $x \in U(b, \epsilon)$ then $f(x) \notin U(b, \epsilon)$.

3. $\Phi(f) \cap \overline{U}([a, b], \epsilon) = a$.

4. f is a proximity map on $\overline{U}([a, b], \epsilon)$.

Then let p be a point of $[a, b]$ other than a whose distance from b is greater than ϵ (see *Property 2* above). Select a point $q \in |s_2| - \overline{U}(b, \epsilon)$ and, noting that $|\text{St}(\sigma(b))| - \overline{U}(b, \epsilon)$ is an open, connected subset of the locally pathwise connected space $|K|$, let Q be a path in $|\text{St}(\sigma(b))| - \overline{U}(b, \epsilon)$ from q to p. The Simplicial Approximation Theorem assures us that there is no loss of generality in assuming that Q is a union of line segments joined end-to-end. Because $V(b) - \overline{U}(b, \epsilon)$ is also open and connected in $|K|$, there is a path P from $f(b)$ to p in $V(b) - \overline{U}(b, \epsilon)$ made up of line segments (Figure 1). Observe that

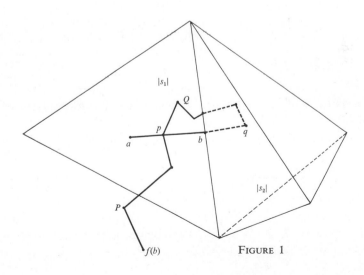

FIGURE 1

$[p, b, q] \cdot Q$ is a loop at p. For ω a loop in a space X and m a nonzero integer, define ω^m to be the loop $\omega \cdot \omega \cdots \omega$ (m times) when $m > 0$ and $\omega^{-1} \cdot \omega^{-1} \cdots$ ω^{-1} (m times) when $m < 0$ (recall that $\omega^{-1}(t) = \omega(t - 1)$). Set $i = i(|K|, f, a) \neq 0$, which is an integer by B.1, and define a path r from $f(b)$ to p by

$$r = P \cdot ([p, b, q] \cdot Q)^i.$$

Since r is a union of line segments, its length $\ell(r)$ is defined to be the sum of the lengths of the segments. Let $r: I \to |K|$ be the map such that $r(I) = r$ and the length of the portion of r from $f(b)$ to $r(t)$ is $t \cdot \ell(r)$. Define a map $f_1: |K| \to |K|$ by

$$f_1(x) = \begin{cases} f(x) & \text{if } x \notin U(b, \epsilon) \\[2mm] f\left[\left(\frac{2}{\epsilon} d(x, b) - 1\right)x + \left(2 - \frac{2}{\epsilon} d(x, b)\right)b\right] & \text{if } \frac{\epsilon}{2} \leq d(x, b) \leq \epsilon \\[2mm] r\left[1 - \frac{2}{\epsilon} d(x, b)\right] & \text{if } 0 \leq d(x, b) \leq \frac{\epsilon}{2}. \end{cases}$$

Then the condition $\overline{U}(b, \epsilon) \subseteq |\mathrm{St}(\sigma(b))|$ assures us that f_1 is well-defined. It is not difficult to show that f and f_1 are homotopic on $U(b, \epsilon)$. We know that f has no fixed points on $U(b, \epsilon)$, so the only place in $U(b, \epsilon)$ where f_1 could have a fixed point would be on $U(b, \epsilon/2) \cap r$. A fixed point here would be a solution to the equation $x = r\left(1 - \frac{2}{\epsilon} d(x, b)\right)$. We are only interested in solutions on $U\left(b, \frac{\epsilon}{2}\right) \cap r \cap |s_1| \subseteq [p, b]$. If $i > 0$, the distance along r from $f(b) = r(0)$ to x is $\ell(P) + k(\ell([p, b, q] \cdot Q)) + d(p, x)$ for each $k = 0, 1, \ldots, i - 1$, since r passes through the point $x \in [p, b]$ once for each repetition of the loop $[p, b, q] \cdot Q$. What we want, then, is a point $x \in [p, b] \cap \overline{U}\left(b, \frac{\epsilon}{2}\right)$ such that

$$\ell(P) + k(\ell([p, b, q] \cdot Q)) + d(p, x) = \left(1 - \frac{2}{\epsilon} d(x, b)\right)\ell(r).$$

Substituting $d(p, x) = d(p, b) - d(x, b)$ and solving, we get

$$d(x, b) = \frac{(i - k)\ell([p, b, q] \cdot Q) - d(p, b)}{\frac{2}{\epsilon} \ell(r) - 1} \quad \left(< \frac{\epsilon}{2}\right),$$

so that, for each $k = 0, \ldots, i - 1$ we have a distinct point $x_k \in [p, b] \cap$

$U(b, \epsilon/2)$ such that $f_1(x_k) = x_k$, and these are the only fixed points of f_1 on $[p, b]$. Near x_k, f_1 is just a very close approximation to the identity map, so by the argument that preceded this lemma, $i(|K|, f_1, x_k) = -1$. Similarly, when $i < 0$, we also have fixed points x_k, $k = 0, 1, \ldots, -i - 1$; but now f_1 behaves near x_k like the map f_1 in our computation preceding the lemma, and therefore $i(|K|, f_1, x_k) = 1$. In either case $i(|K|, f_1, U([a, b], \epsilon) \cap |s_1|) = 0$, by the additivity axiom, because

$$\sum_{k=0}^{|i|-1} i(|K|, f_1, x_k) = -i = -i(|K|, f_1, a).$$

Now f_1 is certainly a proximity map on $U\left(b, \dfrac{\epsilon}{2}\right)$ (notice where P and Q are located), and it is a proximity map on $U([a, b], \epsilon) - U\left(b, \dfrac{\epsilon}{2}\right)$ because f is a proximity map on $U([a, b], \epsilon)$. We may therefore apply Lemma 2, several times if necessary, to obtain a map $f_2 : |K| \rightarrow |K|$ homotopic to f_1 on $U([a, b], \epsilon)$, which is still a proximity map on $U([a, b], \epsilon)$, and which has only one fixed point — call it x_0 — in $\overline{U}([a, b], \epsilon)$. By the homotopy axiom, $i(|K|, f_2, x_0) = 0$, so B.4 furnishes us with a map $f_3 : |K| \rightarrow |K|$ homotopic to f_2 on $\overline{U}([a, b], \epsilon)$ and close enough to f_2 so that f_3 is still a proximity map on $U([a, b], \epsilon)$ with the additional property that $\Phi(f_3) \cap \overline{U}([a, b], \epsilon) = \varnothing$. Finally, f_3 is a proximity map on $U(b, \epsilon)$ so, by Lemma 2, there is a map $f' : |K| \rightarrow |K|$ homotopic to f_3, and therefore to f, on $U([a, b], \epsilon)$ such that $\Phi(f') \cap \overline{U}([a, b], \epsilon) = c$ for some $c \in U(b, \epsilon) \cap |s_2|$ and such that f' is a proximity map on $\overline{U}([a, b], \epsilon)$. ∎

The techniques described in Lemmas 2 and 3 required that the map f with which we were working be a proximity map on certain sets. We now turn to the case where f is not assumed to be a proximity map anywhere. The idea is to deform the given map by a homotopy so that the new map is a proximity map on these sets and then apply the previous results to the new map.

We still have a connected geometric complex $|K|$. Let $s \in K$ and let $a \in |s|$, $b \in \text{cl} |s|$.

Define a retraction $R : \overline{U}([a, b], \epsilon) \rightarrow [a, b]$ in the following manner:

(1) If $b \in |s|$, let $R(x)$ be the unique point of $[a, b]$ closest to x.

(2) If $b \in \partial |s|$ define $R(x)$ as follows:

    (a) If $x \in |s| - [a, b]$, take $y \in |\sigma(b)|$ so that, in the plane determined by x, a, b in R^n, the line defined by x and y is parallel to the line determined by a and b. Then let z be the point on the line determined by a and b such that $xybz$ is a parallelogram. Define $R(x) = z$ if $z \in [a, b]$ and $R(x) = a$ otherwise.

(b) If $x \in [a, b]$, let $R(x) = x$.

(c) If $x \notin |s|$, let $R(x) = b$.

Observe that if ϵ is chosen small enough, then for each $x \in \overline{U}([a, b], \epsilon)$, $[x, R(x)] \subseteq |K|$. For any $\eta > 0$ smaller than ϵ, define

$$W([a, b], \eta) = \{x \in \overline{U}([a, b], \epsilon) \mid d(x, R(x)) < \eta\}$$

and denote its closure by $\overline{W}([a, b], \eta)$. The set $W([a, b], \eta)$ is a neighborhood of $[a, b]$ in $|K|$. If $b \in |s|$, then $W([a, b], \eta) = U([a, b], \eta)$. For $M \subseteq [a, b]$ define

$$W([a, b], \eta, M) = \{x \in W([a, b], \eta) \mid R(x) \in M\}.$$

Let $[a, b] \subset R^n$ and $x \in [a, b]$. Then there exists a unique number, call it t_x, in I such that $x = (1 - t_x)a + t_x b$. Furthermore, given $t \in I$, there is a unique point, call it x_t, defined by $x_t = (1 - t)a + tb$.

Before we can build up the more general kind of machinery, we need a lemma as follows:

Lemma 4. *Let s be a simplex of K of dimension greater than one and let $a \in |s|$, $b \in \mathrm{cl}\,|s|$. Suppose that we have maps $f: |K| \to |K|$ and $H: I \times I \to |K|$ and closed subsets M and N of $[a, b]$ such that*

(1) $H(t, 0) = f(x_t)$ *for all $t \in I$*

(2) $H(t_x, u) \neq x$ *for all $x \in N$, $u \in I$*

(3) $H(t_x, u) \in V(x)$ *for all $x \in M$, $u \in I$.*

There then exists a map $f': |K| \to |K|$ and a real number $\eta > 0$ such that

(4) f' *is homotopic to f on $W([a, b], \eta)$*

(5) $\Phi(f') \cap \overline{W}([a, b], \eta, N) = \varnothing$

(6) f' *is a proximity map on $\overline{W}([a, b], \eta, M)$*

(7) $f'(x) = H(t_x, 1)$ *for all $x \in [a, b]$.*

Proof Condition (2) and the compactness of N imply the existence of $\epsilon > 0$ such that $d(H(t_x, u), x) > \epsilon$ for all $x \in N$, $u \in I$. Similarly, because of condition (1), we can choose $\eta_1 > 0$, $\eta_1 < \epsilon$, so that if $x \in \overline{W}([a, b], \eta_1, N)$ then $d(f(x), x) > \epsilon$. Since f is a proximity map on M, by conditions (1) and (3) there exists $\eta_2 > 0$ such that f is a proximity map on $\overline{W}([a, b], \eta_2, M)$ (compare the first part of the proof of Lemma 3). We can find $\eta_3 > 0$ so that $\overline{U}([a,\ b],\ 2\eta_3) \subseteq |\mathrm{St}(\sigma(b))|$ and therefore $\overline{W}([a,\ b],\ \eta_3) \subseteq |\mathrm{St}(\sigma(b))|$. Let η be the smallest of η_1, η_2, and η_3. We claim that the map that we want, $f': |K| \to |K|$ homotopic to f on $W([a,\ b],\ \eta)$, can be defined by

$$f'(x) = \begin{cases} f(x) & \text{if } x \notin W([a,\ b],\eta) \\[2ex] f\left[\left(\dfrac{2}{\eta}\,d(x, R(x))\right)x + \left(2 - \dfrac{2}{\eta}\,d(x, R(x))\right)R(x)\right] \\[1ex] \hspace{6em} \text{if } \dfrac{\eta}{2} \le d(x, R(x)) \le \eta \\[3ex] H\left[t_{R(x)},\ 1 - \dfrac{2}{\eta}\,d(x, R(x))\right] & \text{if } 0 \le d(x, R(x)) \le \dfrac{\eta}{2}. \end{cases}$$

If $\dfrac{\eta}{2} \le d(x, R(x)) \le \eta$ and $R(x) \in N$, then $f'(x) = f(x')$ for some $x' \in [R(x),\ x]$; thus

$$d(x',\ f(x')) \le d(x',\ x) + d(x, f'(x)),$$

and by the choice of η, $d(x', f'(x)) > \epsilon > \eta$ while $d(x, x') < \eta$, so $f'(x) \ne x$. If $0 \le d(x, R(x)) \le \dfrac{\eta}{2}$ and $R(x) \in N$, then $f'(x) = H(R(x), u)$ and

$$d(H(R(x), u), R(x)) > \epsilon > \eta,$$

so $d(x, f'(x)) > \dfrac{\eta}{2} > 0$. This completes the verification of conclusion (5). Recall that we chose η so that f is a proximity map on $\overline{W}([a,\ b],\ \eta,\ M)$. Clearly $f'(x) \in V(x)$ if $\dfrac{\eta}{2} \le d(x, R(x)) \le \eta$ and $R(x) \in M$. If $0 \le d(x, R(x)) \le \dfrac{\eta}{2}$ and $R(x) \in M$, then $f'(x) = H(t_{R(x)}, u) \in V(x)$ by condition (3). This finishes the argument for conclusion (6) and, since (7) is evident in the definition of f', we are through. ∎

The first of the two main results of this section is:

Lemma 5. *Let $s \in K$ be a maximal simplex of dimension at least three and let $f: |K| \to |K|$ be a map. If $a, b \in |s|$ are isolated fixed points of f such that $[a,\ b]$ contains no other fixed point of f and $\{[a,\ b]\} = \{f[a,\ b]\}$, then there exists a map $f': |K| \to |K|$ and $\delta > 0$ such that f' is homotopic to f on $U([a,\ b],\ \delta)$ and $\Phi(f') \cap U([a,\ b],\ \delta) = a$.*

Proof Since $\{f[a, b]\} = \{[a, b]\}$, there is a map $H_0: I \times I \to |K|$ such that $H_0(t_x, 0) = f(x)$ and $H_0(t_x, 1) = x$ for all $x \in [a, b]$, and $H_0(0, u) = a$ and $H_0(1, u) = b$ for all $u \in I$. Choose $\delta > 0$ small enough so that

(1) $\Phi(f) \cap \bar{U}([a, b], \delta) = a \cup b$

(2) $f[U(a, \delta) \cup U(b, \delta)] \subseteq |s|$

(3) if $x \in [a, b]$ and $d(x, a) \leq 2\delta$ or $d(x, b) \leq 2\delta$, then $H(t_x, u) \in \text{cl } |s|$ for all $u \in I$.

Let p and q be points of $[a, b]$ such that $d(p, a) = d(q, b) = \dfrac{\delta}{2}$. If $x \in [a, b]$ and $f(x) \neq x$, let $\alpha(x)$ be the point where the ray from x through $f(x)$ intersects $\partial |s|$. Now define $g: [a, b] \to |K|$ by

$$g(x) = \begin{cases} f(x) & \text{if } f(x) \notin |s| \\ \alpha(x) & \text{if } f(x) \in |s| \text{ and } x \in [p, q] \\ \alpha(p) & \text{if } x \in [a, p] \\ \alpha(q) & \text{if } x \in [q, b]. \end{cases}$$

Next we define $H_1: I \times I \to |K|$ by $H_1(t, u) = (1 - u)f(x_t) + ug(x_t)$, which makes sense because either $f(x_t) = g(x_t)$ or $f(x_t) \cup g(x_t) \subseteq \text{cl } |s|$. Observe that, if $x_t \in [p, q]$ such that $f(x_t) \in \text{cl } |s|$ and if we consider the set S consisting of the ray from x_t through $f(x_t)$ with $f(x_t)$ removed, then, for $u > 0$, $H_1(t, u)$ and x_t lie in different components of S. Furthermore, $H_1(t, 0) = f(x_t) \neq x_t$, so we see that $H_1(t, u) \neq x_t$ for all t such that $x_t \in [p, q]$ and for all $u \in I$. Note also that, if $x_t \in [a, p] \cup [q, b]$, then $H_1(t, u) \in \text{cl } |s|$ for all $u \in I$. Now combine the homotopies H_0 and H_1 into

$$H'(t, u) = \begin{cases} H_1(t, 1 - 2u) & \text{if } 0 \leq u \leq \tfrac{1}{2} \\ H_0(t, 2u - 1) & \text{if } \tfrac{1}{2} \leq u \leq 1. \end{cases}$$

By condition (3) on δ, $H'(t, u) \in \text{cl } |s|$ for all t such that $x_t \in [a, p] \cup [q, b]$ and for all $u \in I$. Let $H_3: I \times I \to |K|$ be a simplicial approximation to H'. Since $I \times I$ is a two-dimensional polyhedron and H_3 is simplicial, then $H_3(I \times I) \subseteq |K^2|$, the geometric realization of the 2-skeleton of K. The dimension of s is at least three, so $H_3(I \times I) \cap |s| = \varnothing$. We still need another homotopy, so define $H_2: I \times I \to |K|$ by $H_2(t, u) = (1 - u)g(x_t) + uH_3(t, 0)$. The homotopy is well-defined because the map $H_3(\ , 0): I \to |K|$ is a simplicial approximation to $H'(\ , 0) = H_1(\ , 1) = g$. For the same reason, $\sigma(g(x_t)) = \sigma(H_3(t, 0)) \neq s$, so $H_2(I \times I) \cap |s| = \varnothing$. One final remark: $g([a, p] \cup [q, b]) \subseteq \mathrm{cl}\,|s|$, and we observed that $H'(t, u) \in \mathrm{cl}\,|s|$ when $x_t \in [a, p] \cup [q, b]$ and $u \in I$, so the same will be true of H_3 and H_2. The last homotopy we will build is $H: I \times I \to |K|$, whose definition is just

$$H(t, u) = \begin{cases} H_1(t, 3u) & \text{if } 0 \leq u \leq \tfrac{1}{3} \\[6pt] H_2(t, 3u - 1) & \text{if } \tfrac{1}{3} \leq u \leq \tfrac{2}{3} \\[6pt] H_3(t, 3u - 2) & \text{if } \tfrac{2}{3} \leq u \leq 1 \end{cases}$$

for all $t \in I$. Combining what we already know about H_i, $i = 1,2,3$, we conclude that $H(t, u) \neq x_t$ if $x_t \in [p, q]$ for any $u \in I$, and that $H(t, u) \in \mathrm{cl}\,|s|$ if $x_t \in [a, p] \cup [q, b]$ (again for any $u \in I$). Therefore, we are able to apply Lemma 4 to the homotopy H, to the map f, and to the closed subsets $M = [a, p] \cup [q, b]$ and $N = [p, q]$ of $[a, b]$. We obtain a map $f_1: |K| \to |K|$ homotopic to f on $W([a, b], \eta)$ such that f_1 has no fixed points on $\overline{W}([a, b], \eta, N)$, f_1 is a proximity map on $\overline{W}([a, b], \eta, M)$, and $f_1(x) = H(t_x, 1)$ for all $x \in [a, b]$. The last property means that, for $x \in [a, b]$, $f_1(x) = H_3(t_x, 1)$, where H_3 is a simplicial approximation to H', so

$$f_1(x) = H_3(t_x, 1) \in |\mathrm{St}(\sigma(H'(t_x, 1)))|$$
$$= |\mathrm{St}(\sigma(H_0(t_x, 1)))|$$
$$= |\mathrm{St}(\sigma(x))| \subseteq V(x),$$

and f_1 is a proximity map on all of $[a, b]$. Choose $\eta > 0$ small enough so that $\eta < \delta$, all fixed points of f_1 in $\overline{W}([a, b], \eta)$ are in $U(a, \delta) \cup U(b, \delta)$, and f_1 is a proximity map on $\overline{U}(a, \delta) \cup \overline{U}(b, \delta)$. We will omit the proof of the existence of such an η, but the reader who has made it to this point in the section should have no trouble supplying it. Applying Lemma 2 twice, there is a map $f_2: |K| \to |K|$ homotopic to f_1 on $U(a, \delta) \cup U(b, \delta)$ such that $\Phi(f_2) \cap U(a, \delta) = a$, $\Phi(f_2) \cap U(b, \delta) = b$, and f_2 is a proximity map on $[a, b]$. A finite number of further applications of Lemma 2 produce the required map f' whose only fixed point on $U([a, b], \delta)$ is a. ∎

The final result of the section extends Lemma 3 to maps which are not proximity maps.

Lemma 6. *Let $s_1, s_2 \in K$ be maximal simplices of dimension at least two such that the dimension of $s_1 \cap s_2$ is at least one. Suppose that $f: |K| \to |K|$ is a map with an isolated fixed point at a point $a \in |s_1|$ and that $b \in |s_1 \cap s_2|$ is a*

point with the property that $\Phi(f) \cap [a, b] = a$. *There exists* $\delta > 0$ *and a map*
$f' : |K| \to |K|$ *such that*

    (1) f' *is homotopic to* f *on* $U([a, b], \delta)$

    (2) $\Phi(f') \cap \overline{U}([a, b], \delta) = c$ *for some* $c \in |s_2|$

    (3) *if* $z \in \Phi(f)$, $z \notin U([a, b], \delta)$, *and* z *is* f-*equivalent to* a, *then* z *is* f'-
    equivalent to c. *In particular, let* C *be a path from* z *to* a *such that*
    $\{fC\} = \{C\}$; *then* $\{f'(C \cdot [a, b, c])\} = \{C \cdot [a, b, c]\}$.

Proof   Choose $\delta > 0$ small enough so that

$$\overline{U}(a, 2\delta) \subseteq |s_1|$$
$$\overline{U}(b, \delta) \subseteq |\mathrm{St}(\sigma(b))|$$
$$\Phi(f) \cap \overline{U}([a, b], \delta) = a$$
$$f(\overline{U}(b, \delta)) \cap \overline{U}(b, \delta) = \varnothing$$
$$f(\overline{U}(a, 2\delta)) \subseteq \mathrm{cl}\, |s_1|.$$

For bookkeeping purposes we will need the points p, p' and q in $[a, b]$ characterized by $d(p, a) = \dfrac{\delta}{2}$, $d(p', a) = 2\delta$, and $d(q, b) = \delta$. As in the last proof, for $x \in [a, b]$ and $x \neq a$ such that $f(x) \in \mathrm{cl}\, |s_1|$, define $\alpha(x)$ to be the point where the ray from x through $f(x)$ intersects $\partial\, |s_1|$. If $f(x) \in \mathrm{cl}\, |s_1|$, $f(x) \neq q$, then define $\beta(x)$ to be the intersection of the ray from q through $f(x)$ with the set $\partial\, |s_1|$. Let $v \in \sigma(b)$ be any vertex; then $|v|$ and $\alpha(p)$ are points of $\partial\, |s_1|$, which is homeomorphic to a sphere S^m, $m \geq 1$. So there is an arc A from $|v|$ to $\alpha(p)$ in $\partial\, |s_1|$. By the Simplicial Approximation Theorem, we can take A to consist of nonintersecting line segments joined end-to-end. There is a homeomorphism $h \colon [a, p] \to A$ such that $h(a) = |v|$ and $h(p) = \alpha(p)$. Define a map $g_1 \colon [a, b] \to |K|$ in the following manner:

$$g_1(x) = \begin{cases} f(x) & \text{if } f(x) \notin |s_1| \\[4pt] h(x) & \text{if } x \in [a, p] \\[4pt] \alpha(x) & \text{if } x \in [p, q] \text{ and } f(x) \in \mathrm{cl}\, |s_1| \\[4pt] \beta(x) & \text{if } x \in [q, b] \text{ and } f(x) \in \mathrm{cl}\, |s_1|. \end{cases}$$

The condition on δ that $f(\overline{U}(b, \delta))$ and $\overline{U}(b, \delta)$ be disjoint assures us that β is defined on all of $[q, b]$. Now $g_1^{-1}(U(b, \delta))$ is an open subset of $[a, b]$ and hence a union of disjoint "open intervals" (line segments with their end points removed). Since $[a, b]$ is compact, only a finite number of the intervals, denote them by $(a_1, b_1), \ldots, (a_m, b_m)$, can contain any points of the set $g_1^{-1}(b)$. Let $G = U(b, \delta) - |s_1|$ and note that, since $g_1([a, b]) \cap |s_1| = \varnothing$, then $g_1((a_j, b_j)) \subset G$ for all $j = 1, \ldots, m$. Note also that, for all j, $g_1(a_j)$ and $g_1(b_j)$ are in ∂G. We next wish to prove that ∂G is pathwise connected. We chose δ small enough formerly so that $\text{cl}(G) \subseteq |\text{St}(\sigma(b))|$. Let $x_1, x_2 \in \partial G$; then $x_i \in |t_i|$ for some $t_i \in \text{St}(\sigma(b))$, $i = 1, 2$. Because the sets $\partial U(b, \delta) \cap \text{cl} |t_i|$ are pathwise connected and contain points of $\sigma(b)$, we can take $y_i \in \partial U(b, \delta) \cap |\sigma(b)| \cap \text{cl} |t_i|$ and find paths in ∂G from x_1 to y_1 and from y_2 to x_2. The simplex $s_2 \in \text{St}(\sigma(b))$ is of dimension at least two, so $\partial U(b, \delta) \cap |s_2|$ is pathwise connected and we can connect y_1 to y_2 by a path in ∂G to complete the argument. Of course $\overline{U}(b, \delta)$ is contractible along line segments ending at b, so, since $x \in |s| \subseteq |\text{St}(\sigma(b))|$ implies $[x, b] \in \text{cl} |s|$, $\text{cl}(G)$ is contractible. Let $C_j : [a_j, b_j] \to \partial G$ be a map such that $C_j(a_j) = g_1(a_j)$ and $C_j(b_j) = g_1(b_j)$, for $j = 1, \dots, m$. For each j, there is a map H^j: $[t_{a_j}, t_{b_j}] \times I \to \text{cl}(G)$ such that $H^j(t, 0) = g_1(x_t)$, $H^j(t, 1) = C_j(x_t)$ for all t for which $x_t \in [a_j, b_j]$ and $H^j(t_{a_j}, u) = g_1(a_j) = C_j(a_j)$ and $H^j(t_{b_j}, u) = g_1(b_j) = C_j(b_j)$ for all $u \in I$. Define $g_2 : [a, b] \to |K|$ by

$$
g_2(x) = \begin{cases} g_1(x) & \text{if } x \notin \bigcup_{j=1}^{m} [a_j, b_j] \\ C_j(x) & \text{if } x \in [a_j, b_j] \text{ for some } j. \end{cases}
$$

Then $g_2^{-1}(b) = \varnothing$, and g_2 is homotopic to g_1 by means of the homotopy $H_2 : [a, b] \times I \to |K|$ defined by

$$
H_2(x, u) = \begin{cases} g_1(x) = g_2(x) & \text{if } x \notin \bigcup_{j=1}^{m} [a_j, b_j], u \in I \\ H^j(t_x, u) & \text{if } x_t \in [a_j, b_j] \text{ for some } j. \end{cases}
$$

If $x \in [p, b]$ and $x \neq b$ then $x \in |s_1|$. And as we know, $H_2(x, u) \notin |s_1|$ for all such x and all $u \in I$. The choice of δ so that $f(\overline{U}(b, \delta)) \cap \overline{U}(b, \delta) = \varnothing$ assures us that $f(b) \notin [q, b]$, so $g_1(b) \neq b$. Since $H_2(b, u) = g_2(b) = g_1(b) \neq b$ for all $u \in I$, we have shown that $H_2(x, u) \neq x$ for all $x \in [p, b]$ and all $u \in I$. If $x \in [a, p']$, then $g_1(x) = h(x) \in \partial |s_1|$. Either $g_2(x) = g_1(x) \in \partial |s_1|$, or $g_1(x) \in U(b, \delta) \cap \partial |s_1|$ and $g_2(x) \in \partial G$, so $H_2(x, u) \in \text{cl}(G)$ for all $u \in I$. Now $\text{cl}(G) \subseteq |\text{St}(\sigma(b))|$, so we conclude that, if $x \in [a, p']$, then $\sigma(H_2(x, u)) \cap s_1 \neq \varnothing$ for all $u \in I$. We are still in the homotopy-building business. Define $H_1 : [a, b] \times I \to |K|$ by $H_1(x, u) = (1 - u)f(x) + ug_1(x)$. A quick look at the definition of g_1 will convince the reader that H_1 is well-defined. Next define $H_3 : [a, b] \times I \to |K|$ by $H_3(x, u) = g_2(x_{(1-u)t_x})$ and, finally, let H: $[a, b] \times I \to |K|$ be the composition

$$
H(x, u) = \begin{cases} H_1(x, 3u) & \text{if } 0 \leq u \leq \tfrac{1}{3} \\ H_2(x, 3u - 1) & \text{if } \tfrac{1}{3} \leq u \leq \tfrac{2}{3} \\ H_3(x, 3u - 2) & \text{if } \tfrac{2}{3} \leq u \leq 1. \end{cases}
$$

It is clear from the definition of g_1 that, if $x \in [p, b]$, then $H_1(x, u) \neq x$ for all $u \in I$ and, since $g_2([a, b]) \cap |s_1| = \varnothing$ and $g_2(b) \neq b$, that $H_3(x, u) \neq x$ as well. For $x \in [a, p']$, we have $\sigma(H_1(x, u)) \subseteq s_1$ for all $u \in I$, while if $x \in [a, p']$ then $x_{(1-u)t_x} \in [a, p']$. So $\sigma(H_3(x, u)) \cap s_1 \neq \varnothing$ for all $u \in I$. We have proved that $H(x, u) \neq x$ for all $x \in [p, b]$, $u \in I$, and that $\sigma(H(x, u)) \cap s_1 \neq \varnothing$ for all $x \in [a, p']$ and $u \in I$. The map f, the homotopy H, and the closed sets $M = [a, p']$ and $N = [p, b]$ satisfy the hypotheses of Lemma 4, so we know that there is a map $f_1 : |K| \to |K|$ which is homotopic to f on $W([a, b], \eta)$ such that $\Phi(f_1) \cap \overline{W}([a, b], \eta, [p, b]) = \varnothing$ and f_1 is a proximity map on $\overline{W}([a, b], \eta, [a, p'])$. Also, for $x \in [a, b]$,

$$f_1(x) = H(x, 1) = H_3(x, 1) = g_2(x_0) = g_2(a).$$

Recall that $g_1(a) = |v|$ for a vertex v of $\sigma(b)$, so

$$f_1(x) = g_2(a) = g_1(a) \in \mathrm{cl}\, |\sigma(b)| \subset \mathrm{cl}\, |s_1|.$$

In a rather trivial way, then, we find that f_1 is a proximity map on $[a, b]$. By taking η so small that

$$W([a, b], \eta) - W([a, b], \eta, [p, b]) \subseteq U(a, \delta)$$

we can be sure that all the fixed points of f_1 in $W([a, b], \eta)$ are, in fact, in the set $U(a, \delta)$. At the same time we can make sure that η is small enough so that f_1 will be a proximity map on $\overline{U}(a, \delta)$. By Lemma 2 there is a map $f_2 : |K| \to |K|$ homotopic to f_1 on $U(a, \delta)$ such that $\Phi(f_2) \cap U(a, \delta) = a$ and f_2 is a proximity map on $\overline{U}(a, \delta)$. It is easy to verify the hypotheses of Lemma 3 for the map f_2 in order to establish the existence of a map $f' : |K| \to |K|$ homotopic to f_2 on $\overline{U}([a, b], \delta)$, such that $\Phi(f') \cap \overline{U}([a, b], \delta) = c$, where $c \in |s_2| \cap U(b, \delta)$ and f' is a proximity map on $\overline{U}([a, b], \delta)$. The map f' has the property described in conclusion (2), and the verification of conclusion (1) poses no problem.

We must, however, do some work in order to prove that f' satisfies conclusion (3). The line in R^n determined by a and b intersects $\partial U(a, \delta)$ (which is in $|s_1|$) at two points. One of the points is in $[a, b]$. The one that is not we call "e." We are given $z \in \Phi(f)$, $z \notin U([a, b], \delta)$, and a path C from z to a with the property that $\{fC\} = \{C\}$. Since f' is homotopic to f on $U([a, b], \delta)$, and $e \notin U([a, b], \delta)$, the homotopy between f' and f induces a homotopy between $f(C \cdot [a, e])$ and $f'(C \cdot [a, e])$, which is a fixed end-point homotopy. Thus

$$\{f(C \cdot [a, e])\} = \{f'(C \cdot [a, e])\}. \tag{1}$$

The map f is a proximity map on $[e, a] \subset \overline{U}(a, \delta)$. Therefore we can define a path $D : I \to |K|$ from $f(e)$ to e by $D(r) = \alpha(e, f(e), 1 - r)$, where α is the map obtained in Lemma 1. Consider the loop $\Lambda = D^{-1} \cdot f([e, a]) \cdot [a, e]$ based at e. Define $J: I \times I \to |K|$ as follows:

$$J(t, u) = \begin{cases} \alpha(x'_t, f(x'_t), 1 - 2u) & \text{if } 0 \leq u \leq \tfrac{1}{2} \\ x'_{2(1-u)t} & \text{if } \tfrac{1}{2} \leq u \leq 1, \end{cases}$$

where $x'_t = (1 - t)e + ta$. Then $J(\partial(I \times I)) = \Lambda$, and Λ must represent the identity element of $\pi_1(|K|, e)$, so

$$\{f([e, a]) \cdot [a, e]\} = \{D\} \qquad \text{(compare VI. Ex. 3)}. \tag{2}$$

Our final observation is that f' is a proximity map on $[e, a, b, c] \subseteq \overline{U}([a, b], \delta)$. By the argument we used to obtain equation (2) we have

$$\{f'([e, a, b, c]) \cdot [c, b, a, e]\} = \{D\}. \tag{3}$$

The obvious identities $\{[a, e] \cdot [e, a]\} = \{[a, a]\}$ and $\{[b, a, a]\} = \{[b, a]\}$ are used several times in the following computation:

$$\{f'(C \cdot [a, b, c]) \cdot [c, b, a] \cdot C^{-1}\}$$

$$= \{f'(C \cdot [a, e] \cdot [e, a, b, c]) \cdot [c, b, a, e] \cdot [e, a] \cdot C^{-1}\}$$

$$= \{f'(C \cdot [a, e]) \cdot f'([e, a, b, c]) \cdot [c, b, a, e] \cdot [e, a] \cdot C^{-1}\}$$

$$= \{f'(C \cdot [a, e]) \cdot D \cdot [e, a] \cdot C^{-1}\} \qquad \text{(by (3))}$$

$$= \{f(C \cdot [a, e]) \cdot D \cdot [e, a] \cdot C^{-1}\} \qquad \text{(by (1))}$$

$$= \{f(C \cdot [a, e]) \cdot f([e, a]) \cdot [a, e] \cdot [e, a] \cdot C^{-1}\} \qquad \text{(by (2))}$$

$$= \{f(C \cdot [a, e] \cdot [e, a]) \cdot [a, e] \cdot [e, a] \cdot C^{-1}\}$$

$$= \{f(C) \cdot C^{-1}\}.$$

But we were given that $\{fC\} = \{C\}$, so $\{fC \cdot C^{-1}\}$ is the unit element of $\pi_1(|K|, z)$, and therefore $\{f'(C \cdot [a, b, c])\} = \{C \cdot [a, b, c]\}$. ∎

D. THE CONVERSE OF THE LEFSCHETZ THEOREM

The substantial amount of technique that we have developed in the first three sections now enables us to prove the main result of the chapter.

We will say that a connected geometric complex $|K|$ is of *type S* if the dimension of K is at least three and if, for each vertex v of K, $\partial |St(v)|$ is connected, where, we recall, $St(v)$ denotes the collection of all simplices of K which contain v. A polyhedron X is of *type S* if it is homeomorphic to a geometric complex of type S. We know, by VI.C.2 and VI.E.4, that if $f: X \to X$ is a map, then $N(f)$ is a lower bound for the number of fixed points of each map homotopic to f. Our main theorem states that if X is of type S, then $N(f)$ is the best possible lower bound.

Theorem 1. *If X is a polyhedron of type S and $f: X \to X$ is a map, then there exists a map $g: X \to X$ homotopic to f such that g has exactly $N(f)$ fixed points.*

Proof There is no loss of generality in assuming that $X = |K|$, the geometric realization of a simplicial complex. By A.2 and III.A.4, there is a map $f_1: |K| \to |K|$ such that f_1 is homotopic to f, f_1 has only a finite number of fixed points, and each fixed point of f_1 lies in a maximal simplex of $|K'|$ where K' is a refinement of K, and therefore in a maximal simplex of K. Let $x_1, x_2 \in \Phi(f_1)$, both of nonzero index, be f_1-equivalent so there is a path C from x_1 to x_2 such that $\{C\} = \{f_1 C\}$. Since $|K|$ is of type S, there is an n-simplex s in K where $n \geq 3$. We can assume that s is maximal in K. Since $\Phi(f_1)$ is finite, we can choose $x'_1, x'_2 \in |s|$ so that $[x'_1, x'_2] \cap \Phi(f_1) = \varnothing$. Let C_1 be a path from x_1 to x'_1. We wish to construct a path D_1 from x_1 to x'_1 consisting of line segments joined end-to-end such that the interior of each segment is in the geometric realization of a maximal simplex of K, each segment end point is in the geometric realization of a simplex of K of dimension at least one, $D_1 \cap \Phi(f_1) = x_1$, and $\{D_1\} = \{C_1\}$. There exists $t_1 > 0$ so that $C_{11} = \{C_1(t) \mid 0 \leq t \leq t_1\}$ is in the closure of the maximal simplex s_1 of K whose geometric realization contains x_1 and $C_1(t_1) \in \partial |s_1|$. There is a line segment $D_{11}(t)$, $0 \leq t \leq t_1$, starting at x_1 such that $D_{11} \cap \Phi(f_1) = x_1$, $D_{11}(t) \in |s_1|$ for all t such that $0 \leq t < t_1$, $\sigma(D_{11}(t_1))$ is of dimension at least one, and the closure of its geometric realization contains $C_1(t_1)$. There exists $t_2 > t_1$ and a maximal simplex $s_2 \in K$ such that

$$C_{12} = \{C_1(t) \mid t_1 \leq t \leq t_2\} \subseteq \text{cl } |s_2|$$

and $C_1(t_2) \in \partial |s_2|$. If $D_{11}(t_1) \in \text{cl } |s_2|$ then there is a line segment $D_{12}(t)$, $t_1 \leq t \leq t_2$, starting at $D_{11}(t_1)$, disjoint from $\Phi(f_1)$; and such that $D_{12}(t) \in |s_2|$ for $t_1 < t < t_2$, where $\sigma(D_{12}(t_2))$ is of dimension at least one; and the closure of its geometric realization contains $C_1(t_2)$. However, if $\sigma(C_1(t_1))$ is a vertex of K, then it need not be true that $D_{11}(t_1) \in \text{cl } |s_2|$. We know that, because $|K|$ is of type S, $\partial |\text{St}(C_1(t_1))|$ is connected in that case; so there are maximal simplices $s_2^1, \ldots, s_2^r$ of K in $\text{St}(\sigma(C_1(t_1)))$ with $D_{11}(t_1) \in \text{cl } |s_2^1|$ and $s_2^i \cap s_2^{i+1}$ of dimension at least one for $i = 1, \ldots, r-1$ and $s_2^r = s_2$. Therefore we can, in this case, find a path $D_{12}(t)$, $t_1 \leq t \leq t_2$, starting at $D_{11}(t_1)$, made up of line segments such that — except at end points — each point is in the geometric realization of a maximal simplex of K; the end points of segments are in the geometric realizations of simplices of dimension at least one; $D_{12} \cap \Phi(f_1) = \varnothing$; and the closure of $|\sigma(D_{12}(t_2))|$ contains $C_1(t_2)$. Continuing in this manner we obtain the required path $D_1 = D_{11} \cup D_{12} \cup \cdots \cup D_{1k}$. Note that $\{D_1\} = \{C_1\}$ because each D_{1i} is homotopic to each C_{1i} by "straight line" homotopies (hence the homotopies match up at end points). By exactly the same construction we can also obtain a path D_2

from x_2 to x_2' made up of line segments such that the interior of each segment is in the geometric realization of a maximal simplex of K, each segment end point is in the geometric realization of a simplex of dimension at least one, $D_2 \cap \Phi(f_1) = x_2$, and $\{D_2\} = \{C^{-1}C_1[x_1', x_2']\}$. A finite number of applications of C.6, one for each segment making up D_1, produce a map $f_2: |K| \rightarrow |K|$ homotopic to f_1 on $U(D_1 \cup D_2, \delta)$ such that the only fixed points of f_2 on $\overline{U}(D_1 \cup D_2, \delta)$ are x_1' and x_2. By conclusion (3) of C.6, we know that $\{f_2(C^{-1}D_1)\} - \{C^{-1}D_1\}$. Again using C.6, this time applied to the segments of D_2, we obtain a map $f_3: |K| \rightarrow |K|$ homotopic to f_2 (and thus f_1) on $U(D_1 \cup D_2, \delta)$ such that the only fixed points of f_3 on $\overline{U}(D_1 \cup D_2, \delta)$ are x_1' and x_2'. By conclusion (3) of C.6 (employed with respect to the map f_2 and the path $C^{-1}D_1$) we get $\{f_3(D_1^{-1}CD_2)\} = \{D_1^{-1}CD_2\}$. Since $\{D_1\} = \{C_1\}$ and $\{D_2\} = \{C^{-1}C_1[x_1', x_2']\}$, we can substitute as follows:

$$\{f_3([x_2', x_1'])C_1^{-1}CC^{-1}C_1\} = \{f_3(D_2^{-1}C^{-1}D_1)\}$$
$$= \{D_2^{-1}C^{-1}D_1\}$$
$$= \{[x_2', x_1']C_1^{-1}CC^{-1}C_1\}$$

and conclude that $\{f_3([x_2', x_1'])\} = \{[x_2', x_1']\}$. Recalling that $x_1', x_2' \in |s|$, we discover that we are permitted to apply C.5 to f_3 to obtain a map $f_4: |K| \rightarrow |K|$ such that f_4 is homotopic to f_3 on $U([x_1', x_2'], \delta')$, where $\delta > \delta' > 0$ and f_4 has one fixed point in $\overline{U}([x_1', x_2'], \delta')$. To summarize, f_4 is homotopic to f_1, it has exactly the same fixed points as f_1 except for x_1 and x_2, and in place of x_1 and x_2 it has one other fixed point which still lies in the geometric realization of a maximal simplex of K. After a finite number of applications of this technique, we have a map $f': |K| \rightarrow |K|$ homotopic to f which has at most one fixed point of nonzero index in each fixed point class. Finally, suppose that $x \in \Phi(f')$ and $i(|K|, f', x) = 0$; then by B.4 and III.A.4 there is a map f_1' which agrees with f' outside of an arbitrarily small neighborhood U of x, is homotopic to f' on U, and has no fixed points in U. Applying B.4 to each $x \in \Phi(f')$ of index zero, we construct a map $g: |K| \rightarrow |K|$ homotopic to f' such that each fixed point class of g consists of a single fixed point of nonzero index; so the corresponding class is essential. Therefore, by the definition of the Nielsen number, g has exactly $N(g)$ fixed points. ∎

Let X be a polyhedron such that $T(X) = \pi_1(X)$, e.g., X is simply-connected, or X is an H-space (VII.A.9). Let $f: X \rightarrow X$ be any map; then $T(f) = \pi_1(X)$ by VII.A.8. If $L(f) = 0$, Corollary VII.A.5 states that $N(f) = 0$. Thus, because of Theorem 1, we have

Theorem 2   (The Converse of the Lefschetz Fixed Point Theorem).   *Let X be a polyhedron of type S such that $T(X) = \pi_1(X)$. If $f: X \rightarrow X$ is a map such that*

$L(f) = 0$, *then there exists a map* $g: X \to X$, *homotopic to* f, *which is fixed point free.*

Let $H^n = \{(x_1, \ldots, x_n) \in R^n \mid x_n \geq 0\}$. A polyhedron X is called an *n-manifold* if, for any point $x \in X$, there is a neighborhood U of x in X such that U is homeomorphic either to R^n or H^n.

Corollary 3. *If X is an n-manifold, $n \geq 3$, and $f: X \to X$ is a map, then there exists $g: X \to X$ homotopic to f such that g has exactly $N(f)$ fixed points. If, in addition, $T(X) = \pi_1(X)$ and $L(f) = 0$, then g will be fixed point free.*

Proof The result will be an obvious consequence of Theorems 1 and 2 once we establish that an *n*-manifold, $n \geq 3$, is a polyhedron of type S. Let $|K|$ be a geometric complex homeomorphic to X. First observe that — since $|K|$ is a manifold — maximal simplices of K are all of dimension $n \geq 3$; so K is of dimension at least three. Let v be a vertex of K. We know that $|\mathrm{St}(v)|$ is open in $|K|$, so there is a neighborhood U of $|v|$ in $|\mathrm{St}(v)|$ which is homeomorphic either to R^n or to H^n. Assume that there is a homeomorphism $h: R^n \to U$. We can define h so that $h(0) = |v|$. Let $x \in h(S^{n-1})$; then $x \in |s|$ for some $s \in \mathrm{St}(v)$, so we can write $s = \{v, v_1, \ldots, v_k\}$ and $x = \lambda v + \sum_{i=1}^{k} \lambda_i v_i$. The intersection of the ray from $|v|$ through x and the set $\mathrm{cl}\,|s|$ consists of points of the form $[(\lambda - 1)r + 1]v + r\sum_{i=1}^{k} \lambda_i v_i$, where $0 \leq r \leq (1 - \lambda)^{-1}$. Let $\alpha(x) = (1 - \lambda)^{-1} \sum_{i=1}^{k} \lambda_i v_i$; then $\alpha(x) \in |t|$, where $t = \{v_1, \ldots, v_k\}$. Since $t \subset s$ then $|t| \subset \partial\,|s|$, but since $v \notin t$ then $t \notin \mathrm{St}(v)$, so $\alpha(x) \in \partial\,|\mathrm{St}(v)|$. In this way, we define a map $\alpha: h(S^{n-1}) \to \partial\,|\mathrm{St}(v)|$. Next take $y \in \partial\,|\mathrm{St}(v)|$. Let $x \in [|v|, y] \cap h(S^{n-1}) \neq \varnothing$. Then, by definition, $y = \alpha(x)$. We have proved that α is onto and hence that $\partial\,|\mathrm{St}(v)|$ is connected. The argument in the case where U is homeomorphic to H^n is very similar, so we omit it. We have established that an *n*-manifold is of type S whenever $n \geq 3$. ∎

E. DEFORMATIONS

Recall that if X is a polyhedron and if $f: X \to X$ is the identity map then $L(f)$ is called the *Euler characteristic* $\chi(X)$ of X. The Lefschetz Fixed Point Theorem therefore implies that if $\chi(X) \neq 0$ then every deformation on X has a fixed point. We will refer to this special case of the Lefschetz Fixed Point Theorem as the *Lefschetz Deformation Theorem*. The converse of the Lefschetz Deformation Theorem is, of course, a weaker result than the converse of the

Lefschetz Fixed Point Theorem, so one might ask whether this weaker theorem would still be true under conditions less demanding than the hypotheses "type S" and "$T(X) = \pi_1(X)$" that we needed for D.2.

We will say that a connected geometric complex $|K|$ is of *type W* if every maximal simplex of K is of dimension at least two and if $|K|$ is "strongly connected" in the sense that, given s, s', maximal simplices of K, there exist maximal simplices $s_1, \ldots, s_r$ such that $s_1 = s$, $s_r = s'$, and $s_i \cap s_{i+1}$ is of dimension at least one for all $i = 1, \ldots, r - 1$.

If K contains a maximal 1-simplex $s = \{v_0, v_1\}$, then either $|K|$ is homeomorphic to I or, for at least one of the vertices v_i, $i = 0, 1$, the set $\partial |St(v_i)|$ consists of more than just the other vertex; but then $\partial |St(v_i)|$ is disconnected. A complex $|K|$ of type S contains the geometric realization of a 3-simplex and thus is not homeomorphic to I. We conclude that, for a geometric complex $|K|$ of type S, every maximal simplex of K is of dimension at least two. By the method described in the proof of D.1 for constructing the paths D_1 and D_2 it can be shown that, if $\partial |St(v)|$ is connected for all vertices v of K, then $|K|$ is strongly connected. We have proved that a geometric complex of type S is of type W. A complex of type W need not be of type S, for example if $|K|$ is homeomorphic to the polyhedron in Figure 2.

A polyhedron X is of *type W* if there is a geometric complex $|K|$ of type W homeomorphic to X.

Theorem 1 (**The Converse of the Lefschetz Deformation Theorem**). *If X is a polyhedron of type W and $\chi(X) = 0$, then X admits a fixed point free deformation.*

Proof Just as in the proof of D.1 we will work not with X, but with a geometric complex $|K|$, this time of type W, homeomorphic to it. Theorem A.2 gives us a map $f: |K| \to |K|$ with only a finite number of fixed points, all in the geometric realizations of maximal simplices of K, such that $d(f, 1_{|K|}) < \epsilon$. We choose $\epsilon > 0$ small enough so that f is a proximity map on all of $|K|$ and hence a deformation (C.1). Let $x_0, x \in \Phi(f)$ where x is of nonzero index. Then, since $|K|$ is of type W, there are maximal simplices $s_1, \ldots, s_r \in K$ with $s_1 = \sigma(x)$, $s_r = \sigma(x_0)$, and $s_i \cap s_{i+1}$ of dimension at least one for all $i = 1, \ldots, r - 1$. Choose $y_1 \in |s_1 \cap s_2|$ so that $[x, y_1] \cap \Phi(f) = x$, $y_2 \in |s_2 \cap s_3|$ such that $[y_1, y_2] \cap \Phi(f) = \varnothing$, and so on until we finally choose $y_{r-1} \in |s_{r-1} \cap s_r|$ so that $[y_{r-2}, y_{r-1}] \cap \Phi(f) = \varnothing$ and $[y_{r-1}, x_0] \cap \Phi(f) = x_0$. Applying C.3 a finite number of times, we obtain a deformation f_1 of $|K|$ which agrees with f outside of a neighborhood U of $[x, y_1, \ldots, y_{r-1}, x_0]$ small enough to exclude all fixed points of f other than x and x_0, and whose fixed points on U consist of x_0 and a point $x' \in |\sigma(x_0)|$. By C.2 there is a deformation of $|K|$ which agrees with f_1 outside of U, and whose only fixed

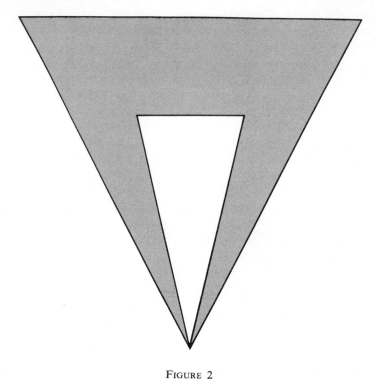

FIGURE 2

point in U is x_0. Applying the same technique to each fixed point of f of nonzero index other than x_0, we end up with a deformation f' of $|K|$ such that all the fixed points of f', except possibly x_0, are of index zero. But in that case,

$$i(|K|, f', x_0) = L(f') = \chi(|K|) = \chi(X) = 0,$$

so a fixed point free deformation g of $|K|$ exists by a finite number of applications of B.4 and III.A.4. ∎

It is clear from the proof above that if X is a polyhedron of type W, it still admits a deformation with a single fixed point, even if $\chi(X) \neq 0$.

Corollary 2. *If X is an n-manifold such that $\chi(X) = 0$, then X admits a fixed point free deformation.*

Proof If $n \geq 3$ then we know that X is of type S (D.3) and therefore of type W, so the result is immediate from Theorem 1. If $n = 2$, take $|K|$ homeomorphic to X. The argument of D.3 still shows that $\partial |St(v)|$ is connected for each vertex v of K, and that each maximal simplex of K is of dimension 2. Thus all 2-manifolds are of type W, so again we apply Theorem 1. There are only two 1-manifolds: I and S^1. We know that $\chi(I) = 1$ and $\chi(S^1) = 0$. In Section II.D we constructed a fixed point free deformation of S^1, so our proof is complete. ∎

The converse of the Lefschetz Deformation Theorem holds for a large class of polyhedra which are not necessarily manifolds.

Corollary 3. *If X is a connected polyhedron such that $\chi(X) = 0$, then $X \times I$ admits a fixed point free deformation.*

Proof It is not difficult to see that $X \times I$ is a polyhedron and that, given a triangulation (K, τ) of X, it can be triangulated so that, if (K', τ') is the triangulation and $t \in K'$, then $(\tau \times 1)^{-1}\tau' |t|$ is a subset of $|s| \times I$ for some $s \in K$ (here 1 denotes the identity map on I). Since maximal simplices of K must be of dimension at least one, a maximal simplex t of K' is of dimension at least two because $(\tau \times 1)^{-1}\tau' |t|$ is open in $|K| \times I$. Identify $|K|$ with the subset $|K| \times 0$ of $|K| \times I$ and define $\pi : |K| \times I \to |K|$ by $\pi(x, r) = x$. If $t, t' \in K'$ are maximal simplices, then $\pi |t|$ and $\pi |t'|$ are geometric realizations of maximal simplices of K; so we can find maximal simplices $s_1, \ldots, s_k$ of K such that $|s_1| = \pi |t|, |s_k| = \pi |t'|$, and $s_i \cap s_{i+1} \neq \varnothing$ for $i = 1, \ldots, k - 1$. The set $s_1, \ldots, s_k$ determines — in a straightforward manner — a set $t_1, \ldots, t_{k'}$ of maximal simplices of K' such that $t_1 = t$, $t_{k'} = t'$, and $t_i \cap t_{i+1}$ is of dimension at least one for $i = 1, \ldots, k' - 1$. Therefore $|K'|$ is strongly connected and hence of type W. We have proved that $X \times I$ is of type W. Define $j : |K| \to |K| \times I$ by $j(x) = (x, 0)$. Clearly

$$j^* : H^*(|K|; Q) \to H^*(|K| \times I; Q)$$

is an isomorphism. Therefore $\chi(X) = 0$ implies that $\chi(X \times I) = 0$. By Theorem 1 there is a fixed point free deformation $f : X \times I \to X \times I$. ∎

F. THE FIXED POINT PROPERTY

As an immediate consequence of the Lefschetz Fixed Point Theorem and Theorems D.1 and D.2, we have the following powerful tools for studying the fixed point property:

Theorem 1.   *Let X be a polyhedron of type S. Then X has the fixed point property if and only if $N(f) \neq 0$ for all maps $f\colon X \to X$.*

Theorem 2.   *Let X be a polyhedron of type S such that $T(X) = \pi_1(X)$. Then X has the fixed point property if and only if $L(f) \neq 0$ for all maps $f\colon X \to X$.*

We will prove a theorem which allows us to build many compact ANRs with the fixed point property.   First we need

Lemma 3.   *Let A be a closed subset of X, a compact ANR, and let $r\colon X \to A$ be a strong deformation retraction (see Section I.H).   Denote by j the inclusion of A in X.   Let $g\colon X \to X$ be any map and define $f = rgj\colon A \to A$.   Then $N(f) = N(g)$.*

Proof   Observe that $rj\colon A \to A$ is the identity map and that jr is homotopic to the identity map on X.   Define $g' = jfr\colon X \to X$.   We claim that $N(g') = N(f)$. Observe that $\Phi(g') = \Phi(f)$.   Suppose x and x' are f-equivalent fixed points; then there is a path C from x to x' in A such that $\{C\} = \{fC\}$, but $rC = C$ and thus $g'C = fC$, which implies that x and x' are g'-equivalent.   Conversely, if x and x' are g'-equivalent fixed points, then there exists a path C in X from x to x' such that $\{C\} = \{g'C\}$, so

$$\{rC\} = \{rg'C\} = \{g'C\} = \{f(rC)\},$$

which means that x and x' are f-equivalent.   Let F be a fixed point class of f and g', and let $F \subset U$, where U is an open set in X such that $\mathrm{cl}(U) \cap \Phi(f) = F$.   By the commutativity axiom,

$$i(X, g', U) = i(X, jfr, U)$$
$$= i(A, frj, j^{-1}(U))$$
$$= i(A, f, U \cap A),$$

which proves that the index of F is the same whether we think of it as a fixed point class of f or as a fixed point class of g'.   We have verified our claim that $N(f) = N(g')$.   Finally, since jr is homotopic to the identity map, $g' = jfr = jrgjr$ is homotopic to g, so $N(g') = N(g)$ by VI.E.4.   ∎

Let $f: X \to Y$ be a map and denote by $M(f)$ the *mapping cylinder* of f, that is, the space obtained from $(X \times I) \cup Y$ by identifying $(x, 0)$ with $f(x)$ for all $x \in X$. If X and Y are compact ANRs, so also is $M(f)$.

Theorem 4.   *Let X be a compact ANR and let Y be a polyhedron of type S which has the fixed point property. If $f: X \to Y$ is any map, then the mapping cylinder $M(f)$ has the fixed point property.*

Proof It is easy to see that there is a stong deformation retraction $r: M(f) \to Y$. Given any map $g: M(f) \to M(f)$, then $N(g) = N(rgj)$ by Lemma 3, where j is the inclusion of Y in $M(f)$. Since Y is a polyhedron of type S with the fixed point property, $N(rgj) \neq 0$ by Theorem 1, so $N(g) \neq 0$ and g has a fixed point. ▌

Since $X \times I$ is the mapping cylinder of the identity map on X, we have

Corollary 5.   *If X is a polyhedron of type S with the fixed point property, then $X \times I$ has the fixed point property.*

For example, if M is an n-manifold, $n \geq 3$, and if M has the fixed point property, then $M \times I$ also has the fixed point property (see the proof of D.3).

Considering Corollary 5, the following question comes immediately to mind:

QUESTION I.   *If X is a polyhedron with the fixed point property, does $X \times I$ have the fixed point property?*

Another way to build new spaces with the fixed point property is the following (the proof is left to the reader):

Let $A \vee B$ be defined as in Section I.M.

Theorem 6.   *If $X = A \vee B$ is a space such that A and B have the fixed point property, then X has the fixed point property.*

One might therefore ask:

QUESTION II.   *If X is a polyhedron and P and Q are subpolyhedra such that $X = P \cup Q$, and if P, Q, and $P \cap Q$ have the fixed point property, does X have the fixed point property?*

Recall from Section II.C that the complex projective spaces CP^{2n} have the fixed point property. We now consider the suspension $\sum CP^{2n}$. The J_2-cohomology is given by

$$H^p(\textstyle\sum CP^{2n}; J_2) = \begin{cases} J_2 & \text{if } p = 0 \\ J_2 & \text{if } p = 2k + 1, \quad k = 1, 2, \ldots, 2n \\ 0 & \text{otherwise.} \end{cases}$$

Furthermore, if we let $\alpha \in H^3(\sum CP^{2n}; J_2)$ be nonzero, then $(Sq^2)^k(\alpha)$ is the nonzero element of $H^{2k+3}(\sum CP^{2n}; J_2)$ for $k = 1, \ldots, 2n - 1$, where $Sq^2 \colon H^r(X; J_2) \to H^{r+2}(X; J_2)$ is the Steenrod square. Let $f \colon \sum CP^{2n} \to \sum CP^{2n}$ be any map. Then $f^*(\alpha) = a\alpha$ and $f^*((Sq^2)^k(\alpha)) = a(Sq^2)^k(\alpha)$ by the naturality of the Steenrod squares. So, as in II.C, $L(f; J_2) \neq 0$ and $\sum CP^{2n}$ *has the fixed point property*. The example suggests the following question:

QUESTION III.   *If X is a polyhedron with the fixed point property, does $\sum X$ have the fixed point property?*

We will now show that the answer to all three questions is "No."

Consider C^n as the subset of C^{n+1} consisting of ordered $(n + 1)$-tuples $(z_1, \ldots, z_n, z_{n+1})$ of complex numbers such that $z_{n+1} = 0$. From the definition of the complex projective spaces we can see that this imbedding of C^n in C^{n+1} gives rise to an imbedding of CP^{n-1} in CP^n. Consider the disjoint union of $CP^1 \times CP^1$, CP^2, and CP^4. Choose $(x_1, x_2) \in CP^1 \times CP^1$. Identify all $x \in CP^1 \subset CP^2$ with $(x, x_2) \in CP^1 \times CP^1$ and all $x' \in CP^1 \subset CP^4$ with $(x_1, x') \in CP^1 \times CP^1$. Call the resulting quotient space X.

The Q-cohomology of X can be described as follows: $H^0(X; Q) \cong Q$ of course. Next we have that $H^p(X; Q) = 0$ if p is odd or $p > 8$. For the remaining $p > 0$, the Betti numbers are

$$b_2(X) = 2, \quad b_4(X) = 3, \quad b_6(X) = 1, \quad b_8(X) = 1.$$

Let α and β generate $H^2(X; Q)$. It can be proved that α and β can be chosen so that α^2, $\alpha \cup \beta$, β^2 is a basis for $H^4(X; Q)$; that β^3 generates $H^6(X; Q)$ and β^4 generates $H^8(X; Q)$; and that

$$\alpha^3 = \alpha^4 = \alpha \cup \beta^2 = \alpha^2 \cup \beta = 0.$$

From the Betti numbers we see that $\chi(X) = 8$.

Let $i \colon CP^4 \to X$ be inclusion and consider $i^* \colon H^2(X; Q) \to H^2(CP^4; Q) \cong Q$. There is a generator $\beta' \in H^2(CP^4; Q)$ such that $i^*(\beta) = \beta'$ and $i^*(\alpha) = 0$. There is a retraction $r \colon X \to CP^2$ defined by sending $CP^1 \times CP^1$ onto $CP^1 \times x_2$ and CP^4 onto (x_1, x_2), and a generator $\alpha' \in H^2(CP^2; Q)$ such that $r^*(\alpha') = \alpha$.

We take $f: X \to X$ to be any map, and we wish to show that $L(f) \neq 0$. Consider $f^*: H^2(X; Q) \to H^2(X; Q)$, then write $f^*(\alpha) = a\alpha + b\beta$ and $f^*(\beta) = c\alpha + d\beta$. Then $\text{Tr}(f^*) = a + d$.

Next, we compute

$$i^* f^* r^*(\alpha') = i^*(a\alpha + b\beta) = b\beta'.$$

Since induced homomorphisms preserve cup products, we therefore know that $i^* f^* r^*(\alpha'^3) = b^3 \beta'^3$. But $\alpha'^3 \in H^6(CP^2; Q) = 0$, so $b^3 \beta'^3 = 0$. Since β' generates $H^2(CP^4; Q)$ then, as we stated in Section II.C, β'^3 generates $H^6(CP^4; Q)$. So it must be that $b = 0$.

In order to compute $L(f)$ we wish to determine the traces of f^* on $H^p(X; Q)$ for $p = 4, 6, 8$. For $H^4(X; Q)$ we use the fact that $b = 0$ to discover that

$$f^*(\alpha^2) = (a\alpha + b\beta)^2 = a^2\alpha^2$$

$$f^*(\alpha \cup \beta) = (a\alpha + b\beta) \cup (c\alpha + d\beta)$$

$$= ac\alpha^2 + ad(\alpha \cup \beta)$$

$$f^*(\beta^2) = (c\alpha + d\beta)^2$$

$$= c^2\alpha^2 + 2cd(\alpha \cup \beta) + d^2\beta^2.$$

The matrix of $f^*: H^4(X; Q) \to H^4(X; Q)$ with respect to the basis α^2, $\alpha \cup \beta$, β^2 is therefore $\begin{bmatrix} a^2 & 0 & 0 \\ ac & ad & 0 \\ c^2 & 2cd & d^2 \end{bmatrix}$.

Because $\alpha^3 = \alpha^4 = \alpha \cup \beta^2 = \alpha^2 \cup \beta = 0$ we have $f^*(\beta^3) = d^3\beta^3$ and $f^*(\beta^4) = d^4\beta^4$, and thus we know the behavior of f^* on $H^6(X; Q)$ and on $H^8(X; Q)$. We find that

$$L(f) = 1 + (a + d) + (a^2 + ad + d^2) + d^3 + d^4$$

$$= \left(a + \frac{1}{2} + \frac{d}{2}\right)^2 + \frac{1}{4}(4d^4 + 4d^3 + 3d^2 + 2d + 3).$$

Define $g: R \to R$ by $g(x) = 4x^4 + 4x^3 + 3x^2 + 2x + 3$. Then $g(x) \geq \frac{5}{2}$ for all $x \in R$, so

$$L(f) = \left(a + \frac{1}{2} + \frac{d}{2}\right)^2 + \frac{g(d)}{4} \geq \frac{5}{8} > 0,$$

and f has a fixed point. We have proved that X has the fixed point property.

The Euler characteristic of ΣCP^{2n}, by the description of $H^*(\Sigma CP^{2n}; J_2)$ above and Exercise 1, is $\chi(\Sigma CP^{2n}) = 1 - 2n$. Let X be the polyhedron of the previous paragraphs and define $Z = X \vee \Sigma CP^8$. Then Z has the fixed point property by Theorem 6 (since X and ΣCP^8 do). But, by I. Ex. 7, $\chi(Z) = 0$, so E.3 tells us that $Z \times I$ fails to have the fixed point property. We have answered Question I.

For Question II, triangulate X and ΣCP^8, take the image of a 1-simplex in each, identify points of the images by means of a homeomorphism, and call the resulting polyhedron Z'. Now X, ΣCP^8, and $X \cap \Sigma CP^8 = I$ all have the fixed point property, but $\chi(Z') = 0$ (I. Ex. 7), and Z' is of type W. So, by E.1, Z' admits a fixed point free deformation which answers Question II in the negative.

Finally, let $Z'' = X \vee \Sigma CP^6$. Then Z'' has the fixed point property by Theorem 6. However, $\chi(Z'') = 2$, so for $\Sigma Z''$, which is a polyhedron of type W, we have $\chi(\Sigma Z'') = 0$ (Exercise 5), and E.1 again implies a negative answer, this time to Question III.

NOTES

As the term "Hopf-Construction" suggests, Theorem A.2 is due to Hopf [28]. It is not known whether the analogous theorem is true for ANRs. The alternate definition of the index of an isolated fixed point, which is worked out in Section B, is essentially the one Hopf used in [28]. A less general form of D.1 was discovered by Wecken [51]; the present result is due to Shi [48]. Corollary D.3 is also true for maps on topological manifolds. This was proved by Brown [12], using earlier work of Weier [52]. Theorem E.1 has a long history. Hopf proved it in 1927 for the case where X is a differentiable manifold [29]. The form of the result given here was first proved by Wecken [51]. There are other, quite different, proofs of E.2 by Brown and Fadell [14], and by Samelson [47]. The counterexamples described in Section F were constructed by Lopez [41]. A counterexample to the nonpolyhedral version of Conjecture I had been demonstrated earlier by Connell [15]. With respect to Conjecture II, Bing has constructed a one-dimensional continuum X (not a polyhedron) with the fixed point property such that there is a disc D meeting X in an arc, and yet $D \cup X$ does not have the fixed point property [2].

For further information on the fixed point property for polyhedra see: E. Fadell, *Some examples in fixed point theory*, Pacific J. Math. **33** (1970), 89–100 and G. Bredon, *Some examples for the fixed point property*, to appear.*

* This paragraph added by author at time of proofreading.

EXERCISES

1. Let K be a simplicial complex and define $b_p(K; J_2)$ to be the dimension of $H^p(K; J_2)$ as a vector space over J_2. Prove that $\chi(K) = \sum_{p \in J} (-1)^p b_p(K; J_2)$.

2. An n-manifold X is *closed* if, for each $x \in X$, there is a neighborhood of x homeomorphic to R^n. If X is a closed n-manifold, the Poincaré Duality Theorem states that $b_p(X; J_2) = b_{n-p}(X; J_2)$ for all $p = 0$, $1, \ldots, n$. Prove that, if X is a closed n-manifold, n odd, then X admits a fixed point free deformation.

3. Prove that, if $|K|$ is a connected geometric complex (other than a point), then $\Sigma |K|$ is of type W.

4. Prove Theorem F.2.

5. For a polyhedron X, define $\Sigma^0 X = X$, $\Sigma^1 X = \Sigma X$, and in general $\Sigma^{n+1} X = \Sigma(\Sigma^n X)$. Prove that $\chi(\Sigma^{2n} X) = \chi(X)$ and $\chi(\Sigma^{2n+1} X) = 2 - \chi(X)$ for all $n \geq 0$.

6. Two spaces X and Y are of the *same homotopy type* if there exist maps $a: X \to Y$ and $b: Y \to X$ such that ba and ab are homotopic to identity maps. Prove that, if X and Y are polyhedra of type S, and if X and Y are of the same homotopy type, then X has the fixed point property if and only if Y has the fixed point property.

7. Give an example of polyhedra X and Y of the same homotopy type such that X has the fixed point property but Y does not.

8. Prove that if $X \times Y$ has the fixed point property, so do X and Y.

9. Prove that, if ΣX has the fixed point property, then X also has the fixed point property

10. Give an example of a polyhedron $X = P \cup Q$ (P and Q subpolyhedra), with $P - Q$ and $Q - P$ both nonempty — such that X has the fixed point property — but none of P, Q, or $P \cap Q$ have the fixed point property.

11. Give an example of a polyhedron X with the fixed point property such that $X \times X$ fails to have the fixed point property.

Dold's Lemma

We will be concerned with the following diagram (Figure 1) where $X \subset U \subseteq R^n$, X is a connected polyhedron, and U is open. The maps j and k are inclusions. For $\mu_n \in H^n(R^n, R^n - 0)$ and $\nu_n \in H^n(S^n)$ (the generators defined in Section IV.B) let $\epsilon(z) = \mu_n \otimes z$ for $z \in H^r(U)$, and for $z' \in H^r(X)$ let $\epsilon^{-1}(\nu_n \otimes z') = z'$. Let $a: (U, U - X) \times X \to (R^n, R^n - 0)$ be given by $a(u, x) = u - x$. The definitions of t and Δ are the same as in Section I.M. The symbol "1" denotes the identity isomorphism. The homomorphism $\Phi_{(XU)}$ is defined to make the diagram commute.

It may appear that the diagram makes somewhat less than complete sense because, for example, $a^*(H^n(R^n, R^n - 0))$ is a subgroup of

$$\bigoplus_{p+q=n} H^p(U, U - X) \otimes H^q(X)$$

rather than a subgroup of just $H^{n-r}(U, U - X) \otimes H^r(X)$. But

$$(1 \otimes t^*)(H^p(U, U - X) \otimes H^q(X) \otimes H^r(U))$$
$$= H^p(U, U - X) \otimes H^r(U) \otimes H^q(X),$$

while $\Delta^*(H^p(U, U - X) \otimes H^r(U)) = 0$ unless $p = n - r$, so we are only leaving out of the direct sum those terms which will be annihilated later in

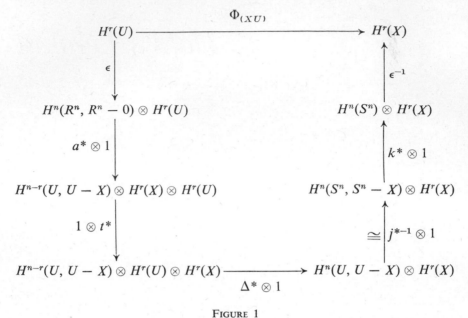

FIGURE 1

the composition anyway. Similarly, the domain of $\Delta^* \otimes 1$ is really

$$\bigoplus_{p+q=n} H^p(U, U - X) \otimes H^q(U) \otimes H^r(X),$$

but the only part of the domain which is in the image of $(1 \otimes t^*)(a^* \otimes 1)$ is $H^{n-r}(U, U - X) \otimes H^r(U) \otimes H^r(X)$, so we omit the other terms of the direct sum.

The result which it is the purpose of this appendix to prove is as simple to state as it is complicated to verify.

Theorem 1. *Let $i_{XU}: X \to U$ be inclusion and let r be any integer. Then*

$$\Phi_{(XU)} = i^*_{(XU)}: H^r(U) \to H^r(X).$$

Let X' be a closed subset of X and let U' be an open subset of R^n containing U. We claim that

$$\Phi_{(XU)} i^*_{(UU')} = \Phi_{(XU')} \tag{1}$$

$$i^*_{(X'X)} \Phi_{(X'U)} = \Phi_{(X'U)}. \tag{1'}$$

The proof in each case is immediate from the corresponding commutative diagram below (Figures 2 and 3, respectively). The unlabeled homomorphisms are all inclusion induced.

We can draw the following conclusions from (1) and (1'). Suppose that we could show that $\Phi_{(XU)} = i^*_{(XU)}$. Then by (1) we would have $\Phi_{(XU')} = i^*_{(XU)}i^*_{(UU')}$. But $i_{(UU')}i_{(XU)} = i_{(XU')}$, so

$$\text{if} \quad \Phi_{(XU)} = i^*_{(XU)} \quad \text{then} \quad \Phi_{(XU')} = i^*_{(XU')}. \tag{2}$$

Similarly, by (1'),

$$\text{if} \quad \Phi_{(XU)} = i^*_{(XU)} \quad \text{then} \quad \Phi_{(X'U)} = i^*_{(X'U)}. \tag{3}$$

If it were true that $\Phi_{(XU')} = i^*_{(XU')}$, then, by (1), we would have $\Phi_{(XU)}i^*_{(UU')} = i^*_{(XU')}$. Using the fact that $i^*_{(XU')} = i^*_{(XU)}i^*_{(UU')}$, we obtain

$$\text{if} \quad \Phi_{(XU')} = i^*_{(XU')} \quad \text{then} \quad [\Phi_{(XU)} - i^*_{(XU)}]i^*_{(UU')} = 0. \tag{4}$$

In other words, the homomorphisms $\Phi_{(XU)}$ and $i^*_{(XU)}$ are identical on $i^*_{(UU')}(H^r(U')) \subseteq H^r(U)$. A similar argument using (1') in place of (1) proves

$$\text{if} \quad \Phi_{(X'U)} = i^*_{(X'U)} \quad \text{then} \quad i^*_{(X'X)}[\Phi_{(XU)} - i^*_{(XU)}] = 0. \tag{5}$$

Another way of stating (5) is to say that the image of the homomorphism

$$[\Phi_{(XU)} - i^*_{(XU)}]: H^r(U) \to H^r(X)$$

is contained in the kernel of $i^*_{(X'X)}$. Thus, if we knew that $i^*_{(X'X)}$ were one-to-one, then $\Phi_{(X'U)} = i^*_{(X'U)}$ would imply that $\Phi_{(XU)}$ and $i^*_{(XU)}$ were identical.

The rest of the proof is accomplished in six steps:

STEP 1.   Assume that X is the point $0 \in R^n$ and let $V = \{x \in R^n \mid |x| < \beta\}$, where $\beta > 0$ is chosen small enough so that $0 \in V \subseteq U$. The only nontrivial homomorphisms occur when $r = 0$. If we consider the composition

$$(V, V - 0) \times 0 \xrightarrow{\Delta \times 1} (V, V - 0) \times V \times 0 \xrightarrow{1 \times t}$$

$$(V, V - 0) \times 0 \times V \xrightarrow{a \times 1} (R^n, R^n - 0) \times V,$$

then we see that $(a \times 1)(1 \times t)(\Delta \times 1)(v, 0) = (v, v)$ for all $v \in V$. The composition is therefore homotopic in $(V, V - 0) \times V$ to the inclusion map $b: (V, V - 0) \times 0 \to (R^n, R^n - 0) \times V$. Since it is clear that the diagram

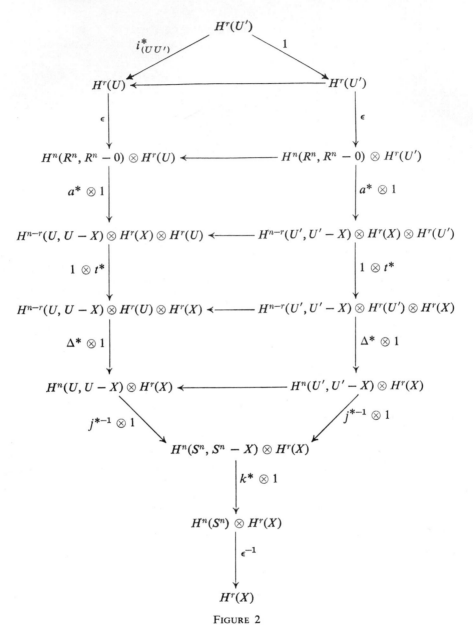

Figure 2

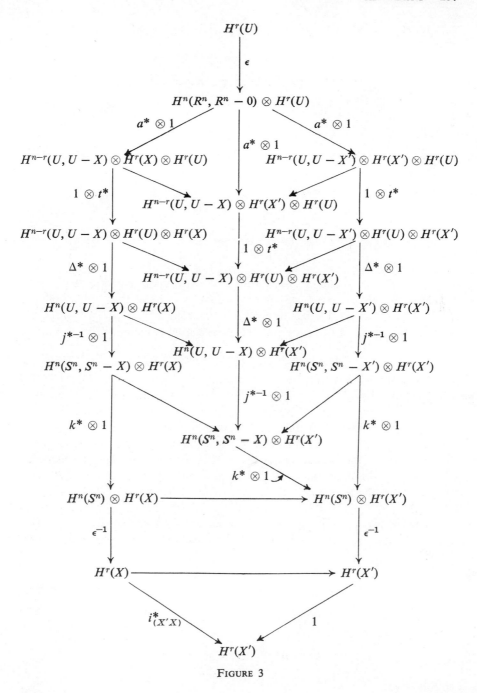

FIGURE 3

commutes, we see that $i^*_{(OV)} = \Phi_{(OV)}$. The fact that $i^*_{(OU)} = \Phi_{(OU)}$ is immediate from (2).

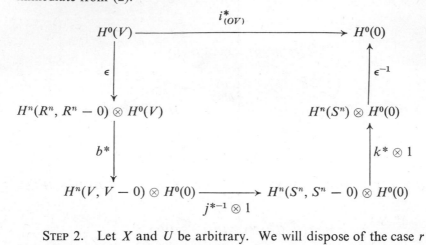

STEP 2. Let X and U be arbitrary. We will dispose of the case $r = 0$. Let $X' = 0 \in R^n$. Then by Step 1 we have $\Phi_{(X'U)} = i^*_{(X'U)}$. So by (5) $i^*_{(X'X)}[\Phi_{(XU)} - i^*_{(XU)}] = 0$. Since X is connected, $i^*_{(X'X)} : H^0(X) \to H^0(X')$ is an isomorphism, and so, in particular, its kernel is trivial. Therefore

$$\Phi_{(XU)} = i^*_{(XU)} : H^0(U) \to H^0(X).$$

We assume for the rest of the proof that $r \geq 1$.

STEP 3. Let $B^{n-r} = \{x \in R^{n-r} \mid |x| < 1\}$. Assume that U is homeomorphic to $S^r \times B^{n-r}$ by a homeomorphism that takes X onto $S^r \times q$ for some $q \in B^{n-r}$. Assume further that there is a point $p \in S^r$ and a neighborhood V of (p, q) in R^n so that $V \cap (S^r \times q)$ and $V \cap (p \times B^{n-r})$ are contained in orthogonal linear subspaces of R^n. There is no less of generality (by changing the coordinates of R^n) in assuming that $(p, q) = 0 \in R^n$ and that, if $x \in V \cap (S^r \times q) \subset R^n$, then $x = (x_1, \ldots, x_r, 0, \ldots, 0)$, while, if $y \in V \cap (p \times B^{n-r}) \subset R^n$, then $y = (0, \ldots, 0, y_{r+1}, \ldots, y_n)$ (see Figure 4).

The definition of $\Phi_{(XU)}$ in this special case is given by Figure 5. The maps Δ_1 and Δ_2 are diagonal maps. Subdiagram (1) commutes because the diagram

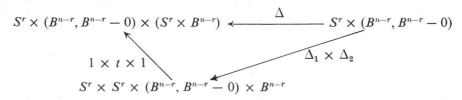

commutes.

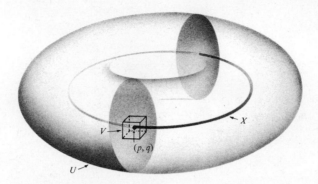

FIGURE 4

If we consider the composition

$$H^{n-r}(R^{n-r}, R^{n-r} - 0) \otimes H^r(S^r) \xrightarrow{\quad j^{*-1} \quad}$$

$$H^n(S^n, S^n - 0) \xrightarrow{\quad k^* \quad} H^n(S^n),$$

then it follows from the definition of the generators $\mu_p \in H^p(R^p, R^p - 0)$ and $\nu_q \in H^q(S^q)$ in Section IV.B that $k^*j^{*-1}(\mu_{n-r} \otimes \nu_r) = \nu_n$. The homeomorphism $h\colon B^{n-r} \to R^{n-r}$ given by $h(x) = \dfrac{x}{1 - |x|}$ induces an isomorphism

$$h^*\colon H^{n-r}(R^{n-r}, R^{n-r} - 0) \to H^{n-r}(B^{n-r}, B^{n-r} - 0).$$

Define a generator

$$\mu'_{n-r} = h^*(\mu_{n-r}) \in H^{n-r}(B^{n-r}, B^{n-r} - 0).$$

Consider the map

$$a\colon [S^r \times (B^{n-r}, B^{n-r} - 0)] \times S^r \to (R^n, R^n - 0).$$

In order to find out how a^* behaves it is sufficient, by excision, to look at its restriction to V. Because of the way we defined V, a is the same on that set as the map from R^n to itself which takes a point $(x_1, \dots, x_n) \in R^n$ to the point $(-x_1, \dots, -x_r, x_{r+1}, \dots, x_n)$. Thus a^* is a composition of r homomorphisms from $H^n(R^n, R^n - 0)$ to itself — each of which takes an element to its

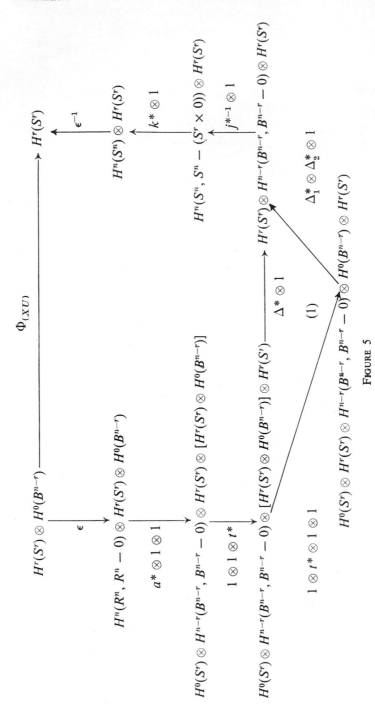

FIGURE 5

own inverse (see Section I.M). In order words a^* is just multiplication by $(-1)^r$. In particular,

$$a^*(\mu_n) = (-1)^r 1 \otimes \mu'_{n-r} \otimes \nu_r.$$

To see what $\Phi_{(XU)}$ does, we first compute

$$\begin{aligned}
&(\Delta^* \otimes 1)(1 \otimes 1 \otimes t^*)(a^* \otimes 1 \otimes 1)\epsilon(\nu_r \otimes 1)\\
&\quad = (\Delta^* \otimes 1)(1 \otimes 1 \otimes t^*)(a^* \otimes 1 \otimes 1)(\mu_n \otimes (\nu_r \otimes 1))\\
&\quad = (-1)^r(\Delta^* \otimes 1)(1 \otimes 1 \otimes t^*)(1 \otimes \mu'_{n-r} \otimes \nu_r \otimes (\nu_r \otimes 1))\\
&\quad = (-1)^r(-1)^{r^2}(\Delta^* \otimes 1)(1 \otimes \mu'_{n-r} \otimes (\nu_r \otimes 1) \otimes \nu_r)\\
&\quad = (-1)^{r+r^2}(\Delta_1^* \otimes \Delta_2^* \otimes 1)(1 \otimes t^* \otimes 1 \otimes 1)(1 \otimes \mu'_{n-r} \otimes \nu_r \otimes 1 \otimes \nu_r)\\
&\quad = (-1)^{r+r^2}(-1)^{r(n-r)}(\Delta_1^* \otimes \Delta_2^* \otimes 1)(1 \otimes \nu_r \otimes \mu'_{n-r} \otimes 1 \otimes \nu_r)\\
&\quad = (-1)^{r+r^2+r(n-r)}(\nu_r \otimes \mu'_{n-r} \otimes \nu_r).
\end{aligned}$$

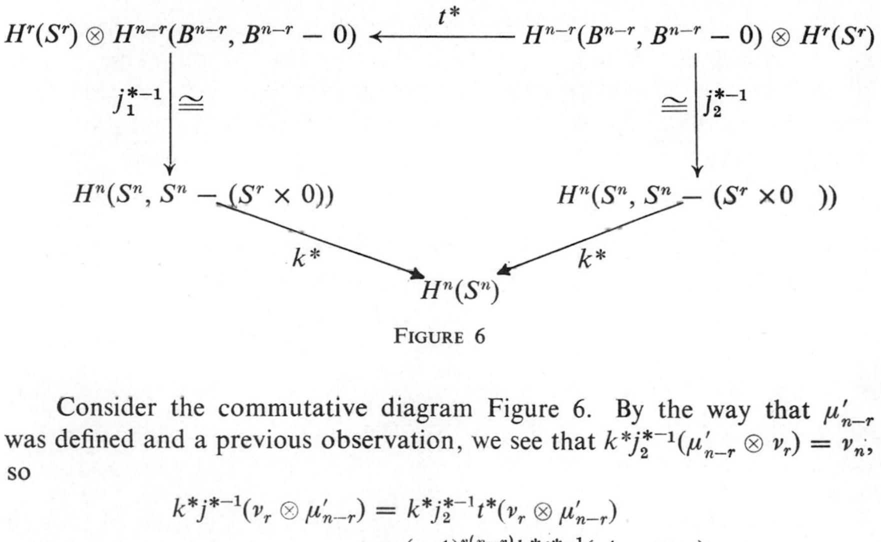
$H^r(S^r) \otimes H^{n-r}(B^{n-r}, B^{n-r} - 0)$
t^*
$H^{n-r}(B^{n-r}, B^{n-r} - 0) \otimes H^r(S^r)$
j_1^{*-1} $\cong$
$\cong$ j_2^{*-1}
$H^n(S^n, S^n - (S^r \times 0))$
$H^n(S^n, S^n - (S^r \times 0))$
k^*
k^*
$H^n(S^n)$

FIGURE 6

Consider the commutative diagram Figure 6. By the way that μ'_{n-r} was defined and a previous observation, we see that $k^*j_2^{*-1}(\mu'_{n-r} \otimes \nu_r) = \nu_n$, so

$$\begin{aligned}
k^*j^{*-1}(\nu_r \otimes \mu'_{n-r}) &= k^*j_2^{*-1}t^*(\nu_r \otimes \mu'_{n-r})\\
&= (-1)^{r(n-r)}k^*j_2^{*-1}(\mu'_{n-r} \otimes \nu_r)\\
&= (-1)^{r(n-r)}\nu_n.
\end{aligned}$$

Finally, we have

$$\begin{aligned}
\Phi_{(XU)}(\nu_r \otimes 1) &= \epsilon^{-1}(k^* \otimes 1)(j^{*-1} \otimes 1)(\Delta^* \otimes 1)\\
&\qquad (1 \otimes 1 \otimes t^*)(a^* \otimes 1 \otimes 1)\epsilon(\nu_r \otimes 1)\\
&= (-1)^{r+r^2+r(n-r)}\epsilon^{-1}(k^*j^{*-1} \otimes 1)(\nu_r \otimes \mu'_{n-r} \otimes \nu_r)\\
&= (-1)^{r+r^2+r(n-r)}(-1)^{r(n-r)}\epsilon^{-1}(\nu_n \otimes \nu_r)\\
&= (-1)^{r+r^2+2r(n-r)}\nu_r.
\end{aligned}$$

But $r + r^2 + 2r(n - r)$ is even, so $\Phi_{(XU)}(v_r \otimes 1) = v_r$. On the other hand, if $i_{(XU)}: S^r \to S^r \times B^{n-r}$ is inclusion, then $i^*_{(XU)}(v_r \otimes 1) = v_r$ also. We have completed the proof that $\Phi_{(XU)} = i^*_{(XU)}$ in this case, because it is sufficient to show that the homomorphisms agree on a generator of $H^r(S^r) \cong Q$.

STEP 4.   Let $|\sigma(n)^r|$ be the geometric realization of the r-skeleton of $\sigma(n)$, the simplicial complex with $n + 1$ vertices such that $|\sigma(n)|$ is homeomorphic to an n-cell. Let S^r be the boundary of the geometric realization of an $(r + 1)$-simplex of $\sigma(n)$. Denote by $\delta > 0$ the infimum of the set $\{d(x, y) \mid x \in |\sigma(n)^r|, y \in R^n - U\}$ (U is an open set containing $X = |\sigma(n)^r|$). Define $W = \{x \in R^n \mid d(x, S^r) < \delta\}$. Then W is an open subset of U homeomorphic to $S^r \times B^{n-r}$. We can apply Step 3 to conclude that $\Phi_{(S^rW)} = i^*_{(S^rW)}$. Therefore, by (2), $\Phi_{(S^rU)} = i^*_{(S^rU)}$, which by (5) implies that

$$i^*_{(S^r|\sigma(n)^r|)}[\Phi_{(|\sigma(n)^r|U)} - i^*_{(|\sigma(n)^r|U)}] = 0: H^r(U) \to H^r(S^r)$$

for the boundary S^r of each $(r + 1)$-simplex in $|\sigma(n)|$.

From Section I.M we have that $H^r(\sigma(n)^r) = \bigoplus H^r(S^r)$, where there is a term in the direct sum for each $(r + 1)$-simplex in $\sigma(n)$. We also know how $i^*_{(S^n|\sigma(n)^r|)}$ behaves. Let $\alpha_1, \ldots, \alpha_p$ be a basis for $H^r(U)$, and let $\beta_1, \ldots, \beta_m$ be generators for $H^r(\sigma(n)^r)$ corresponding to the various S^r. Let $i^*_j: H^r(\sigma(n)^r) \to H^r(S^r)$ be the homomorphism such that $i^*_j(\beta_k) = 0$ if $k \neq j$ and $i^*_j(\beta_j) = \beta_j$. Now write, for $1 \leq s \leq p$,

$$\Phi_{(|\sigma(n)^r|U)}(\alpha_s) = a_1\beta_1 + \cdots + a_m\beta_m$$
$$i^*_{(|\sigma(n)^r|U)}(\alpha_s) = b_1\beta_1 + \cdots + b_m\beta_m.$$

We know that, for $j = 1, \ldots, m$,

$$0 = i^*_j[\Phi_{(|\sigma(n)^r|U)} - i^*_{(|\sigma(n)^r|U)}] = i^*_j[(a_1 - b_1)\beta_1 + \cdots + (a_m - b_m)\beta_m]$$
$$= (a_j - b_j)\beta_j.$$

So $a_j = b_j$, which implies $\Phi_{(|\sigma(n)^r|U)}(\alpha_s) = i^*_{(|\sigma(n)^r|U)}(\alpha_s)$. Since $i^*_{(|\sigma(n)^r|U)}$ and $\Phi_{(|\sigma(n)^r|U)}$ agree on a basis for $H^r(U)$, we must conclude that $i^*_{(|\sigma(n)^r|U)} = \Phi_{(|\sigma(n)^r|U)}$.

STEP 5.   Let $X = |K|$, where K is a subcomplex of $\sigma(n)^r$, and let U be an arbitrary open set in R^n containing $|K|$. Since $\sigma(n)^r$ contains no $(r + 1)$-simplex, then, $C_{r+1}(\sigma(n)^r) = 0$. As a consequence, by the Identification Theorem (Section I.L), $H^{r+1}(|\sigma(n)^r|, |K|) = 0$. If we look at the exact sequence of the pair $(|\sigma(n)^r|, |K|)$, we have

$$H^r(|\sigma(n)^r|) \xrightarrow{i^*_{(|K|,|\sigma(n)^r|)}} H^r(|K|) \to H^r(|\sigma(n)^r|, |K|) = 0.$$

So $i^*_{(|K|),|\sigma(n)^r|)}$ is onto.

As we observed in I.H, there is a regular neighborhood of $|\sigma(n)^r|$ in $|\sigma(n)|$ and a strong deformation retraction of it onto $|\sigma(n)^n|$. Since $|\sigma(n)|$

is obviously a strong deformation retract of R^n, there is, therefore, an open set V in U and a strong deformation retraction $\rho_{(V|\sigma(n)^r|)}\colon V \to |\sigma(n)^r|$. Similarly, there is an open subset W of V and a strong deformation retraction $\rho_{(W|K|)}\colon W \to |K|$.

The diagram

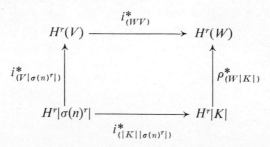

commutes, because $\rho^*_{(W|K|)} = i^{*-1}_{(W|K|)}$. Since $i^*_{(V|\sigma(n)^r|)}$ and $\rho^*_{(W|K|)}$ are isomorphisms and we have shown that $i^*_{(|K||\sigma(n)^r|)}$ is onto, we have now proved that $i^*_{(WV)}$ is also onto.

Step 4 states that $\Phi_{(|\sigma(n)^r|V)} = i^*_{(|\sigma(n)^r|V)}$; so by (3), $\Phi_{(|K|V)} = i^*_{(|K|V)}$. Hence (4) implies that $[\Phi_{(|K|W)} - i^*_{(|K|W)}]i^*_{(WV)} = 0$, that is, that $\Phi_{(|K|W)}$ and $i^*_{(|K|W)}$ agree on the image of $i^*_{(WV)}$. We just proved that $i^*_{(WV)}$ is onto, so $\Phi_{(|K|W)} = i^*_{(|K|W)}$. The fact that $\Phi_{(|K|U)} = i^*_{(|K|U)}$ is now immediate from (2).

Step 6. Let X be any polyhedron, let (K, τ) be a triangulation of X, and take any $r \geq 1$. We identify $|K|$ with $X \subset U \subseteq R^n$. Let $|K^r|$ be the geometric realization of the r-skeleton of K. Now K is contained in $\sigma(n)$ and K^r is a subcomplex of $\sigma(n)^r$. It is obvious that $C_r(K^r) = C_r(K)$, so $H^r(|K|, |K^r|)$ is trivial. Thus, if we look at the exact sequence of the pair $(|K|, |K^r|)$, we have

$$0 = H^r(|K|, |K^r|) \to H^r(|K^r|) \xrightarrow{i^*_{(|K^r||K|)}} H^r(|K^r|),$$

which means that $i^*_{(|K^r||K|)}$ is one-to-one.

Step 5 tells us that $\Phi_{(|K^r|U)} = i^*_{(|K^r|U)}$, so by (5), $i^*_{(|K^r||K|)}[\Phi_{(|K|U)} - i^*_{(|K|U)}] = 0$. But $i^*_{(|K^r||K|)}$ is one-to-one, so $\Phi_{(|K|U)} = i^*_{(|K|U)}$. Having identified $|K|$ with X (by means of the homeomorphism τ) this completes the proof of the theorem since it follows that

$$\Phi_{(XU)} = i^*_{(XU)}\colon H^r(U) \to H^r(X).$$

Uniqueness of the Index

We proved in Chapters IV and V the fact that there exists an index on the collection $\mathscr{C}_A$ of ANRs, that is, there is a function $i: \mathscr{C}'_A \to Q$ with the properties described in the five axioms stated in Section IV.A. Our goal is to prove that the index is unique. In other words, if $i, i': \mathscr{C}'_A \to Q$ are functions for which the axioms are true, and if (X, f, U) is any triple in $\mathscr{C}'_A$, then $i(X, f, U)$ and $i'(X, f, U)$ are the same rational number.

The method used in the proof of uniqueness is rather like the one we employed to prove existence. First, we will show that the index $i: \mathscr{C}'_C \to Q$ on the collection of all connected geometric complexes is unique; we then make use of this information, together with the Domination Theorem, to prove uniqueness on the larger collection of all connected ANRs.

A. UNIQUENESS ON GEOMETRIC COMPLEXES

Define by $\mathscr{C}'_C$ the collection of all triples $(|K|, f, U)$, where $|K|$ is a connected geometric complex, $f: |K| \to |K|$ is a map, and U is an open subset of $|K|$ such that $\Phi(f) \cap \partial U = \varnothing$. Assume that $i: \mathscr{C}'_C \to Q$ is a function which has the properties described by the five axioms for a fixed point index listed in Section IV.A. We will show how to compute $i(|K|, f, U)$ directly from the axioms. That will certainly imply that the fixed point index is unique.

Given a space X and a function $f: X \to R^n$, we will always denote by the corresponding capital letter $F: X \to R^n$ the function such that $F(x) = x - f(x)$ for all $x \in X$. Let $\mathbf{0}$ denote the origin in R^n.

Lemma 1. *If U is an open subset of R^n containing $\mathbf{0}$ and $f: U \to R^n$ is a linear function whose only fixed point is $\mathbf{0}$, then $\mathbf{J}F(\mathbf{0})$, the jacobian of F at $\mathbf{0}$, is not zero.*

Proof Suppose that $\mathbf{J}F(\mathbf{0}) = 0$. Since f is linear on U and $f(\mathbf{0}) = \mathbf{0}$, there exists a linear transformation $g: R^n \to R^n$ such that $g(x) = f(x)$ for all $x \in U$. We observe that $G: R^n \to R^n$ is also a linear transformation; so, letting dG denote the differential of G, we have $dG(x) = G$ for all $x \in R^n$. Since G is identical with F in a neighborhood of $\mathbf{0}$, the determinant of G is

$$\det(G) = \mathbf{J}G(\mathbf{0}) = \mathbf{J}F(\mathbf{0}) = 0$$

and G is a singular linear transformation. Therefore there exists a vector subspace S of R^n of dimension at least one such that $G(S) = \mathbf{0}$. Thus, for $x \in S \cap U$, we have

$$\mathbf{0} = G(x) = x - g(x) = x - f(x),$$

which means that the points of $S \cap U$ are fixed points of f, in contradiction to the hypothesis that $\mathbf{0}$ is the only fixed point. ∎

The reader may easily verify (compare IV. Ex. 5)

Lemma 2. *If $0 \in (a, b) \subset R^1, f: [a, b] \to [a, b]$ is differentiable at 0, $f(0) = 0$ and $F'(0) > 0$, then there exists $\epsilon > 0$ and a homotopy $H: I \to \mathrm{Map}([a, b], [a, b])$ such that $H(0) = f$, $H(1)$ maps $[a, b]$ to 0 and $H(t)(\epsilon) \neq \epsilon$, $H(t)(-\epsilon) \neq -\epsilon$ for all $t \in I$.*

If $r \neq 0$ is a real number, define $\alpha(r) = \dfrac{r}{|r|}$. Note that we may identify a closed interval $[a, b] \subset R^1$ with the geometric complex $|\sigma(1)|$.

Lemma 3. *Let $0 \in (a, b) \subset R^1$. Let $f: [a, b] \to [a, b]$ be a map differentiable at 0, $f(0) = 0$, and $F'(0) \neq 0$. If $i: \mathscr{C}'_C \to Q$ is any index, then $i([a, b], f, (-\epsilon, \epsilon)) = \alpha(F'(0))$ for a sufficiently small $\epsilon > 0$.*

Proof If $F'(0) > 0$, then, using Lemma 2 and the homotopy, additivity and normalization axioms,

$$
\begin{aligned}
i([a, b], f, (-\epsilon, \epsilon)) &= i([a, b], H(1), (-\epsilon, \epsilon)) \\
&= i([a, b], H(1), [a, b]) \\
&= L(H(1)).
\end{aligned}
$$

Since $[a, b]$ is contractible, then $L(H(1)) = 1$ (see Section II.C). If $F'(0) < 0$, then there exists $\epsilon > 0$ such that $f(-\epsilon) < -\epsilon$ and $f(\epsilon) > \epsilon$. Define a map

$g: [a, b] \to [a, b]$ as follows: If $x \in [-\epsilon, \epsilon]$, let $g(x) = f(x)$. Choose $c \in (\epsilon, f(\epsilon))$, define $g(f(\epsilon)) = c$, and extend g linearly over $[\epsilon, f(\epsilon)]$. Finally, extend g over $[a, b]$. By the additivity axiom,

$$i([a, b], g, (-\epsilon, f(\epsilon))) = i([a, b], g, (-\epsilon, \epsilon)) + i([a, b], g, (\epsilon, f(\epsilon))).$$

Since $g(\epsilon) > \epsilon$ and $g(f(\epsilon)) < f(\epsilon)$, an argument like the one in the first part of the proof shows that $i([a, b], g, (\epsilon, f(\epsilon))) = 1$. Next, observe that $g(-\epsilon) < -\epsilon$ and $g(f(\epsilon)) < f(\epsilon)$. So, choosing $e \in (g(-\epsilon), -\epsilon)$, the homotopy $H(t)(x) = (1 - t)g(x) + te$ (for $x \in [a, b]$) has the following properties: $H(0) = g$, $H(1)$ is the constant map at e, and $H(t)(-\epsilon) \neq -\epsilon$ and $H(t)(f(\epsilon)) \neq f(\epsilon)$ for all $t \in I$. Therefore, by the homotopy axiom,

$$i([a, b], g, (-\epsilon, f(\epsilon))) = i([a, b], H(1), (-\epsilon, f(\epsilon))).$$

However, $H(1)$ has no fixed points on $[-\epsilon, f(\epsilon)]$. So, by the additivity axiom, $i([a, b], H(1), (-\epsilon, f(\epsilon))) = 0$. Consequently, $i([a, b], g, (-\epsilon, \epsilon)) = -1$ and, by the localization axiom, $i([a, b], f, (-\epsilon, \epsilon)) = -1$. ∎

Lemma 4. *Suppose, for $j = 1, 2$, that $0 \in (a_j, b_j) \subset R^1$, $f_j: [a_j, b_j] \to [a_j, b_j]$ is differentiable at 0, $f_j(0) = 0$, and $F_j'(0) < 0$. Let $X = [a_1, b_1] \times [a_2, b_2]$. There exists $\epsilon > 0$ and a homotopy $H: I \to \mathrm{Map}(X, X)$ such that $H(0) = f_1 \times f_2$, $H(1)$ is the constant map at 0, and $H(t)(p) \neq p$ for $t \in I$ and all p on the boundary of $V = [-\epsilon, \epsilon] \times [-\epsilon, \epsilon] \subseteq X$.*

Proof The hypothesis $F_j'(0) < 0$ implies that there exists $\epsilon > 0$ such that $f_j(x) > x$ for $0 < x \leq \epsilon$ and $f_j(x) < x$ when $-\epsilon \leq x < 0$. Let B_ϵ denote the closed ball in R^2 of radius ϵ centered at 0 and let $S_\epsilon = \partial B_\epsilon$. Define $r: V \to B_\epsilon$ to be the retraction such that, if $p \notin B_\epsilon$, then $r(p)$ is the point where the ray from 0 through p intersects S_ϵ. Define $s: B_\epsilon \to V$ to be radial projection. If $p \in B_\epsilon$ then $p = \gamma e^{i\theta}$ for some $\gamma \in [0, \epsilon]$ and $\theta \in [0, 2\pi)$. For a real number t, define $\rho_t: B_\epsilon \to B_\epsilon$ to be the rotation $\rho_t(\gamma e^{i\theta}) = \gamma e^{i(\theta + t\pi)}$. Finally, define $H: I \to \mathrm{Map}(V, X)$ as follows

$$H(t)(p) = \begin{cases} (f_1 \times f_2) s \rho_t r(p) & \text{if } 0 \leq t \leq \frac{1}{2} \\ 2(1 - t)H(\frac{1}{2})(p) & \text{if } \frac{1}{2} \leq t \leq 1 \end{cases}$$

and extend H to a map $H: I \to \mathrm{Map}(X, X)$ so that $H(0) = f_1 \times f_2$ and $H(1)$ is constant. ∎

Note that, if X and Y are geometric complexes, then $X \times Y$ is not, strictly speaking, a geometric complex, but it is a polyhedron and there is obviously a standard way to identify $X \times Y$ with a geometric complex.

Lemma 5. *Let X and Y be geometric complexes. If $f: X \rightarrow X$ is a map, U is open in X such that $\Phi(f) \cap \mathrm{cl}(U)$ is a single point $x_0 \in U$ and if $k: Y \rightarrow Y$ is the map such that $k(Y) = y_0$, then $i(X \times Y, f \times k, U \times Y) = i(X, f, U)$ for any index i on $\mathscr{C}_C$.*

Proof Define $\pi: X \times Y \rightarrow X$ to be projection and let $j: X \rightarrow X \times Y$ be given by $j(x) = (x, y_0)$. By the commutativity axiom,

$$i(X \times Y, f \times k, U \times Y) = i(X \times Y, j\pi(f \times k), U \times Y)$$
$$= i(X, \pi(f \times k)j, j^{-1}(U \times Y))$$
$$= i(X, f, U). \quad \blacksquare$$

Lemma 6. *For $j = 1, \ldots, n$, let $0 \in (a_j, b_j) \subset R^1$ and $f_j: [a_j, b_j] \rightarrow [a_j, b_j]$ be maps differentiable at 0, and let $f_j(0) = 0$ and $F'_j(0) \neq 0$. Let $X = \prod_{j=1}^{n} [a_j, b_j] \subset R^n$ and $f = f_1 \times \cdots \times f_n: X \rightarrow X$. If U is a neighborhood of 0 in R^n such that $\Phi(f) \cap \mathrm{cl}(U) = 0$, then we have $i(X, f, U) = \alpha(\mathbf{J}F(0))$ for $i: \mathscr{C}'_C \rightarrow Q$ any fixed point index.*

Proof Certainly,

$$\mathbf{J}F(0) = F'_1(0)F'_2(0) \cdots F'_n(0).$$

By the commutativity axiom, $i(X, f, U)$ is independent of the ordering of the $f_j's$, so assume $F'_j(0)$ is negative for $j = 1, \ldots, m$ and positive for $j = m + 1, \ldots, n$ (where it may be that $m = 0$ or $m = n$). Thus we see that $\alpha(\mathbf{J}F(0)) = (-1)^m$. Write $m = 2r + \delta$, where $\delta = 0$ or $\delta = 1$. Applying Lemma 2 $n - m$ times and then applying Lemma 4 r times, we obtain $\epsilon > 0$ and a homotopy $H: I \rightarrow \mathrm{Map}(X, X)$ such that $H(0) = f$, $H(1)(X) = 0$ if $\delta = 0$, and $H(1) = f_1 \times k$; where k maps $\prod_{j=2}^{n} [a_j, b_j]$ to $0 \in R^{n-1}$, if $\delta = 1$ and $H(t)(p) \neq p$ for p on the boundary of $U = (-\epsilon, \epsilon) \times \cdots \times (-\epsilon, \epsilon)$. Thus, if m is even, $i(X, f, U) = i(X, H(1), U) = 1$ by the homotopy, additivity, and normalization axioms, and by the fact that X is contractible. If m is odd,

$$i(X, f, U) = i(X, f_1 \times k, U)$$
$$= i([a_1, b_1], f_1, (-\epsilon, \epsilon)) = -1$$

by the homotopy axiom, and by Lemma 5 and Lemma 3. In either case, $i(X, f, U) = (-1)^m$. $\quad \blacksquare$

Lemma 7. *Suppose $0 \in (a_j, b_j) \subset R^1$ for $j = 1, \ldots, n$ and let $X = \prod_{j=1}^{n} [a_j, b_j]$. Let $f: X \rightarrow X$ be a map such that $f(0) = 0$, f is continuously differentiable on a* *neighborhood of* **0**, *and* $\mathbf{J}F(0) \neq 0$. *There exists a homotopy* $H: I \to \mathrm{Map}(X, X)$ *and an open subset* V *of* X *containing* **0** *such that* $H(0) = f$, $H(1) = g_1 \times \cdots \times g_n$ *where* $g_j: [a_j, b_j] \to [a_j, b_j]$ *is a map*, $H(t)(0) = 0$, $\mathbf{J}: I \to R^1$ *defined by* $\mathbf{J}(t) = \mathbf{J}(H(t))(0)$ *is a continuous nonvanishing function, and* $H(t)$ *is one-to-one on* V *for all* $t \in I$.

Proof Write
$$f(x_1, \ldots, x_n) = (f_1(x_1, \ldots, x_n), \ldots, f_n(x_1, \ldots, x_n)),$$
where $f_j: X \to [a_j, b_j]$. Let $S(n)$ denote the symmetric group on n symbols. For $\varphi \in S(n)$, define $h_t^\varphi: X \to X$ by
$$h_{1-t}^\varphi(x_1, \ldots, x_n) = (f_1(tx^{\varphi(1)}), \ldots, f_n(tx^{\varphi(n)})),$$
where
$$tx^{\varphi(j)} = (tx_1, \ldots, tx_{\varphi(j)-1}, x_{\varphi(j)}, tx_{\varphi(j)+1}, \ldots, tx_n) \in X.$$
Let $F_{jk} = -\dfrac{\partial f_j(0)}{\partial x_k}$ if $j \neq k$ and let $F_{jj} = 1 - \dfrac{\partial f_j(0)}{\partial x_j}$. Then
$$\mathbf{J}H_{1-t}^\varphi(0) = \pi(\varphi)F_{1\varphi(1)} \cdots F_{n\varphi(n)} + \sum_{\psi \neq \varphi} \pi(\psi)t^n F_{1\psi(1)} \cdots F_{n\psi(n)},$$
where $\pi(\varphi)$ is 1 if φ is an even permutation and -1 if φ is odd. It is clear that $h_0^\varphi = f$ and that $h_1^\varphi = g_1 \times \cdots \times g_n$ where
$$g_j(x_j) = f_k(0, \ldots, 0, x_j, 0, \ldots, 0)$$
and $\varphi(k) = j$. Also, $\mathbf{J}^\varphi(t) = \mathbf{J}H_t^\varphi(0)$ is certainly a continuous function of t. However, there may exist $t_\varphi \in I$ such that $\mathbf{J}^\varphi(t_\varphi) = 0$. Observe first that the hypothesis $\mathbf{J}F(0) \neq 0$ implies that $t_\varphi < 1$. Next note that we have in fact defined $n!$ different homotopies h_t^φ, one for each element of $S(n)$. The question is whether there exist $n!$ numbers t_φ, $0 \leq t_\varphi < 1$, such that $\mathbf{J}^\varphi(t_\varphi) = 0$. We claim that there do not. The system of equations $\mathbf{J}^\varphi(t_\varphi) = 0$, $\varphi \in S(n)$, can be written in the following form: Order the elements of $S(n)$ and let $\mathfrak{F} = (F_1, \ldots, F_{n!})$ where $F_j = F_{1\varphi(1)} \cdots F_{n\varphi(n)}$ and φ is the jth element of $S(n)$. Also write $t_\varphi = t_j$ in this case. The system can be written $T\mathfrak{F} = 0$ where

$$T = T(t_1, \ldots, t_n) = \begin{bmatrix} 1 & t_1 & \cdots & t_1 \\ t_2 & 1 & \cdots & t_2 \\ \cdot & \cdot & & \cdot \\ \cdot & \cdot & & \cdot \\ \cdot & \cdot & & \cdot \\ t_{n!} & t_{n!} & \cdots & 1 \end{bmatrix}.$$

Since $\mathbf{J}F(0) \neq 0$, it must be that $\mathfrak{F} \neq 0$; so there is a solution to $T\mathfrak{F} = 0$ if and only if $\det(T) = 0$. Observe that if all $t_j < 1$, then

$$\det T(1, t_2, \ldots, t_{n!}) = \prod_{j=2}^{n!} (1 - t_j) > 0.$$

If we write

$$\det T(1, t_2, \ldots, t_{n!}) = \det T(t_2, \ldots, t_{n!}) - B_{n!},$$

then

$$B_{n!} = t_2(\det T(1, t_3, \ldots, t_{n!})) + \cdots + t_{n!}(\det T(1, t_2, \ldots, t_{n!-1})).$$

Since $0 \leq t_j < 1$ for $j = 2, \ldots, n!$ then $\det(T) = 0$ implies $B_{n!} \neq 0$ and

$$t_1 = \frac{\det T(t_2, \ldots, t_{n!})}{B_{n!}} > 1,$$

which establishes a contradiction and verifies our claim. Thus there exists the required homotopy h_t so that $\mathbf{J}H_t(0) \neq 0$ for all $t \in I$. It remains to find a single neighborhood V of 0 on which each H_t is one-to-one. By hypothesis there exists $\delta > 0$ such that, if $p \in R^n$ and $|p| \leq \delta$, then f is continuously differentiable at p. Let $B_\delta = \{p \in R^n \mid |p| \leq \delta\}$ and define $D: B_\delta \times \cdots \times B_\delta \times I \to R^1$ by

$$D(p_1, \ldots, p_n, t) = \det \begin{bmatrix} \dfrac{\partial H_t(p_1)}{\partial x_1} & \cdots & \dfrac{\partial H_t(p_1)}{\partial x_n} \\ \cdot & & \cdot \\ \cdot & & \cdot \\ \cdot & & \cdot \\ \dfrac{\partial H_t(p_n)}{\partial x_1} & \cdots & \dfrac{\partial H_t(p_n)}{\partial x_n} \end{bmatrix}.$$

Note that $D(0 \times \cdots \times 0 \times I) \subset R^1 - 0$. Let C be the component of $D^{-1}(R^1 - 0)$ containing $0 \times \cdots \times 0 \times I$. Then there exists $\epsilon > 0$ such that $|p_j| < \epsilon$, for $j = 1, \ldots, n$, implies $(p_1, \ldots, p_n, t) \in C$ for all $t \in I$. Let $V = \{p \in R^n \mid |p| < \epsilon\}$. Then the Inverse Function Theorem tells us that each H_t is one-to-one on V. ∎

Theorem 8. *Let $0 \in U \subset |K| \subset R^n$, where U is open in R^n. If $f: |K| \to |K|$ is continuously differentiable on U, $f(0) = 0$, and $\mathbf{J}F(0) \neq 0$; then $i(|K|, f, U) = \alpha(\mathbf{J}F(0))$ for any index $i: \mathscr{C}'_C \to Q$.*

Proof   Choose $0 \in (a_j, b_j) \subset R^1$ so that $X = \prod_{j=1}^{n} [a_j, b_j]$ is contained in U. Let $Y = f^{-1}(X) \cap X$. Then there is an open subset of R^n containing 0 in Y.

Construct a map $k: X \to X$ such that $k(x) = f(x)$ for all $x \in Y$. By Lemma 7, there is a homotopy $h_t: X \to X$ such that $h_0 = k$ and $h_1 = g_1 \times \cdots \times g_n$, where $g_j: [a_j, b_j] \to [a_j, b_j]$, $h_t(0) = 0$, and H_t is one-to-one on a neighborhood V of 0 for all $t \in I$. Therefore **0** is the only fixed point of each map h_t on V and, by the homotopy axiom, $i(X, k, W) = i(X, h_1, W)$, where W is any open set such that $\mathbf{0} \in W \subset \mathrm{cl}(W) \subset V$. Applying Lemma 6, $i(X, h_1, W) = \alpha(\mathbf{J}H_1(\mathbf{0}))$. Lemma 7 also states that $\mathbf{J}(t) = \mathbf{J}H_t(\mathbf{0})$ is a continuous non-vanishing function of t; so $\alpha(\mathbf{J}H_1(\mathbf{0})) = \alpha(\mathbf{J}H_0(\mathbf{0}))$. But $h_0 = k$ and k agrees with f near **0**; therefore $\alpha(\mathbf{J}H_0(\mathbf{0})) = \alpha(\mathbf{J}F(\mathbf{0}))$. On the other hand, if we extend k to a map $k: |K| \to |K|$, then the commutativity axiom implies that $i(|K|, k, W) = i(X, k, W)$. Applying the localization axiom, $i(|K|, f, W) = i(|K|, k, W)$. We have proved that $i(|K|, f, W) = \alpha(\mathbf{J}F(\mathbf{0}))$. ∎

Theorem 9 (Uniqueness of the Index on Geometric Complexes). *Let i, i': $\mathscr{C}'_C \to Q$ be indices and let $(|K|, f, U) \in \mathscr{C}'_C$. Then*

$$i(|K|, f, U) = i'(|K|, f, U).$$

Proof Since the boundary of U is compact and contains no fixed point of f, there exists $\epsilon > 0$ such that (for all $x \in \partial U$) $d(x, f(x)) > \epsilon$. By VIII.A.2 there is a map $g: |K| \to |K|$ with a finite number of fixed points — all in maximal simplices of $|K|$ — close enough to f so that, by III.A.4, g is ϵ-homotopic to f and therefore $i(|K|, f, U) = i(|K|, g, U)$ by the homotopy axiom.

Furthermore, the proof of VIII.A.2 shows that g is a simplicial map which is linear in a neighborhood of each fixed point. Let $x_1, \ldots, x_r$ be the fixed points of g on U. Then, by the additivity axiom $i(|K|, g, U) = \sum_{j=1}^{r} i(|K|, g, U_j)$, where $x_j \in U_j$ and $\mathrm{cl}(U_j) \cap \Phi(g) = x_j$. We can choose the cell U_j small enough so that $\mathrm{cl}(U_j) \cup g(\mathrm{cl}(U_j)) \subset Y_j$, where Y_j is a closed $n(j)$-cell and g is linear on Y_j. There are retractions $\rho_\gamma: Y_j \to \mathrm{cl}(U_j)$ and $\rho_\delta: |K| \to Y_j$. Let $\gamma = g\rho_\gamma: Y_j \to Y_j$ and $\delta = \gamma\rho_\delta: |K| \to |K|$. The localization axiom tells us that $i(|K|, g, U_j) = i(|K|, \delta, U_j)$. Furthermore, for $\eta_j: Y_j \to |K|$ the inclusion map, the commutativity axiom implies that

$$
\begin{aligned}
i(|K|, \delta, U_j) &= i(|K|, \eta_j \gamma \rho_\delta, U_j) \\
&= i(Y_j, \gamma \rho_\delta \eta_j, \eta_j^{-1}(U_j)) \\
&= i(Y_j, \gamma, U_j).
\end{aligned}
$$

Observe that $\gamma(x) = g(x)$ for $x \in U_j$, so that γ is linear on U_j. There is a linear homeomorphism h_j taking a neighborhood of Y_j onto an open subset of $R^{n(j)}$ so that $h_j(x_j) = \mathbf{0}$. Let $a_j = h_j \gamma h_j^{-1}: h_j(Y_j) \to h_j(Y_j)$. Then, by the commutativity axiom, $i(Y_j, \gamma, U_j) = i(h_j(Y_j), a_j, h_j(U_j))$. Since a_j is linear on $h_j(U_j)$, we have $\mathbf{J}A_j(\mathbf{0}) \neq 0$ by Lemma 1 and so, by Theorem 8,

$$i(|K|, g, U_j) = i(h_j(Y_j), a_j, h_j(U_j))$$
$$= \alpha(\mathbf{J}A_j(\mathbf{0})).$$

We have proved that

$$i(|K|, f, U) = \sum_{j=1}^{r} \alpha(\mathbf{J}A_j(\mathbf{0})).$$

Furthermore, since we employed no property of the function i other than the axioms for a fixed point index,

$$i'(|K|, f, U) = \sum_{j=1}^{r} \alpha(\mathbf{J}A_j(\mathbf{0}))$$

as well. ∎

B. UNIQUENESS ON ANRs

Theorem 1 (Uniqueness of the Index on ANRs).   *Let $i, i' : \mathscr{C}'_A \to Q$ be indices and let $(X, f, U) \in \mathscr{C}'_A$; then*

$$i(X, f, U) = i'(X, f, U).$$

Proof   Given $\delta > 0$ there is, by III.B.1, a geometric complex $|K|$ (the geometric realization of the nerve of a certain cover of X) which δ-dominates X by means of maps $\varphi : X \to |K|$ and $\psi : |K| \to X$. If we choose $\delta = \delta(f, U)$ from V.A.1 then $(X, \psi\varphi f, U) \in \mathscr{C}'_A$. The complex $|K|$ is an ANR by III.A.2, so we have

$$i(|K|, \varphi f \psi, \psi^{-1}(U)) = i(X, \psi\varphi f, U)$$

as a consequence of the commutativity axiom. Let $H : X \times I \to X$ be the δ-homotopy between the identity map on X and $\psi\varphi$. If $x \in \partial U$ then $d(x, f(x)) > \delta$ by V.A.1, while

$$d(f(x), H(f(x), t)) = d(H(f(x), 0), H(f(x), t)) < \delta,$$

so $H(f(x), t) \neq x$ for all $t \in I$. Define $H' : X \times I \to X$ by $H'(x, t) = H(f(x), t)$. Then $H'(x, 0) = f(x)$, $H'(x, 1) = \psi\varphi f(x)$; and for all $x \in \partial U$, $H'(x, t) \neq x$ for all $t \in I$. The homotopy axiom implies that $i(X, \psi\varphi f, U) = i(X, f, U)$. We have proved that

$$i(X, f, U) = i(|K|, \varphi f \psi, \psi^{-1}(U)).$$

Repeating the same argument with i' in place of i proves that

$$i'(|K|, \varphi f \psi, \psi^{-1}(U)) = i'(X, f, U).$$

The restrictions of i and i' to $\mathscr{C}'_C$ are indices on the collection of connected geometric complexes, and $(|K|, \varphi f \psi, \psi^{-1}(U)) \in \mathscr{C}'_C$. Therefore, by A.9,

$$i(|K|, \varphi f \psi, \psi^{-1}(U)) = i'(|K|, \varphi f \psi, \psi^{-1}(U)),$$

and so $i(X, f, U) = i'(X, f, U)$ as required. ∎

NOTES

The Uniqueness Theorem for indices on the collection of connected geometric complexes is due to O'Neill [44]. The proof of uniqueness above is based on techniques from [40] and is entirely different from O'Neill's original proof. The extension to the ANR case was accomplished by Browder in [9].

1. W. Barnier, *The Jiang subgroup for a map*, Doctoral Dissertation, University of California, Los Angeles, 1967.
2. R. Bing, *The elusive fixed-point property*, Amer. Math. Monthly, **76** (1969), 119–132.
3. K. Borsuk, *Sur un continu acyclique qui se lasse transformer topologiquement en lui même sans points invariants*, Fund. Math. **24** (1935), 51–58.
4. R. Bourgin, *Un indice dei punti uniti*, I, II, III, Accad. Lincei Roma Sci. Fis. Mat. Nat. **19** (1955), 435–440; **20** (1956), 43–48; **21** (1956), 395–400.
5. R. Brooks, *Coincidences, roots, and fixed points*, Doctoral Dissertation, University of California, Los Angeles, 1967.
6. ———— and R. Brown, *A lower bound for the Δ-Nielsen number*, Trans. Amer. Math. Soc. **143** (1969), 555–564.
7. L. Brouwer, *Über Abbildungen von Mannigfaltigkeiten*, Math. Ann. **71** (1912), 97–115.
8. F. Browder, *On a generalization of the Schauder fixed point theorem*, Duke Math. J. **26** (1959), 291–303.
9. ————, *On the fixed point index for continuous mappings of locally connected spaces*, Summa Brasil. Math. **4** (1960), 253–293.
10. ————, *The topological fixed point index and its application in functional anaylsis*, Doctoral Dissertation, Princeton University, 1948.
11. R. Brown, *Divisible H-spaces*, Proc. Amer. Math. Soc., to appear.
12. ————, *On a homotopy converse to the Lefschetz fixed point theorem*, Pacific J. Math. **17** (1966), 407–411.
13. ————, *On the Nielsen fixed point theorem for compact maps*, Duke Math. J., **36** (1969), 699–708.
14. ———— and E. Fadell, *Non-singular path fields on compact topological manifolds*, Proc. Amer. Math. Soc. **16** (1965), 1342–1349.
15. E. Connell, *Properties of fixed point spaces*, Proc. Amer. Math. Soc. **10** (1959), 974–979.
16. J. Cronin, *Fixed points and topological degree in nonlinear analysis*, Amer. Math. Soc., 1964.
17. A. Deleanu, *Théorie des points fixes sur les rétractes de voisinage des espaces convexoides*, Bull. Soc. Math. France **87** (1959), 235–243.
18. A. Dold, *Fixed point index and fixed point theorem for Euclidean neighborhood retracts*, Topology **4** (1965), 1–8.
19. E. Fadell, *On a coincidence theorem of F. B. Fuller*, Pacific J. Math. **15** (1965), 825–834.
20. F. Fuller, *An index of fixed point type for periodic orbits*, Amer. J. Math. **89** (1967), 133–148.

21. ————, *The existence of periodic points*, Ann. Math. **57** (1953), 229–230.

22. ————, *The homotopy theory of concidences*, Ann. Math. **59** (1954), 488–513.

23. A. Granas, *The Hopf-Lefschetz fixed point theorem for noncompact ANR's*, Proceedings of the Conference on Infinite Dimensional Topology at Baton Rouge, La., 1967.

24. D. Gottlieb, *A certain subgroup of the fundamental group*, Amer. J. Math. **87** (1965), 840–856.

25. O. Hanner, *Some theorems on absolute neighborhood retracts*, Ark. Mat. **1** (1951), 389–408.

26. H. Hopf, *Eine Verallgemeinerung der Euler-Poincaréschen Formel*, Nachr. Ges. Wiss. Göttingen 1928, 127–136.

27. ————, *Über den Rang geschlosscher Liescher Gruppen*, Comment. Math. Helv. **13** (1940), 119–143.

28. ————, *Über die algebraische Anzahl von Fixpunkten*, Math. Z. **29** (1929), 493–524.

29. ————, *Vektorfelder in n-dimensionalen Mannigfaltigkeiten*, Math. Ann. **96** (1927), 225–250.

30. Jiang Bo-Ju, *Estimation of the Nielsen numbers*, Chinese Math. **5** (1964), 330–339.

31. S. Kinoshita, *On some contractible continua without the fixed point property*, Fund. Math. **40** (1953), 96–98.

32. R. Knill, *On the Lefschetz coincidence point formula*, Doctoral Dissertation, University of Notre Dame, 1964.

33. S. Lefschetz, *Algebraic Topology*, Amer. Math. Soc., 1942.

34. ————, *Continuous transformations of manifolds*, Proc. Nat. Acad. Sci. U.S.A. **9** (1923), 90–93.

35. ————, *Intersections and transformations of complexes and manifolds*, Trans. Amer. Math. Soc. **28** (1926), 1–49.

36. ————, *Manifolds with a boundary and their transformations*, Trans. Amer. Math. Soc. **29** (1927), 429–462.

37. ————, *On the fixed point formula*, Ann. Math. **38** (1937), 819–822.

38. ————, *Topology*, Amer. Math. Soc., 1930.

39. J. Leray, *Sur la forme des espaces topologiques et sur les points fixes des représentations*, J. Math. Pures et appl. **24** (1945), 95–167.

40. ————, *Sur les équations et les transformations*, J. Math. Pures et appl. **24** (1945), 201–248.

41. W. Lopez, *An example in the fixed point theory of polyhedra*, Bull. Amer. Math. Soc. **73** (1967), 922–924.

42. J. Mycielski, *Some properties of connected compact groups*, Colloq. Math. **5** (1958), 162–166.

43. J. Nielsen, *Untersuchungen zur Topologie des geschlossen zweiseitigen Flache*, I, II, III, Acta Math. **50** (1927), 189–358; **53** (1929), 1–76; **58** (1932), 87–167.

44. B. O'Neill, *Essential sets and fixed points*, Amer. J. Math. **75** (1953), 497–509.

45. H. Poincaré, *Deuxième complement a l'Analysis Situs*, Proc. London Math. Soc. **32** (1900), 277–308.

46. K. Reidemeister, *Automorphismen von Homotopiekettenringen*, Math. Ann. **112** (1936), 586–593.

47. H. Samelson, *On small maps of manifolds*, Pacific J. Math. **15** (1965), 1401–1403.

48. Shi Gen-Hua, *On the least number of fixed points and Nielsen numbers*, Chinese Math. **8** (1966), 234–243.

49. E. Spanier, *Algebraic Topology*, New York, 1966.

50. T. van der Walt, *Fixed and Almost Fixed Points*, Amsterdam, 1963.

51. F. Wecken, *Fixpunktklassen*, I, II, III, Math. Ann. **117** (1941), 659–671; **118** (1942), 216–234 and 544–577.

52. J. Weier, *Fixpunkttheorie in topologische Mannigfaltigkeiten*, Math. Z. **59** (1953), 171–190.

INDEX

Abelian group, 103, 110
    as coefficients of cohomology, 13, 17
    as fundamental group, 107, 110
    module over, 15, 24
Absolute neighborhood retract (ANR)
    cartesian product of, 84
    cohomology of, 42
    definition of, 37, 49
    dimension of, 50
    domination by polyhedra, 37, 41, 75-76, 165
    Euler characteristic of, 45
    examples
        Hilbert cube, 39, 43
        H-spaces, 101
        mapping cylinder, 147
        polyhedra, 38-39
        topological groups, 47, 49, 109
    fixed point property of, 43-44
    fixed points of maps on, 44, 86, 150
    homotopies of maps on, 40, 50, 84, 91, 95
    imbedding in Hilbert cube, 38-39, 41
    index theory of, 54, 75, 84, 87, 165
        uniqueness of, 165, 172-173
    Lefschetz number of map on, 42, 50, 52, 84, 114
    Lefschetz Theorem for, 37, 42, 49
    maps on, 87-89, 94, 97, 122
    Nielsen number of map on, 85, 87, 95-96, 114
    pathwise-connectedness of, 43-44, 93
    retraction of, 39, 50, 146
    ULC property of, 39, 43
Additivity axiom
    computation with, 53, 73, 100, 131
    in defining special indices, 87, 122
    motivation for, 53
    in proof of invariance, 77-79
    in proving uniqueness, 166-168, 171
    relation to Lefschetz theory, 53
    statement of, 52
    verification of, 57, 65, 81
    in verifying commutativity, 82-83
Admissable triple, 52, 74, 165
Alternating sign morphism, 2-3, 5, 8, 27
Antipodal map, 32, 36
Arc, 28, 136
Aspherical space
    definition of, 101
    examples
        circle, 107
        figure-eight, 114
        Klein bottle, 108
        two-manifold, 108, 114
    polyhedron, 102-103, 106

Axioms
    for fixed point index, 51-52, 73, 165, 172

Ball, 167
Barycentric homeomorphism, 11
Barycentric mapping, 40-41
Barycentric subdivision
    modulo a subcomplex, 116
    of a simplicial complex, 9, 11, 15, 24, 28, 115-116
    of a triangulation, 11
Base point, 97, 101, 104
Basis
    for cohomology with field coefficients, 6, 22
    for free module, 2-3, 8, 29
    for rational cohomology, 30, 44, 46, 148-149, 162
    for vector space, 5-6, 66-67
Betti number, 45, 148
Binomial coefficient, 49
Binomial formula, 49
Boundary
    of disc, 36, 167-168
    of open set, 51-52, 56, 171
    of simplex, 22, 162
Bounded, 40, 75, 127
Brouwer Fixed Point Theorem, 31, 34-35, 43

Cardinality, 103, 105
Cartesian product of pairs, 16-17, 21
Cartesian product topology, 80
Cell
    as geometric complex, 12-13, 22, 162
    n-dimensional, 31, 35, 43, 171
Center of a group, 101, 106
Centralizer of a subgroup, 101, 109
Chain complex, 3-6, 8-10, 13, 17
Chain map
    between chain complexes, 3-6, 8
    definition of, 3
    induced by barycentric subdivision, 9, 15
    induced by map, 13, 17
    induced by simplicial function, 9, 15, 24
Circle, 46, 107
Closed manifold, 151
Closed set
    in ANR, 38, 50, 80-81, 84, 146
    in compact space, 40, 75, 98-100
    in euclidean space, 166-167, 171
    in polyhedron, 39, 80, 154
    in relation to the fixed-point set, 56-57, 59, 74
    in segment, 132, 135, 138
Closure
    of open cell, 108, 127, 140
    of open set, 56, 59, 124, 132
    of set, 19
    symbol for, 52, 87

Cohomology, 31, 148
    of chain complex, 5, 9, 13, 17
Cokernel, 103
Commutativity axiom
    computation with, 146
    in proof of invariance, 77, 79
    in proof of uniqueness, 168, 171-172
    relation to Lefschetz number, 53
    statement of, 53
    verification of, 62, 65, 82-84
Compact
    cartesian products, 80
    Lie group, 50
    metric space, 37, 39-40, 43, 49-50, 75, 98
    property of geometric realization, 11
    property of interval, 59, 136
    space, 38, 56, 93
    subset of euclidean space, 19, 26
    subset of polyhedron, 63-64, 132, 171
    topological group, 47, 49-50, 109, 111
Complex conjugate, 107
Complex number, 31, 46, 107, 148
Complex projective space, 31, 33, 148
Component, 127, 134, 170
Congruence, 107
Connected
    ANR, 43-44, 54, 75, 98, 165
    geometric complex, 119, 122-124, 131, 139,
        151, 165, 173
    Lie group, 50
    open set, 93, 129
    polyhedron, 56, 75, 101-103, 106, 118,
        145, 153
    property of interval, 94
    property of figure-eight, 114
    property of Klein bottle, 108
    property of projective space, 32
    property of surfaces, 108, 114
    property of unitary groups, 113
    set, 139-140, 143, 145
    space, 52, 74, 158
    subset of ANR, 93
    topological group, 47, 49-50, 109, 111
Connected sum, 108
Constant map, 23, 64, 84, 122-123, 167
Constant path, 89-92, 96, 99, 105
Continuous
    family of homeomorphisms, 120
    function, 59, 123, 127-128
    real-valued function, 40, 75, 169-170
Continuously differentiable, 168, 170
Continuum, 150
Contractible
    ANR, 43
    polyhedron, 31
    property of closed cells, 31, 120, 166, 168
    property of euclidean spaces, 54, 120
    space, 22, 137
Contraction, 43

Convex hull, 41
Convex set, 41
Coordinate, 38, 158
Coset, 104
Cover, 40, 50
Cup product, 14-15, 32, 149
Cyclic group, 31, 104, 110

Deformation, 115, 142-145
    definition of, 32
    fixed-point-free, 32-33, 36, 143-145, 150-
        151
    Nielsen number of, 96
    examples
        sphere, 32-33, 96
        sphere with handles, 36
        projective spaces, 33-34
Degenerate simplex, 8
Degree, 48-49
Determinant, 33, 166
Diagonal map, 14, 22, 47, 68, 158
Diagonal matrix, 48
Diameter, 12
Differentiable manifold, 150
Differentiable map, 74, 166-168
Differential, 166
Dimension
    of cohomology with J_2-coefficients, 151
    of polyhedron, 118-119, 134
    of simplex, 118-119
        greater than one, 128, 132, 135, 137,
            143, 145
        at least one, 135, 140-141, 143, 145
        at least three, 133-134, 142
    of rational cohomology, 10, 44-45
    of simplicial complex, 50, 118, 139, 142
    of topological space, 50, 113, 150
    of vector space, 66-67, 166
Direct sum
    of cyclic groups, 110
    of groups, 59, 153, 162
    of homotopy groups, 23
    symbol for, 14, 21
Disc, 150
Disconnected, 143
Distance, 39-40, 54, 119, 130
Divisible group, 47, 49-50
Dold's Lemma, 69, 71, 153
Domain, 154
Domination, 42
    definition of, 40
    ϵ-, 40-41, 43, 50, 75-77, 80-81, 172
    theorem, 40-43, 49, 76, 165
Dual
    of graded vector space, 65
    of vector space, 67-68
Dual basis, 2-3, 66-67

Eigenvalue, 44, 46

181

of type S, 139, 141, 146-147, 151
of type W, 143, 145, 150
Polynomial, 44-45
Principal ideal domain, 1-4
Product map, 17
Proximity map, 124, 126-129, 131-133, 135, 138-139, 143

Q-acyclic, 30-31, 43-44, 50, 74
Quaternion, 31
Quaternionic projective space, 31, 33
Quotient graded module, 1, 4, 17
Quotient group, 103
Quotient map, 19, 55
Quotient morphism, 17
Quotient space, 107-108, 121, 148
Quotient topology, 19, 31, 107

Radial projection, 167
Radius, 167
Rank, 10
Rational cohomology, 21, 27, 119, 122
Rational number, 8, 53, 56, 65, 165
Ray, 127, 134, 136, 142, 167
Real number, 10, 26, 37, 47, 120, 126, 132
as angle of rotation, 32, 167
as parameter of line, 119
sign of, 166
Real projective space, 31, 33, 108, 113
Refinement
of cover, 50
of simplicial complex, 116-118, 140
Regular neighborhood, 12, 39, 162
Reidemeister number, 103-104, 113
Related fixed point classes, 87, 90-95, 99, 105-106
Related fixed points, 89-91, 94, 99-100
Relation, 108-109, 114
Relative singular cohomology, 16
Retract, 34-35, 39, 43, 50
Retraction
onto ANR, 39, 41
onto cell, 131, 167, 171
of disc, 35
of figure-eight, 112
onto geometric complex, 119
of Hilbert cube, 38, 43
of open set, 37-38
onto polyhedron, 56, 60, 63, 65, 67
onto projective space, 148
Root
in a group, 47, 109-111, 113
of a polynomial, 45
Rotation, 47, 120, 167

Separable, 37-38, 56
Sequence, 37, 54, 59
Simplex, 24, 102, 117-119, 124, 128, 139
of barycentric subdivision, 9, 24, 116

of cell, 12, 22, 162
definition of, 8
degenerate, 8
diameter of, 12
dimension of, 8, 118, 128, 132, 135, 140, 142-143
of figure-eight, 28
geometric realization of, 11
maximal, 117-119, 124, 127, 140, 142-143
of nerve, 40-41
number of, 10, 119
oriented, 8-9
skeletal, 116
Simplicial approximation, 12-13, 15-16, 26, 118-119, 134
Simplicial Approximation Theorem, 13, 129, 136
Simplicial complex, 10, 24, 116, 151
barycentric subdivision of, 9, 11, 15, 24, 116
definition of, 8
dimension of, 50
geometric realization of, 10, 39
maximal simplex of, 117
nerve of cover, 40
number of simplices in, 10
refinement of, 116-117
simplicial function on, 9, 15
skeleton of, 116
subcomplex of, 11, 24, 116
in triangulation, 11
triangulating a cell, 12-13, 22, 38, 162
triangulating figure-eight, 28
Simplicial function
definition of, 9
on figure-eight, 28
in Hopf-construction, 117-118
induces chain map, 15, 24
induces map, 12, 15
Simplicial map, 13, 28, 50, 117, 134, 171
Simply-connected, 141
Singular cohomology, 13, 15, 17, 119, 122
Singular linear transformation, 33, 166
Skeletal simplex, 116, 119
Skeleton, 22, 101, 116-117, 162-163
Sphere, 19, 22, 32, 136
with handles, 36, 114
Steenrod square, 148
Strong deformation retraction, 12, 147, 162
Strongly connected, 143, 145
Surface, 108
Suspension, 121, 148
Symmetric group, 169
Symmetric polynomial, 44

Tensor product
of homomorphisms, 20
of modules, 14, 54
Tietze's Extension Theorem, 38